Items should be returned on or before the last date
shown below. Items not already requested by other
borrowers may be renewed in person, in writing or by
telephone. To renew, please quote the number on the
barcode label. To renew online a PIN is required.
This can be requested at your local library.
Renew online @ **www.dublincitypubliclibraries.ie**
Fines charged for overdue items will include postage
incurred in recovery. Damage to or loss of items will
be charged to the borrower.

Leabharlanna Poiblí Chathair Bhaile Átha Cliath
Dublin City Public Libraries

Dublin City
Baile Átha Cliath

Central Library, Henry Street,
Lár-Leabharlann, Sraid Annraoi
Tel. 8734333

Date Due	Date Due	Date Due
JUN		
20. JUN 09		
0 9 FEB 2009 SEP		
	28. JUL 11	
	25. JUN 12	
	15. DEC 12	
	26JAN13	

Straight
Talking
Wild

ABOUT THE AUTHOR

Hailing from County Louth, Éanna Ní Lamhna is a self-styled expert on just about everything. She is best known for her environmental expertise as a broadcaster on both the television series *Creature Feature*, which ran for five years from 1999 to 2004, and the radio programme *Mooney Goes Wild*, now in its twelfth year. Her ability to bring her subject to life is legendary and her no-nonsense approach to romantic views about wildlife are well known. She is currently the president of An Taisce, The National Trust for Ireland, and is giving that association a new realistic image, which properly reflects its attitude to environmental issues in Ireland.

Originally a botanist, Éanna has become a jack-of-all-trades over the years since leaving university; lecturing to environmental planning students in DIT, conducting Leaving Cert ecology trips and inspiring environmental awareness in primary schools. She is married with three children and lives in Dublin.

Éanna is the author of two books published by TownHouse, *Talking Wild – Wildlife on the Radio* (2002) and *Wild and Wonderful* (2004).

Straight Talking Wild

More Wildlife on the Radio

Éanna Ní Lamhna

TOWN HOUSE DUBLIN

First published in 2006 by

TownHouse, Dublin
THCH Ltd
Mount Pleasant Business Centre
Mount Pleasant Avenue
Ranelagh
Dublin 6
Ireland

www.townhouse.ie

1 2 3 4 5 6 7 8 9 10

ISBN: 1-86059-260-0 / 978-186059-260-7

Cover image © Bill Brown / Getty Images
Cover and text design by Sin É Design
Printed by Creative Print and Design (Wales), Ebbw Vale

CONTENTS

Acknowledgements 15

Introduction 19

1 Wildlife on the wirelesss 37

2 In the beginning 39

3 Drama in the garden – an everyday story of birdlife 45

4 Bird food – the à la carte approach 49

5 Miss Moffat's revenge – spiders 53

6 The terrible truth about bluebottles and flies 57

7 Sleepovers and holidays – coping with the cold 61

8 Bats in (and out of) the belfry 67

9 Wildlife isn't only for children 71

10 Adventure on Lambay Island 75

11 Introducing the crow family 79

12 Strange but true – bugs and their idiosyncrasies 87

13 Badgers and other carnivores 91

14 Ageism – insect life cycles 97

15 Rabbits and hares and their unspeakable habits 103

16 Our own personal fauna 109

17 What'll it do to you? 117

18 The water police 123

19 *An Dúlra Blasta* – edible wildlife 129

20 Your home as a wildlife habitat 133

21 Teaching teachers 139

22 Things that sting and things that don't – wasps, bees and ants 143

23   Maligned and misunderstood –
        who'd be an insect?   157

24   Sex and the single plant   161

25   Nature's weirdos – fungi   167

26   The ones St Patrick missed – amphibians
        and reptiles   173

27   Piseoga and folklore   183

28   Why did God make rats?   191

29   Surrounded by water   197

30   Why you can't burn holes in the
        ozone layer from your back garden   201

31   Flying in the Red Sea   209

32   Hummingbirds: real and pretend   215

33   Talking wild in Costa Rica   219

34   Designed to kill   225

35   Beautiful water police   231

36   How to boil an egg in a sock   239

37   Deconstructing the tale of the salmon of
        knowledge   245

38   The exciting life of the courtroom scientist   251

39   Not sailing to Australia   257

40   Sex, drugs and rock'n'roll in the dark garden   263

41   The ones that got away   273

42   Carnival of the carnivores   277

43   Timberrrrrr!   285

44   Having a whale of a time   291

45   The state of our environment   301

46   Teaching students – or *not* teaching them   307

47   Mooney goes wild   311

        Bibliography   317

I dedicate this book to my husband John Harding –
my favourite specimen of the species Homo sapiens

Acknowledgements

My thanks must go to the listeners and contributors to the radio programme, *Mooney Goes Wild*, who unwittingly contributed to this book. Thanks also to Derek Mooney for enduring the ribbing and banter he receives from me on air

Jervis Good regaled me with stories of being a biological scientist. Michael Dillon commiserated with me on my students and added a string of his own student anecdotes. A special thanks to Richard Collins for the constant help and support he has given me in a professional capacity. I have worked with Richard in the world of wildlife since 1974, and he has been unfailingly generous with his help and kind with his criticisms.

INTRODUCTION

What is *Mooney Goes Wild?* What indeed? To say that it is a radio programme on wildlife presented by Derek Mooney who has called it after himself may be strictly true, but this doesn't come near to describing the phenomenon that has become compulsory listening for quarter of a million people – firstly in our Sunday morning slot, then Saturday, and now Friday afternoon – whether they are still in bed, in the car on the way to do the Saturday shopping, or loitering in the kitchen, stretching the chores until eleven o'clock. It is an eclectic mix of serious scientific information, questions and comments from the public, *craic* and banter among the panellists and the presenter, and a repository of amazing facts and figures about wildlife not only in Ireland, but all over the world, and not only about wildlife but about human life too…

It evolved in length and content over the years, with Derek and myself there from the very start and Richard Collins joining not so long afterwards. By May 2006, we had been broadcasting *Mooney Goes Wild* for eleven years. In the earlier years we used to run for thirty minutes, from February to Hallowe'en. We got promoted to forty-five minutes after some years and began to run for the whole year. We had slots on Tuesday afternoons, Saturday evening at six, Sunday afternoon at two, Sunday mornings at eleven (when listeners complained that it interfered with Mass), Saturday morning at ten, and now Friday afternoon at three. Of late we have been broadcasting for an hour at a time with the programme continuing over the summer with an alternative producer/presenter – as Derek must have holidays (because of health and safety regulations no less!). So doing general sums, it would seem that we have been talking wild to the people of Ireland (and indeed further afield) for an unbelievable four hundred and fifty hours, and that doesn't include special programmes such as the dawn chorus, Christmas specials or simultaneous television broadcasts.

What can we have been talking about for all that time? It was interesting to see when we broadcast our ten-year highlights in May 2005 what had changed and what had remained the same. One thing struck me as very obvious – we had no more female input ten years on than we had at the beginning. I was and am the only regular female participant on the programme. Is knowing about wildlife a male thing? Are women reluctant to speak on the radio? Is it an indication of the age profile of the panellists? In the old days the men had all the jobs, so spokespeople on mammals, birds, fish and plants, who represent the institutions they work for, are all male and of a certain age. Or are men just more pushy?

As for things remaining the same, people still ask every year how to get rid of wasps; people still find Maybugs every May and worry if they are an exotic species from abroad; people are still amazed to learn that we have mosquitoes in Ireland (but they don't carry malaria, thank goodness); people still think birds return to their nests every night; and they still think woodlice are ugly! I presume that these are the new listeners we have garnered along the way, as I would hate to think that people have been listening all this time and still retain the old ideas they always had (bats are blind, and will fly into your hair, squirrels hibernate – wrong, wrong, all wrong). One thing that has definitely changed, however, is the notion that learning about wildlife is only for children. Make no mistake about it, this programme is listened to by grown-ups. What child under the age of twenty voluntarily listens to talk radio?

The programme began in 1995 and at that time had a separate producer and presenter. The presenter was and is Derek Mooney, but the producer role evolved. Dick Warner was the first producer and in those far-off, dim days, each programme was planned in detail. It is a live programme, so the time on air has to be organised properly. Dick used to hold post-programme meetings to analyse how it went – not always a good idea coming off the air high on adrenalin! Micheál Holmes produced for a year after Dick, and Colin Morrisson had the producer's chair for a time too. The job of producer seems to be to ensure that the programme runs smoothly, that items keep to time, that connections to outside lines are made, that no libel occurs on air and, indeed, the producer decides what shall be on the programme in the first place, even though he may not necessarily always come up with the ideas for items to be included.

After a couple of years it became apparent that Derek could do the two jobs himself and for the last good number of years the programme is produced and presented by him. This means that the broadcast assistant and the sound operator are really on their toes for the programme – they are guided by hand signals from Derek while he is inside in the studio live on air and they are outside keeping the channels working. In fact, if a good idea occurs to Derek mid-programme, he can nip out of the studio altogether to find the sound effect on CD, leaving his gallant panellists holding the fort. This can take guests by surprise and increases their adrenalin rush. Derek never misses anything, however, and can continue the conversation on his return, as if he had never left, even though we feel we must explain to him what he has been absent for.

One of the things that makes a good programme is the relationship between the panellists with each other and with the presenter. The programme always gives the impression that we are having a great time in the studio, enjoying ourselves and having fun. Is this really the case? Well, a lot of the time it is – the banter between the regular panellists goes on well-defined routes, as at this stage we have grown personalities on air, as it were. Sometimes we agree in advance what we might say on air: will we comment on each other's appearance or what we are wearing, for example, but what happens on air is usually spontaneous. We do have a certain code of conduct; panellists try not to contradict each other too openly. If a question is asked that requires referring to the many books we bring in as a security blanket, one panellist will try to hold the fort until the other has time to find the page in the book with the information on it. As panellists we like to give the impression that we know everything, although Derek doesn't necessarily approve of this and is well capable of telling the public at large that we are looking in the books. He usually means this a compliment to whoever has asked the question that caused us to rush for our books in the first place.

Does anything ever go wrong on the programme? Surely over the years there have been accidents and howlers. Strange as this might sound, this is not the case. Derek as the producer is always so concerned that we might all be struck with amnesia or that every phone line might go down, that he packs every running order with enough material for two programmes. So if anything could be described as going wrong, it is that people are asked to come on the phone or stand by the phone at home and then we never get to them. The earlier material has proved so riveting, and we the panellists have known so much about whatever topics are mentioned, that time runs out before we can come to them. There has never been an occasion when we have run out of material before the time is up. In fact we are more likely to be begging an extra few seconds from the following programme. There are always people ringing in on the phone lines with questions and responses to what is being said on the programme too, most of which, although answered by Jarlath Holland and Terry Flanagan, never get to go on air. I am sure we could just come in cold and have a programme for an hour with just our heads and the phone-calls and emails, but so far we haven't risked it. Mind you, in spite of having circulated a comprehensive running order a day or two before the programme so that we have time to bone up on whatever is coming up, the programme is quite likely to open with a question on why a fly walks on a bald man's head, or whether the spiders on your bedroom ceiling are likely to fall on top of you as you sleep. You can never be fully prepared!

One of the items that was very popular in the early years of the programme was the answering-machine mission. This was contrived to sound like a message left on the programme's answering machine reporting some strange phenomenon that required a visit from me to resolve. This was always great fun. Derek and I would arrange to go to the person's house to observe and resolve the conundrum. Someone may have rung in, say, to ask how to get rid of house martins that were soiling the front of the house, or to tell us about a jumping egg they had found in their garden, or the fact that the birds sang specially for them and only started when they opened the door. I would phone and agree to arrive at a certain time and then we would land out to the house.

Spontaneity is an important part of these visits. Hearing the story first and then doing it again for the radio is not the same. So quite often we'd record the thing for real from the beginning. I would begin by standing on someone's doorstep and speaking loudly to myself, as it were, 'This must be the right house – a pity they wouldn't have the number on the door and I don't see any bell either; I'll have to knock.' And when the person opens the door, I go straight into the mission: 'I've come to see your wasps' nest/singing dog/case-carrying moth – whatever.' I must say, it usually works very well; we rarely announce all this at the wrong front door or get eaten alive by ferocious dogs.

Sometimes of course the thing doesn't happen, although the fox always appears when it is getting dark, or the badger comes up to the back door when we rattle the tin opener, it's not going to happen on this particular occasion. But we will never ever fudge the issue. If it is not there, we cannot pretend it is – we cannot imagine we are looking at something if we are not. And I suppose that is why it works so well – the conviction with which I told the woman with the house martins' nests, made from cowpats and smeared greenly all over her walls, that she could not disturb a protected species, could not be faked. The excitement when, after we'd got through about four cups of tea, the badger finally arrived and snorted directly into the microphone, was real all round. The state of me when I climbed out of the tank in the Dingle aquarium after swimming with the sharks and surviving, wouldn't have been replicated half an hour later. This is good radio and listeners enjoy it.

Making a programme on the dawn chorus was the first big foray the programme made on to a wider canvas. Birdwatch Ireland have always had a series of field trips and learning sessions on the dawn chorus in the month of May and have always got a mention on the programme for this event. But a few years into the programme, Derek felt that this would make magnificent radio and that it should be broadcast live. As the dawn chorus happens at dawn, and as dawn in May is very, very early, it took some skill in persuasion to convince the powers that be that this was desirable, possible, and a wonderful idea. An outside broadcast unit would have to be allocated to the task. Outside broadcast units are well used to travelling for sports events, but they take place at reasonable hours of the day and you know where the action will be. How would it work for the dawn chorus?

We had to pick a site where there would definitely be a wonderful selection of birds singing. Jim Wilson from the Cork branch of Birdwatch Ireland could swear by Cushkinny marsh on Cobh Island. So that is where we went. Never one to do things by halves, Derek decided that we would broadcast live all night long from midnight, even though the birds don't really start to sing until four in the morning. And so it was that we found ourselves with a caravan (that could have been left over from a *Father Ted* set), in the pitch dark at midnight, facing six hours of live broadcasting. The technical staff had placed parabolic microphones in the surrounding woods, and we had a main central microphone about one hundred metres from the caravan. We were standing ready and waiting around the mike with woolly hats, heavy boots and socks, torches and umbrellas to keep off the wind, Derek at one side with headphones hopefully connected back to a studio in Dublin and the rest of us – Richard Collins, Jim Wilson and myself – standing looking at him. Midnight chimed, news and weather and then we were on – for six hours.

Looking back on it now we must have been mad: no scripts, we couldn't have read them anyway, just a huge enthusiasm to tell this whole story of the dawn chorus – why it took place, what happened, who was involved, what bird species, what they sounded like and how you could identify them. We included comments on overhead airplanes, and lights in the sky over Cork. We postulated on what might be abroad in the woods at the moment, we considered vegetation and creepy-crawlies and we interspersed it all with recorded clips to give us a chance to flex our muscles and stop freezing to the ground. At least it was so cold we weren't likely to fall asleep.

Members of the public came and there were fears that they might interrupt the live transmission so they had to be politely told they could watch from a distance as the four ghostly figures in the woolly hats and umbrellas stood in torchlight at a microphone in the middle of the wood in the back of beyond. What were we sounding like? Were we saying the same things twice? Were we contradicting each other or, indeed, ourselves? Was anyone listening? Would it ever end or were we going to be here forever like some crazy Beckett play? And then it all happened at once. Streaks of light came across the eastern sky, the wind dropped altogether and the first blackbird sang. And in the next half hour before it got bright enough to extinguish the torches, the birds woke up in order and sang: pheasants, rooks, coots, and all joining in with the robins, thrushes, wrens, finches and blackbirds. By half four, the worry was over – it was working – the birds were in great form and we could hear a wonderful dawn chorus on all the parabolic mikes, better than in reality, as sounds from further away were accessible to us. It didn't rain, the microphones worked outdoors, our line to the studio in Dublin didn't go down, and we were indeed able to talk non-stop from midnight live on air.

The only thing was, was there anyone listening? So Derek asked, 'If you are listening, stick your mobile phone out the window and let us hear your dawn chorus.' The phone line to the Dublin studio was jammed. We heard a cuckoo in Donegal and skylarks in Connemara. Taxi drivers in Dublin City let us hear what was coming in through their windows. People coming home from night shift rang in. Oh, they were listening out there all right. We forgot our cold feet and our blue fingers and how awful instant coffee tastes after the fifth paper cupful. The dawn chorus in Cushkinny was wonderful. We now had all the warblers in the reedbeds joining in with the woodland birds and it really was a feast for the ears. We let the birds speak for the final twenty minutes and collapsed gratefully into the caravan to hear it as it was being transmitted.

We were broadcasting on Sundays at that time from two o'clock to half two, just before the sports. So a dash back into Cork City, breakfast and forty winks and we were there live (if you could call it that) to comment on how the awfully big adventure went and bask in the praise of the listeners. Since then, we have done the dawn chorus from the Phoenix Park, from Dick Warner's house in Kildare, and indeed from Cobh. We have had a multi-centred approach with outside microphones at several locations. It is always an immensely popular event. Indeed, when we produced a commemorative CD and poster with the *RTÉ Guide* in 2005, 140,000 copies were sold, the first time ever that the *Guide* sold out in every shop. But I never will forget that first occasion at midnight wondering how could we broadcast live for six hours.

In the early days of the programme, we used to have a winter break. In order not to be forgotten, we would always want to come back with some wonderful stunt that could be flagged beforehand and which would remind listeners of our existence. One year Derek had the notion that we would return with a live radio and television programme. We would attend the release of some seals at Bull Island and this would go out simultaneously on radio and television. You cannot imagine how complicated television is, relative to radio – and live television is even more fraught. Throw in animals and the children and grown-ups who were encouraged to come along for the event, and the scenario gets worse. Throw in Bull Island causeway where on the marsh side are all the waders in full winter splendour, and on the beach side is a container with several seals waiting to be released, and maybe half a mile of open ground between them, and you are beginning to get the picture. We need broadcasters everywhere and a co-ordinator in charge. Derek will be the co-ordinator in the road unit changing the gears on the programme, and outside, at the various areas of interest, will be the rest of us. We will of course know all that is going on through a small little earpiece that will crackle in our ears and then we shall talk animatedly and clearly into the lens of the nearest television camera that will be placed strategically nearby.

Come back the dawn chorus; all is forgiven, I thought, as I stood miserably in the rain in a gale-force wind on the causeway. I was delegated to stand with Don Conroy who was – of all things – painting a picture in the downpour, a watercolour, as it happens, of an oystercatcher (I think). I was to talk to Don about oystercatchers and painting when my turn came. Indeed if I could talk to any member of the public too that would be grand. For how long? Oh, for five minutes or so; my earpiece would tell me when the time came and ended. And so there I was with no knowledge of what was happening at all. Had the programme started? Who was talking to whom? What were they saying, so I wouldn't say the same things again when my turn came? We had our own cameraman who would get the nod when it was time for us, so at least that was something. Don had his own earpiece, so he too would be getting guidance. We discussed with each other what we might say and hoped for the best.

Of course when the time came and the red light came on, it was a different scenario. The time we were allocated was changed, but for longer or shorter no-one seemed to know. We couldn't hear a thing through the earpieces. We just went for it as best we could – me peering at Don's streaky painting, down which the rain was running, and discussing oystercatchers. The member of the public who I had lined up to speak kept wondering when they were to speak and nobody had any idea how long the piece was going to be. Were we still on air? Were we just on radio? You couldn't move or make faces as the camera was running and might even be transmitting. What else would we say now? Why weren't they releasing the blasted seal anyway? Eventually the cameraman stopped filming, as apparently the one at the water's edge with the seal was now operational. It had taken Derek longer than he thought to get there and we were on air longer to cover his hectic off-camera dash. A panting Derek finally saw off the seal, which was being released by Brendan Price, and the credits rolled.

We couldn't wait to read the reviews in the papers. Because it was TV as well as radio, we were covered in both sets of critiques. Liam Fay of the *Sunday Times* availed of the opportunity in his review to deliver himself of an opinion of how radio people behave on television. He opined that you could learn so much more about people when you could read their body language. He had read the body language of myself and Don Conroy and had concluded that we were both prima donnas of the highest order. Each of us, apparently, was trying to show off how much we knew without taking heed of what the other was saying. At one point he maintained that I offered poor Don a shoulder cold enough to provide perching for a whole row of arctic seabirds. Television had obviously gone to our heads completely and we were jostling for the limelight. 'Oh God, grant that we can see ourselves as others see us,' was a prayer we were taught in school. I think the reverse of the prayer would have been a salutary learning experience for Liam Fay.

When *Mooney Goes Wild* began in 1995, Brendan Howlin of Labour was Minister for the Environment. The programme didn't attract huge listenership figures then, so although Minister Howlin was very concerned about the public perception of the environment, he did not see our programme as a way of publicising his ideas. He did think that talking on local radio stations was the way forward, and I did a series of slots on local radio about the importance of our environment and how we were all responsible for it. I don't know if it all fell on deaf ears – nobody ever told me they heard me on their local station.

Come 1997, everything had changed. Fianna Fáil came to power with the Progressive Democrats and the environment became the business of several ministerial departments. Noel Dempsey was Minister for the Environment, Síle de Valera was Minister for Arts, Heritage, Culture, the Gaeltacht and the Islands, and Micheal Woods was Minister for Fisheries and Forestry (or Fish and Chips as it was irreverently dubbed). We had all three on the programme at different times – after all, politicians are a form of wildlife too.

Síle de Valera had Dúchas – the renamed and newly empowered Office of Public Works – in her brief. Special areas of conservation and natural heritage areas were being designated by her department. We felt the public should know all about what was going on – what areas, how many, etc. She would come on our programme, yes, but she would only answer questions that had been submitted and approved in advance and only Derek could interview her. The rest of us had to keep our mouths shut. So we didn't get to grill her like we would wish and, indeed, to this day the commencement order for most of the natural heritage areas has yet to be signed and they remain proposed sites. That department is now gone; Dúchas has again been absorbed into the OPW and the junior PD minister Tom Parlon is in charge.

Michael Woods came on our programme one Tree Day to speak about the wonderful things his department was doing with forestry. He didn't need the questions in advance and was willing to talk to any of us. I am sure he didn't need me introducing him as the aptly named Minister Woods, but he concealed any annoyance such a well-worn cliché may have provoked. He was delighted to announce that at 10 per cent forestry cover, we were well on our way to restoring Ireland's wooded landscape. The fact that the EU average at that time was 33 per cent forestry cover wasn't a statistic he wanted to hear, or that the only country in Europe with less woodland than us was Iceland. However, he got very testy when we pointed out that most of this Irish 10 per cent cover was, in fact, coniferous evergreen forestry grown as a crop, that these woodlands consisted of only one or two foreign exotic tree species and that they were not good for wildlife in the way native deciduous woodland would be. We were told we were always whinging and that these growing trees would absorb carbon dioxide from the air and that was good in these days of climate change. However, since then more deciduous woodlands have been planted – the millennium forests were all of native deciduous species – but we weren't graced with another visit from Minister Woods.

Noel Dempsey was a different kettle of fish. He was always willing to come on the programme and announce the wonderful things he was doing for the environment. He spoke about introducing a plastic-bag tax early in his ministry, which was proclaimed by all to be a very good idea. We did vox pops on shoppers emerging from supermarkets with their trolleys laden to the gunwales with plastic-bag-wrapped messages. What were they going to do when the tax came in? Would they pay for all these bags? Of course they wouldn't, but sure the tax would never come – them fellas were always making promises. And indeed it did seem like that for a bit. The minister accompanied us on a clean-up of the Grand Canal during a Spring Clean Week. (And to be fair to me, I did support Fianna Fáil for a while when Noel leaned on me to put on his wellies!) But there was no sign of the tax. The minister put the best face on it on air, but off the record he told us that as it was a tax the Department of Finance had to approve it, and as plastic bags were advertisements for grocers, they were holding things up too – demanding a definition of a plastic bag. Did it have handles? What about meat and fish? We were hardly going to go back to brown-paper parcels of lamb chops tied up with butcher's string. But to be fair to him, he hung in there and the plastic-bag tax came in and people did change their behaviour. On subsequent programmes we followed up what became of the money collected in the tax, and indeed it has been ring-fenced for environmental recycling projects. He had just delivered the tax by 2002 when, after the general election, he was moved to Education and Martin Cullen became Minister for the Environment.

We were dying to get our hands on Martin Cullen, particularly when we heard him say on some news interview that 'all these greenhouse gases are making a hole in the ozone layer'. Wisely for him, probably, he never accepted any of our invitations to come on the programme. In 2004 he moved to Transport and Dick Roche became Minister for the Environment. Minister Roche made his first appearance on the programme in June 2006. He wanted to announce some new special areas of conservation that had been designated in areas of coral on the seabed off the west coast. He was quite willing to come on for the whole hour, didn't need to see any questions in advance and would have no difficulty with whoever would be on the panel in the studio.

Sure why would he? He is a past master at not answering the question. No matter what Derek asked him we got 'on the one hand this and on the other that'. In the end Derek got completely exasperated and said, 'Just give us a yes or a no, let's play the yes or no game.' He did actually manage to get 'well, it's a no actually' out of him, but it was hard going. And this minister does not like to be interrupted. He has a nice trick of putting his hand firmly on your arm to shut you up so that he can speak. He didn't get to the announcement of the new special areas of conservation, in spite of being on for a whole hour – he got sidetracked by chewing gum and green motor cars.

Tom Parlon is the Minister for the OPW and in late 2005 we had a Bums on Bikes programme live from the Phoenix Park. Riding a bicycle is good for you and we had held a competition to see who should be awarded the bikes given to the programme by the OPW and the minister came along to support the event. He was a good sport and even rode a bike live on the radio. But naturally when asked the hard question of where in rural areas it was going to be safe to ride these bikes with all the traffic on the roads and no cycle paths, he referred the question to the Minister for Transport, one Martin Cullen, who never did send us in an answer. Ah yes, politicians – a species of wildlife with their own ways and rules of evolution.

Filming birds in their nests was another brainwave of Derek's. This all began with a jackdaw's nest in County Kildare. The camera would be put in the nest and the whole life inside would be filmed. Originally it was to be in a nest at Dick Warner's house, but it proved impossible to get the camera into the nest without disturbing the nesting pair. In the event, a nest near the premises of *Wild Ireland* magazine was chosen, just off the motorway near Leixlip. It was possible to get the camera into the nest before the eggs were laid, and so life in the nest from egg-laying to fledging could be filmed.

So far so good. But of course this was being recorded for twenty-four hours a day for three or four weeks. For much of the time nothing happened. The pictures were beamed on to a screen in the offices nearby and one could see the eggs there, or the chicks or whatever. Someone needed to look at the hours and hours of tape and edit the highlights. No money could pay for that sort of attention. So the idea of streaming it on to computer and letting the public have access to it by downloading the site was formed. This is what happened, although there wasn't great computer access in homes in the late 1990s. We covered it on the weekly radio show, one of which was broadcast from the site, and we regaled the listeners with stories of what was happening in the nest. The highlights were edited; such events as the eggs hatching out, the day Daddy brought in a dead chaffinch for the babies to eat, the bullying tactics of the two bigger babies who got all the food and crowded out their younger, smaller sibling, which duly died of hunger. Although they had eaten a dead chaffinch, they didn't actually eat their dead sibling and the body was carried away by Daddy some days later. Derek made an appearance on the *Late Late Show* with

Pat Kenny to facilitate the pictures being seen by a wider television audience and the whole thing won the Prix Europa award that year as it had incorporated radio, television and live Internet streaming.

Filming the inside of a bird's nest became something Derek wanted to do more and more of. Naturally, such events required the input of cameras and live access to the website which the programme now has for the past few years. It is not always possible to commit these resources to such a project. Should it therefore be a very rare and exciting bird such as a bird of prey, or a more familiar one, which would be easier to manage? Do you put the camera in (with all the expense and commitment) before the nesting gets underway and hope that the site is used this year, or do you wait until the nest is built and the eggs are about to be laid and risk disturbing the nesting pair? Difficult one to call.

The Marriott Hotel in the Druid's Glen was putting in a kingfisher bank at the river's edge. This was an artificial set of nesting holes with a glass back and an already positioned camera, which would transmit back to the screen in the bar. Would the kingfishers nest there, however? They did in the summers of 2005 and 2006 and provided great wildlife scenes for the golfers and the bar golfers. We described it on our radio programmes and put together a television documentary of the highlights earlier this year.

But still we wanted our own nest, streaming continuously on the *Mooney Goes Wild* website. Derek thought he was in business when a blackbird built a nest in his own garden at home in April 2006. He quickly and carefully set up the camera on the tree opposite and had it showing on a screen in his house. He was in the process of getting streaming set up and recording of activity in the nest underway when disaster struck. The nest was attacked by magpies when the parents were absent and the eggs destroyed. As recording wasn't yet happening, the event wasn't available for Derek to see. The blackbirds went off to build a nest elsewhere. However Derek wasn't to be denied.

He set up a nest box for blue tits that contained a recording camera and connected this up to his computer. And the very next day, Good Friday, two blue tits came prospecting. Derek managed to get the recording operational so everything that happened in the nest could be played back. He also prevailed upon Broadband and RTÉ to do their thing and, by the end of the week, he had the activities in the blue tits' nest streaming live on to the *Mooney Goes Wild* site.

It was like *Big Brother* only much better and more exciting. The public could log on to the website at any hour of the day or night and see what was going on in the nest. We saw the nest being made with painstaking attention to detail. Herself laid the eggs and there was great interest in how many there were and whether they were all the same colour. People texted in with questions, and a running commentary was carried on the weekly programme. In fact, we even broadcast a whole programme from Derek's house and gave a blow-by-blow account of the four eggs we could see.

The eggs hatched out on Tuesday, 16 May and Derek was as excited as if they were his very own children. There was great interest in seeing how many there were – six nestlings were the most that were counted, even though it seemed that perhaps nine eggs were laid. Watching the nestlings being fed and growing was amazing. The site got an enormous number of hits, as by now Irish people are connected to Broadband and are receiving the pictures live on their computers at home, at school, at work – everywhere, it would seem. Derek was always worried in case a magpie would make off with the parents and leave the nestlings as orphans. But they were clever and diligent parents and visited their chicks with food up to five hundred times a day each. Not that anyone counted for a whole day long, but by calculating from an hour's watching, such figures could be obtained.

The babies got bigger and bigger. They got all their coloured feathers. They pranced about in the nest practising flying and stretching their wings. They looked as if they might go at any minute. The whole country was all of a dither. What would happen when the time came? We knew that the parents would sit outside and call to the chicks who would emerge from the box and fly into the garden. Once they left they would never return. The only camera recording the procedure was inside the box and this would only record their departure, as it was too costly for RTÉ to have a second camera fixed outside, waiting for the moment when they should emerge.

They were to fledge on day twenty-two – 7 June. Derek woke to an unnatural silence. No chirping sounds from the screen downstairs. What had happened? He rushed down to see. The birds had flown. But worse, much worse, hadn't there been a surge of electrical power that night shortly after midnight which had caused the sensitive system to shut down and of course it didn't start up again. When Derek turned it on at eight that morning it was to reveal an empty nest. And all the recording had stopped after the power surge, so there was no record of what had happened. A mad dash out to the garden revealed nothing – the whole family had obviously decamped to open area further away. So there was no ending as such, or none that anyone saw. At least we can all assume the best, as we have seen nothing to the contrary. In nature all six babies would not survive and perhaps it was just as well that the story ended where it did. The viewers wouldn't have wanted to see any unhappy bits. It was a really popular slot. It got mentioned on lots of other radio programmes – in fact it wouldn't have amazed Derek one little bit if the fledging had been announced on the nine o'clock news.

The move to Saturday morning and the extension of the programme to one hour resulted in a huge increase in listeners – a quarter of a million of them tuned in, more than listened to the programmes on either side. The advent of email and the website means that huge amounts of listeners correspond with the programme each week, sending in pictures of what they have seen and captured on their cameras and mobile phones. Derek seems to have completely weaned the listeners off sending in dead things to be identified. I think it was the dead and rather smelly chaffinch that finished him off, and he issued a stern edict after that, forbidding such post. Producing educational posters and giving them free with the *RTÉ Guide* has proved a popular way of educating our listeners. Early in 2006, we followed up the success of the dawn-chorus poster and CD with one on waders and, early in May, we had one on creepy-crawlies. And again, more than 100,000 of each were snapped up by an interested public.

The programme has come a long way in the eleven years since it began. As I write there is change in the air again – the programme may change its length or indeed change its slot again. But one thing is certain: if they said it couldn't be done, that you couldn't have a programme on wildlife on radio rather than on television, that there wouldn't be enough material or interest to sustain it beyond one season – well, quite simply, they were wrong.

Éanna Ní Lamhna
October 2006

CHAPTER ONE

Wildlife on the wireless

Until the 1990s, wildlife programmes on the airwaves in Ireland were confined to television. Éamon de Buitléar and Gerrit van Gelderen had pioneered documentaries shot in Ireland with Irish wildlife featuring as the stars. Wildlife on the radio was not considered except in the form of earnest lectures or gardening information, although there was a series in the early 1950s (before my time) where J Ashton Freeman used to talk about wildlife and do bird mimicry.

But, like dancing on the wireless, it could be done. All that was needed was imagination to inspire it and a leap of faith to produce it. But how to go about it at the start of the 1990s? What did the ordinary person in Ireland at that time know about wildlife? What did they want to know? How much of it could they take at a time? How could you do it on the radio? The radio producer, Dick Warner, knew just the man for the job.

Enter Derek Mooney, a rising young presenter in RTÉ with a lively curiosity and a sense of the ridiculous. He was the person to know the questions to ask, the questions that anyone at home might want to ask. The concept got going with a series on places where wildlife lived, called *Habitats*, and another, *The Nature Line*, answering queries written in by listeners. (This was in the days before e-mail.) But it was in May 1995 that the idea of a live interactive programme on wildlife was mooted by Derek Mooney and *Mooney Goes Wild* was born.

This programme would seek out fascinating nuggets of information about Irish wildlife, would keep abreast of current developments, would answer listeners' questions but, above anything else, would not be boring. Items were to be short and snappy, of the 'I never knew that' variety, and would not lecture the listeners. The format was to have Mooney as presenter, with a panel of so-called experts, Mooney being the arbiter of how interesting each piece was.

And it worked, beyond wildest expectations. The series has been running now since May 1995 and I have been on that panel of 'experts' since the beginning. The listenership has reached over 130,000 betimes and, as well as Derek, and latterly Richard Collins, I too have become irrevocably associated with it. 'Are you the woman on the radio? Every time I see a spider I think of you! I feel guilty when I kill creepy-crawlies now, thanks to you...' This sort of thing is the least of what I am accosted with when I venture out and open my mouth.

Wildlife radio has come of age in the last few years, thanks in no small measure to the Mooney show. Wildlife and nature now feature in mainstream broadcasting with Pat Kenny, Marian Finucane and especially Gerry Ryan on 2FM, regularly airing wildlife topics. Another important development has been the Internet, with a profusion of websites developing on all sorts of nature topics and, here too, *Money Goes Wild* has fully availed of this medium. The broadcasting world is changing rapidly; where we go from here is anybody's guess.

But still the words have to come – when I stand up before an audience with my trusty slide projector, or when I am faced with a red light in the studio, I have to make the case for wildlife. So, what do I say? How do I go about it? I explain the world we live in, as it appears to me. I find the lives of other creatures fascinating and I try to convey this as convincingly as possible. And since you can't actually have my voice ringing in your ears all the time, here's the written version.

CHAPTER TWO

In the beginning

There actually was a beginning to wildlife in Ireland as we know it today, and that was 10,000 years ago at the end of the last Ice Age. Ireland had been covered with a layer of ice, a kilometre thick in places, for thousands of years prior to this and no plant, animal or person could live here. Global warming came about – I suppose even then that's what it was, although humans can't be blamed for that one – and caused temperatures to rise and the ice sheets began to melt. Now, this layer of ice had covered all the northern European countries, forcing the plants and animals to live in a much smaller Europe, the unfrozen southern half. The sea level was much lower too because of all the water held in the ice-sheets.

As the ice began to melt along its southern edge and retreat northwards, bare countries were uncovered. Sea levels were so low that Ireland and Britain were not islands but were attached by land-bridges to each other and to mainland Europe. Faced with these wide spaces opening up, the plants and animals corralled for so long in southern Europe began to move northwards.

Those at the edge of the ice made the most progress. And it was a race against time – at least as far as Ireland was concerned. The ice was inexorably melting and the seas were getting deeper all the time. What could get to Ireland before the land-bridges were cut off? Hardy, speedy things had no trouble, and so cold-tolerant trees with wind-borne seeds were our first trees – think of willow and birch. Once we had trees, we had habitat for caterpillars and greenflies and so we had food and shelter for birds. Trees whose seeds were cunningly wrapped in juicy berries arrived, presumably originally in the gut of gourmet birds – trees like mountain ash, holly, hawthorn, blackthorn, yew and elder. Finally the large trees, which formed the continuous leafy canopy in those woodlands, slowly made their way here – oak, ash, elm and pine. But time was running out – the bridges were flooded. The beginning was over. The also-rans included trees like beech, which only made it to England (which lost its land-bridge to Europe much later), sycamore and horse-chestnut, which were still dallying in southern Europe and would now have to wait for millennia for entry visas.

And, of course, animals had the same conditions to endure. If you couldn't fly you'd have to walk, and coming by land was only possible when the land-bridges were still there. So we got stoats but for some reason not weasels; pygmy shrews but no other kind; wolves, bears and foxes; hares but no rabbits; red squirrels but no hedgehogs (they must still have been hibernating!); no dormice, no moles, no frogs, no snakes. Yes, snakes never got here. They were obviously disporting themselves on the Mediterranean shores when the ice began to melt, and by the time they slithered slowly northwards to the Irish Sea, crossing was by ferry only. The English Channel formed much later than the Irish Sea, so the snakes did get as far as Britain and all the way up Europe to Sweden, but they never made it to Ireland – they were too slow getting off the starting blocks.

Earthworms weren't, though, and although their rate of movement can hardly be described as speedy, their starting line was much nearer the edge of the ice, as was the starting point for slugs and snails, all of which species are in abundant supply here.

Of course we only got a selection of what was available in Europe and, indeed, the selection there was no great shakes, compared to what was on offer at similar latitudes across the Atlantic in North America. This was because of the direction of the mountain ranges. In Europe they lie in an east–west direction – think of the Pyrenees and the Alps. During the Ice Age, as the weather got colder, the ice moved downwards over Europe and North America, pushing all before it in a southerly direction. But it was freezing on top of the mountains too and glaciers formed there and moved down the mountainsides.

So the plants and animals fleeing the ice in Europe came to the Pyrenees and the Alps covered in ice, with an ice sheet behind them forcing them southwards – surely the original quandary of being between a rock and a hard place! And many, many species became extinct.

But in North America, the Rockies and the Appalachians run north–south. The plants and the animals could move southwards with no bother and when the ice retreated they all went off northwards again. So today if you go to similar latitudes in North America, not only will you find different species, as you might expect on a different continent, but you will also find a much greater number of species as well.

If you were to fly in a helicopter over Ireland 8,000 years ago what would you see? Well, it would be an island, detached from all further supply of non-flying plant and animal species, but what exactly would you see from the air? You'd see 80 per cent of the country covered in forest – ash, hazel, sessile oak and elm on good soil; pedunculate oak and holly on acid soil; and the mountains covered in pine. The whole of the midlands would be one enormous lake. The melting ice had dumped its loads of sand and gravel in lines called eskers, where rivers once flowed under the ice, and these walls of sand and gravel had stopped the meltwater flowing away, making the low-lying central plain one large lake.

Come back in your helicopter 3,000 years later and a different scene would greet your eyes. The low-lying lakes had all filled in with vegetation, giving us the huge areas of raised bogs we had in the midlands until the advent of machinery, 5,000 years later, destroyed them all in sixty years.

The one thing you would not see in your first helicopter ride would have been much evidence of humans, but man was on the move too and no Irish Sea was going to deter him. Europeans had advanced from Palaeolithic (Early Stone Age) to Mesolithic (Mid-Stone Age) at this stage and it was Mesolithic man who first ventured across the sea to Ireland. (Scientists always use big words where short simple ones would do just as well: 'lithic' merely means stone, 'paleao' is old, 'meso' is middle and 'neo' is new.) The earliest evidence of human campsites in Ireland has been recorded from County Antrim from as long as 9,000 years ago. These were hunter-gatherers with primitive stone tools and they made little or no impact on the landscape. They couldn't cut down trees, so they had to travel by river and gather what they could to eat. Even then disposal of waste was an issue and landfill was the preferred option of disposal. How else can you explain the middens, some of which date back to this time – great heaps of shells carelessly tossed aside when they had finished dining in a favourite cooking spot?

Looking at these kitchen middens today, what strikes me is the size of the periwinkle shells they contain, many of them much bigger than those you commonly see on rocks nowadays. Middens also contain bones and the odd bit of pottery or jewellery that got lost at the feast. We think of these rubbish dumps from long ago as archaeological treasure troves, but will that be the attitude to our landfill sites 5,000 years from now?

This happy state of affairs lasted until 5,000 years ago when a new coloniser made its way to our shores – Neolithic (New or Late Stone Age) man, the first farmers. Humans had got tired of this hunter-gatherer way of life and someone, probably a woman who had got fed up moving the tent to gather food somewhere else, thought, 'Why don't we make the plants grow beside us instead of always having to go and look for them?' and gathered and sowed the seeds of the grasses most commonly eaten. The men used to disappear off on dangerous (and exciting) hunts, sometimes for weeks on end – not very convenient. A much better arrangement would be to have the animals too nearby, and then perhaps improvements could be made to the tent and it would be easier on the children – can't you just imagine it! This is quite possibly how domestication of animals came about.

So successful did this farming way of life prove that populations expanded and more land had to be acquired – hence the movement of peoples across Europe and into Ireland. Even more remarkable was their behaviour when they got here. These were no primitive Mesolithic people – they were New Stone Age men with state-of-the-art stone tools and they knew how to remove trees. Being good ecologists, they knew that ash and hazel grew on the good soil, so they got rid of them first, to let the light in so that grass could grow and their cattle and sheep could graze.

And this was the beginning of the end for plants and animals that got in the way of progress. Some, like wolves and eagles, who were seen as the enemies of lambs and calves, were directly targeted. But it was also the end of the line for animals that needed large areas of untouched woodlands to live in – curtains for the wild boar and the woodpecker.

If the arrival of Neolithic man wasn't bad enough from wildlife's point of view, the weather deteriorated too – it got colder and wetter. It rained much more, particularly on the mountainsides, which were covered in pine forests. The saturated soil became an ideal habitat for Sphagnum moss, which grew over the roots of the trees, blocking the air from them, and so the pine trees died and the blanket bog grew up around them. Things don't rot in a bog, because it is too acidic and there's not enough oxygen, so the pine roots are there to this day – bog deal. The bogs grew over the early farmland cleared by the first Neolithic farmers too, as the excavations at the Céide Fields in north Mayo demonstrate.

Invaders, cold, rain – what else could happen? What else indeed but pestilence and disease? This time it was the elm tree that suffered, presumably with what we know today as Dutch elm disease. Within a short space of time most of the elms disappeared. We know this, because we can see that there is a sudden, huge drop in the amount of elm pollen that was trapped in the bogs at around this time (our bogs contain accurate accounts, in the form of layers of trapped pollen, of all the plants growing around them, their abundance and chronological order). It took nearly 400 years for the elm to recover its place in the native woodlands.

The helicopter ride 3,000 years ago (around 1000 BC) would show a different picture: the start of things to come, habitat destruction, species elimination and a new phenomenon – illegal immigrants. Because trade with Europe increased, stowaways came to Ireland on board the boats and ships, black rats and house mice came in food supplies, and brown rats, frogs and bank voles were to follow subsequently. And as man discovered metal, first bronze and then iron, tilling the soil became possible. You can write the rest of the script yourself. We can blame the Danes, the Normans, the Tudors, the Great Famine, the general perfidy of Albion, for the way the countryside was managed if we like, but the fact remains that, when we got our own hands on the tiller of government, the country was changed out of all recognition. By 1921 we had reduced our 80 per cent woodland to 1.5 per cent. We had introduced another hundred species of plants. Our bogs are now down to 3 per cent of land area from a one-time grand total of 16 per cent. Rabbits, hedgehogs, fallow deer and sika deer had been brought here to grace the menus and fill the cooking pots of the more adventurous.

And if you used to live in a forest – tough. You had two choices – become extinct or adapt. So capercaillies, who had no pine forest, took the first choice, while pine martens and jays just managed to cling on in the few remaining broad-leaved forests. Some of those who chose the second route, pragmatically took what was going. And what was going was hedgerow, miles and miles of linear woodland, taking up 1.5 per cent of the country. Many of the inhabitants of our garden hedges with which we are so familiar, such as robins and blackbirds, were originally woodland birds – surely a case of 'if you can't beat them, join them'.

Our hedgerows are extremely important habitats in the Ireland of today, an Ireland which has very little broad-leaved woodland. Although we are planting new woodlands, most of what we plant consists of coniferous trees, all the same species (foreign ones) and all the same age. So our original woodland flora and fauna are better off in old, long-established field hedges than in the new evergreen woodlands. We maintain that, generally speaking, we like wildlife. We enjoy looking at wild flowers and hearing the birds sing. Why, then, is the removal of the site hedge the first thing we do when we go to build ourselves a new house in a nice rural area? And why, oh why, do we replace it in so many instances with a hedge of evergreen Leyland cypress or – even worse – an ever-yellow one?

CHAPTER THREE

Drama in the garden – an everyday story of birdlife

Many of our garden birds, which seem so tame and happy in our gardens, are actually dispossessed woodland birds. Take the robin, for example. Robins originally lived on woodland edges and, as woodlands diminished and hedgerows increased, they adapted to the change very successfully. In woodlands, communication between birds was by song because they couldn't see each other on account of all the trees and cover in the way and robins still sing, although they are wholly adapted to gardens now. Robins are unusual among songbirds in that both the male and female sing. (In most other bird species it is the male that does the singing.) Although, to be quite accurate, the female robin sings and holds territory only in the winter. She is more docile and quiet during the breeding season, as silence is the price she has to pay to get a mate. The male wouldn't like a female who sings!

We can start off the robin's story in winter. At this time, the robin visits the bird table – the shortage of food overcomes any xenophobic tendencies. But come spring and the lengthening day, the sap rises in the trees and a male robin's thoughts turn to love. But first there must be some land to make a good impression on the intended. Where else but your nice suburban garden?

So he stakes his claim and perches on the trees and bushes along the perimeter and advertises his eligibility with what is, to us, the most melodious

45

song. The song also indicates to other male robins looking for territory the character and, indeed, the bottle of the singer. If another male robin thinks that he can take the singer on, he approaches. Our sitting tenant is outraged. He rushes towards the visitor with his body language screaming aggression. This, however, may not be enough to deter the intruder, and actual hand-to-hand (or claw-to-claw) combat may take place. Robins have been known to kill would-be land-grabbers.

The intruder dealt with, our hero resumes his song. Another robin appears. This time it is a female, checking out the local talent, having been mightily impressed with the song. But – would you believe it? – our hero doesn't know that she is female (both sexes look the same) and he rushes over again, full of aggro, to see off the intruder. Fortunately for the survival of the robin species, female robins know what sex they are and act accordingly. Instead of squaring up to the opera singer, she is suitably demure and submissive and puts your man completely off his stroke. She is tolerated in the furthest extremity of his territory.

It is not long, though, until one thing leads to another and soon he is enthusiastically showing her around the most desirable building sites on his property and feeding her choice titbits. She gets a good idea of what sort of husband he'll be, how good he'll be at finding food for a family and how sharp his eye is at spotting a secure nesting site. Once planning permission has been given, he's off helping with the collection of nest material from which she constructs a nest and fashions it to her body shape. And, of course, he is a very vigorous lover. Frequency of mating can range from once a day to twice an hour around the time of egg formation – he can walk the walk as well as talk the talk!

Robins can have a clutch of up to six eggs and the one-time neighbourhood thug makes a very dependable husband, feeding first herself and, later on, the babies with the creepy-crawly content of your garden. And, in a good year, the performance can be repeated twice and even three times over, with the same missus of course.

By the end of the summer, your robins could have at least ten babies, which together with the original parents, comes to twelve – a six-fold increase in robin population. The oldest ringed robin was thirteen years old when it died. Say yours are not trying for the *Guinness Book of Records* and live for only ten years, and all their offspring and their children set up home in your garden, how many robins will be in your garden at the end of those ten years? Increasing by a factor of six each year, you will start off with two, have twelve by the end of summer one, 72 at the end of the second year, 432 by the end of year three... and well over 120 million by the end of year ten! Well, will you? No, you will have two robins. And will there be a large heap of 120 million dead robins on your front lawn? No, of course not. The truth is that this amazing reproductive capacity of robins cannot possibly be fulfilled.

Go back to year one. With the best will in the world there is no way that twelve robins can find enough food in your garden over the winter (bearing in mind that in the same imaginary scenario there are twelve robins in the adjoining garden looking for food as well). They would die of hunger.

But things don't get to this stage, because most robins don't survive babyhood. They are almost all caught by predators in the inexperienced early days of flying. They are food for the next level in the food chain. It has to be – life is not a Walt Disney cartoon. But, somehow, while we might accept that a sparrowhawk could dine on one of your garden robins, we are most outraged to see and hear the magpies do so. But at least they are hungry, and the robins are part of their food chain. They're not part of the food chain, though, for your beloved pussycat, stuffed to the gills with Kit-e-Kat or the like. He's not hungry, and he doesn't need to dine on baby robins. He just kills robins for the hell of it; he doesn't even eat them. More garden robins are killed by cats (unnecessary pets imposed on the food chain) than are ever killed by magpies. So, think of that if you own a cat before you open your mouth to deplore the marauding magpie.

In fact, the two robins in your garden at the end of the season are most likely to be one parent and one of the young – the luckiest, the most alert, the smartest youngster. In other words, it's the survival of the fittest. And off they go to separate territories for the winter and next spring the story begins all over again.

Of course, the same general principle applies to blackbirds, thrushes, wrens, blue-tits – whatever other birds are in your garden. All these birds are only concerned with their own species. Robins don't care how many blackbirds or thrushes come in. Great tits are only interested in other great tits. The number of bird species in your garden depends on the availability of cover, nesting sites and food – and indeed the absence of the resident predator, the cat, who can spend all day in the garden bird-watching as his dinner is assured by the tin-opener. At least the magpies have to patrol a much larger area and a well-hidden nest and careful, cautious parents can outwit them.

So, is your garden a good habitat for birds? You may think it is. You may be doing the divil and all putting out bread, hanging up nuts in special feeders, even making those bird cakes that you get recipes for in wildlife magazines. But is this only moving the deck-chairs around on the *Titanic*? What have you done to the garden itself to ensure that it is suitable for birds? What grows there? What creepy-crawlies are welcome or at least tolerated? There's no sense in blitzing everything with weedkiller and pesticide and then putting out a few crumbs to salve your conscience. There's more to it than that, I'm afraid!

CHAPTER FOUR

Bird food – the à la carte approach

Birds are the Public Relations Officers for wildlife. People like to see and hear them. They feel familiar with them. We have a manageable number of species here. You can recognise most of those you see and bird books are sufficiently available to make it easy to identify the more unusual ones. They herald the seasons: bird song – spring; swallows – the start of summer; cuckoos and corncrakes – summer surely; and geese, swans and waders enliven our winter days. We're proud of our status as being vital to the bird population of Europe and of having internationally important bird sites.

Much of our radio programme, and many of the phone calls to it, concern birds and their welfare. Irish people feed them assiduously in winter, being careful to buy the right kind of bird seed, free from pesticides. We nannyingly stop feeding them when they're rearing young, lest they might lazily fill their babies' crops with bread rather than high-protein insect food, but actually we can continue to feed birds in the summer if we want to. Chris Mead, the British expert on songbirds, said on our programme once that parent birds weren't eejits – that they were well able to work out the right food to give their babies (although he mightn't have put it quite like that).

And yet, and yet… why are we such two-faced hypocrites? Why do we poison all their food and then moan to the radio programme that the thrushes, say, are getting very scarce? How else would they be, when every slug and snail they consume has already been killed by you with a blue pellet?

In an ideal world, slugs and snails would form part of the normal variety of flora and fauna. They come out at night to feed (as many creatures do to avoid predators, in this case the birds). They are herbivores, so their numbers are controlled by the amount of food that is available to them. In a natural habitat – say, a woodland – there is a natural balance of species. Some of these are palatable to slugs and snails, but not so much that the place is overrun with them.

But in ecological terms, what is your garden? Like primeval man you have cleared away the naturally occurring vegetation, to grow particular things that you like either to see or to eat yourself. If any of the dispossessed, naturally occurring plants dare to try and return, you arrogantly refer to them as weeds and remove them by fair means or foul. You only want your carefully chosen selected plants. And, of course, whether by accident or design or just Murphy's Law, these carefully selected plants in the main are beloved of slugs and snails, who cannot believe their good luck to be living in the midst of such plenty. They go on to raise large families to share in the largesse, always being careful to feed only at night and to hide away when the light comes.

Birds, of course, haven't survived all these millions of years without learning a trick or two and thrushes in particular have specialised in snails. Step number one: get up early and nab them before they hide away. Step number two (and this is a thrush speciality): invest in opening equipment. It's hard to get a snail out of a shell if it has obstinately coiled itself inside, but thrushes have worked out how to do it. Hold it in your beak and bash it against a hard surface like a rock and eat the contents when it smashes open – simple! In fact, in areas like sand dunes where suitable stones are scarce, any available boulder is used by several thrushes and is called a 'thrush's anvil'. You can see the evidence in broken snail shells all round it. Although we have two thrushes, the song thrush and the mistle thrush – and, indeed, the blackbird which is also a thrush species – it is only the song thrush that has developed this technique. Gulls and grey crows drop sea-shells from on high to open them, but songbirds have never learned this trick.

But if you have upset the balance of nature by rearranging the plant species composition of the piece of land around your house (a preoccupation known as gardening), you don't want to hand over the fruits of your labours to voracious slugs and snails. Hence the little blue pellets. Slugs and snails are killed on the spot and thrushes can find them, no bother – even the late birds, never mind the early ones. Too many chemically killed snails can't be good for birds (would you like to eat them?) and, not surprisingly, the number of thrushes diminishes. And even if you conscientiously get up before dawn to bury the poisoned slug corpses by torchlight, you are still diminishing the amount of food available for birds in your garden.

If we consider tillage farming – another unnatural practice, if we look at it purely in ecological terms – the number of herbivorous insects that are encouraged by such monocultures is enormous. A whole field of wheat is Christmas and its birthday for anything that likes wheat, and such creepy-crawlies can reach great numbers if unchecked. The way to check them is considered to be by killing them with poisonous sprays. Consider the amount of crop sprays and pesticides that are sprayed over large areas of intensive agriculture – too often the headlands around the field and even the hedge get a blast too – and the wonder is that we have any insects left at all anywhere for birds to feed on.

What to do? Come on, you can work it out for yourself. Prioritise. Snails and slugs don't eat everything, so select species for your garden accordingly. Provide hiding places for the slugs and snails yourself, such as old mats, even empty grapefruit halves, and evict the tenants in the morning, preferably into open space where the birds can see and grab them. Protect the delicate plants you can't wean yourself off with a mini-glasshouse made from a 2-litre clear plastic drink bottle (with the top cut off to let the rain in) Snails find it hard to get their foot over these. And organic slug killers, such as beer in a saucer, at least do not poison the rest of the food chain. Then you can enjoy your birds with a virtuous glow.

CHAPTER FIVE

Miss Moffat's revenge – spiders

Little Miss Moffat has a lot to answer for. We're fed this nursery rhyme as children and, as a result of the autosuggestion, I'm sure many otherwise normal adults are reduced to the screaming heebie-jeebies by just the sight of a spider. Is this fear justified? Does it stand up to scrutiny? Of course not. Irish spiders are not only harmless, they are our friends and should not be screamed at.

There are, broadly speaking, two sorts of spiders in Ireland. There are the web-spinning spiders, which spin webs to catch food, and there are the hunting spiders, which hunt after their food. These latter can make webs too for nests and suchlike, but they don't catch food in them.

We are all well up enough on spiders to know that they are not insects – they have eight legs, not six as insects do, and so they are, technically, arachnids. But did you know that they have eight eyes too, arranged in a circle on the top of their heads? A sensible place to have eyes if you are watching out for attack from above from hungry birds.

Web-spinning spiders occur in many different groups, distinguished by the shape and complexity of the web they spin. But many of us must be familiar (if we have an eye in our heads at all) with the garden spider, an expert web-spinner, who seems to be especially obvious in the month of September. The spider itself, if you look closely at it, has a white cross on its back making it easy to identify.

Web-spinning is a matter of finding a good location and getting established. To describe it in basic terms, an invisible, sticky, flexible curtain has to be put in place on a highway that is hopefully frequented by lots of flies. The anchor lines must be dropped first. These are lines of good, strong, spider silk, so that the whole edifice has a firm foundation. From the centre, the spider spins out thin sticky strands, which are the trap. This fills the whole space allotted for the web and the spider sits at the side attached to the last silken strand and waits for a fly to blunder in. And when one does, it is the vibrations on the end of the strand attached to the spider that alert it to the presence of food.

Out it charges at once, across the web to the struggling victim who is stuck fast. A quick bite with a dash of venom to the hapless fly's neck and he is no more. He can be eaten on the spot by sucking out all the juicy insides or, if the spider is a trifle full, the fly can be embalmed in lots of new silk and hung up in the spider's larder for leaner times. The fly didn't have a chance from the moment it touched the web; the sticky silk quickly entrapped it. But did you ever wonder how spiders themselves don't get caught in their own webs? There are two reasons, actually. The main anchor lines of the web, substantial threads of silk, are not sticky strands and the spider knows to move along these highways. But what about when it gets to the struggling fly in the sticky bit? The spider has oily feet, which don't stick to the sticky strands, a bit like the way a plaster won't stick to your knee if you put ointment on the cut first.

This means that spiders don't get stuck in each other's webs either, but why would you want to go calling if your neighbour is a savage cannibal? Spiders – particularly females – have no problem eating other spiders that come their way. So if a dashing young spider's thoughts turn to love, should discretion be the better part of valour? Certainly the phrase 'faint heart never won fair lady' could have been coined for the Lothario spider out on the town. How to win the lady without becoming her dinner? Well, like any good suitor he must bring a gift when he comes calling. A nice juicy fly, particularly well wrapped in sticky web, fits the bill, and no courting spider would set off without this. Mating in most species normally involves an extremely close intimate encounter, but our hero really doesn't want to get too close. So in matters amorous, his interesting body design comes into its own. Male spiders can transfer their sperm to the ends of their palps – two antennae-like appendages on either sides of their heads – which literally gives them breathing space during a mating encounter.

So a spider out for a night on the town arms himself with a juicy present, arranges his personal toilette, and comes calling on the neighbouring web. He indicates to herself that he has arrived by vibrating the sticky silk in the web. She thinks that dinner has landed and rushes out to polish off the intruder. Our hero quickly thrusts the gift-wrapped fly at his ladylove and while she is distracted unwrapping the present, mates gingerly with her from as far away as possible, keeping her literally at palp's length. If he hasn't wrapped the present enough, or lingers too long in the love department, herself has no compunction gobbling him up. The adrenalin rush must be mighty.

Actually, it makes no difference to the survival of the species if the female eats the male after mating – in fact the extra protein will come in handy for the ensuing egg laying – because the vital sperm and male genes have already been transferred. But our hero would like to live another day and is very concerned that he should manage a speedy departure. So it is true: female spiders do eat their husbands, but not always.

After all this drama, the female spins a special web and lays the eggs in it. She then leaves the young entirely to their own devices. They hatch out and grow into spiderlings still in the web nest. They are dispersed by an interesting type of explosive action if the nest is touched at a certain stage of development. The young have got bigger inside, the web nest is stretched to bursting point and any outside pressure at all – say, being investigated by a predator – causes the web to burst and the spiderlings to explode out. This ensures their wide dispersal, stops them eating each other and, of course, enables at least some of them to escape if the nest is attacked by predators.

The big black spiders you find under loose floorboards or at the back of the garden shed are hunting spiders. These come out at night and chase their prey – earwigs, beetles, woodlice, anything that will provide a meal – around the garden. And they hunt over the whole garden and the walls of the house, anywhere they can find food. They come in and out of the house through open windows with impunity. They do, that is, until they unfortunately enter the room in the house with the spider trap and indeed the room most likely to have the window open – the bathroom. They race around this room too, unknown to us, chasing prey in the wee small hours of the morning. That is until they have the bad luck to fall into the bath – for then they are trapped. They cannot climb up the slippery sheer sides and, of course, it is always a huge spider that gets trapped in the bath. The small ones seem to be light enough to scramble out.

What should you do about the situation when you are finished screaming? Cruel types wash them down the plughole. Food chain experts (or those who hate earwigs and woodlice even more) catch them in the tooth mug and empty them out the window. But you could spare yourself all the histrionics by simply putting the plug into the plughole. End of problem. This is not because it stops them coming up the plughole – they'd want to be equipped with sub-aqua gear to get through the water trap in the S-bend. No, it quite simply provides them with a ladder – if a spider falls in, it can climb up the chain attached to the plug and escape. A towel casually thrown over the edge would do the trick as well. Simple, really.

Spiders should be high on our list of friendly creepy-crawlies if only for the fact that bluebottles and houseflies are favourite items in their diet, and even I cannot think of a defence for the bluebottle.

None of the spiders in this country do us the slightest harm. Their jaws are not strong enough to bite us anyway deeply, and they haven't enough venom to kill us or do us any harm. They are tiny, really, in the world order of spiders. Our biggest spider would have a body size at most of about 20mm and its legs might be this length again; the whole thing, legs and all, would easily fit in the palm of your hand. The world's biggest spider is the Goliath tarantula. Its body size alone is 90mm, while its leg span can reach 250mm. In other words, were you to put this on your hand its body alone would completely cover your palm, while its legs would be the length of your fingers. Even this spider doesn't harm us: it lives in the northern part of South America and dines on snakes, toads and mice. You have to go to Australia for the really nasty spiders, such as the Sydney funnel-web spider or the red-back spider, or to the southern US for the black widow spider. So get a grip when you see a common-or-garden Irish spider. If this makes you feel bad, don't even think of how you might exist in a country where there are tarantulas!

CHAPTER SIX

The terrible truth about bluebottles and flies

Am I on the side of all creepy-crawlies? Well, even I cannot think of anything good to say about bluebottles. Shall I give you the gory details?

Bluebottles are pretty typical insects – body in three parts, six legs, two wings. Standard enough arrangement. But did you ever notice how much walking a fly does? If you had wings, would you bother much with walking, when you could fly everywhere? So why do the flies do it? What are they up to? Well, flies have very interesting feet. First of all they have hooks on them so that they can grip on to any surface. They can walk up glass windows and walk upside-down on the ceiling. But they have something else on their feet – taste buds. And when you think about it, this is very useful. Our taste buds are on our tongues and if we want to taste anything we have to put it into our mouths, and spit it out again hastily if it proves to taste nasty. How convenient it would be just to touch it with your toe and declare it to be palatable or not.

So that's why flies walk, when they could be flying – they're tasting things. One minute it could be the dog's droppings outside – the next it could be your dinner or the piece of ham cooling on the sideboard. They're not particular where they put their germ-laden feet.

When they do find a piece of meat they fancy (and bluebottles in particular love meat), how are they going to eat it? How well equipped are they in the teeth department? Well, very poorly; actually, they have no teeth. Their tongue is like a rolled-up hollow tube in their mouth, for all the world like a paper party whistle, and they can only feed by sucking up liquid through this hollow tongue. So the meat must be liquefied before eating and they have the very solution to do it with – vomit. They vomit on the piece of meat, the strong acid in this quickly liquefies the surrounding meat, and then they slurp up the vomit and the surrounding meat. Yum. And, if they want a second mouthful, they repeat the process. Then you come along, shoo away the fly and eat the meat yourself. Not any more you won't!

But what if it is a huge piece of meat in the fly's mind? A pity to waste all this good food just because the fly can't eat it all now. Ever with an eye to the future and the survival of the species, the fly takes this opportunity to lay eggs on the meat, thus ensuring a supply of food for its offspring.

This whole phenomenon often only comes to people's attention when the business happens in a confined space. Say a bird falls out of a nest in the chimney and dies behind the blocked-up fireplace. Or a mouse dies under the hot-water cylinder in the hot press. (Did you know that there's a hollow under the cylinder where it can be trapped?) In both cases, from the bluebottle's point of view, there is a supply of meat going a-begging and it will quickly detect it as it begins to go off. Each female can lay up to a hundred eggs and the eggs quickly hatch out into fly maggots – fat white juicy grubs.

These grubs feast away on the dead flesh and, in the fullness of time, maybe a fortnight later, they metamorphose into adult bluebottles. They are attracted towards light, which comes through the opening the original egg-laying bluebottle entered through, and they all swarm out through this to the light. Then you come into your under-used sitting room or summer holiday home and are appalled by the hundreds of bluebottles swarming in the window – or dead if you haven't come in for some time. This will continue to happen in waves until all the meat is eaten off the dead jackdaw or mouse, or until you find it first and dispose of it.

Old birds' nests under the eaves, particularly starlings' nests, can attract greenbottles, which are vegetarian and feed on the nest material itself. However, these are no more welcome a sight in hundreds in your sitting room than are their carnivorous cousins the bluebottles. And, indeed, their buzzing sounds have inspired no poet (no verses about bluebottle-loud glades), but in truth add to our general disgust.

So flies are the dustbin men of nature. They naturally break down and use up waste. If we are untidy with our dustbins and refuse and dump everything in landfill sites, we shouldn't be amazed to see vast quantities of flies. Could they be harnessed to eat up the putrescible waste in a controlled situation and the juicy white maggots fed to ducks as part of our food chain? Just wondering! (In the light of the foregoing we should have the bunting out for the spiders.)

An interesting side effect, as it were, of all this is how certain plants have exploited the situation. Flesh-eating flies are carnivores and don't eat plants, so why would they visit them? And would plants want them anyway? Flowering plants have been most ingenious in the way in which they have evolved to ensure their survival. Plants produce pollen – the male cells – and these need to fall on the female part of the flower in order to form seeds. It is much better if it falls on the female part of another flower of the same species some distance away, than for inbreeding to happen in any individual flower. So some species of plants have evolved means whereby they inveigle meat-eating flies to do this job for them.

Rafflesia is one such flower. This is the largest flower in the world, it looks like a large leathery cabbage and it grows on the forest floor in the tropical rain forests of Asia. When it is fully open and its pollen is ripe and ready for business, it exudes a smell of rotting flesh, so much so that the natives of these parts call it the corpse flower. The flies smell it when it is open and flock there in their thousands. They walk all over it looking for the non-existent rotting meat that they can smell, and in doing so get covered in pollen. Eventually disillusioned, they fly off. But again they smell rotting meat – another open rafflesia flower – and off they go to inspect, covered in pollen from the previous flower. So the rafflesia achieves its objective and gets itself pollen from a different flower. Of course, some of the time the smell must be a real rotting animal or the flies wouldn't survive.

Mind you, you don't have to go to the tropical forests to observe this phenomenon. We have the same carry-on in our own woods in spring, admittedly on a smaller scale. The arum lily, a common spring woodland plant, has a most peculiar projectile emerging from its flowerhead, called the spathe.

This spathe has a rotten smell which is attractive to flies who think it is meat. They fly to it and buzz around it. The smell seems to them to be coming up from below and they seek urgently along the length of the spathe for the food. The neck of the spathe is protected by a rim of stiff hairs, which only bend downwards, so the flies can get in, but they cannot get out.

Eventually some flies arrive on the scene who have already been in an earlier arum lily and, of course, they are covered in that lily's pollen – this is what our lily has been waiting for. Once these slow-learner flies, who have again fallen for the smell-but-no-food trick, come down the spathe and touch their pollen-covered bodies off the female part of the flower, fertilisation of our lily takes place. Now the stiff guard hairs can relax and all the entrapped flies can rise up and escape. They visit other nearby arum lilies, always hoping that this time the smell is of food and so they continue the pollination process.

You can verify that this process is happening in spring by sniffing an arum lily. Only some of us can smell the horrible smell – apparently we have to have a gene for this, and if we do we are quickly deterred. But if you don't have the gene and can't understand what horrible smell your fellow-sniffers are complaining of, give up trying at once. Don't be tempted to give an extra hard sniff or you'll get all the deranged flies stuck to the hairs of your own nostrils. Ah, the joys of fieldwork!

CHAPTER SEVEN

Sleepovers and holidays – coping with the cold

One of the problems with living in Ireland is how to get through the winter. Seasons of mist and mellow fruitfulness don't last that long and cold, bleak winter approaches. Hibernation – sleeping through it – seems an excellent idea. Why don't we all do it? We could rearrange Christmas.

Well, it's not simply a matter of going asleep. If we tried to go to sleep in November and sleep right through non-stop till March, we'd wake up dead from hunger and thirst! It's just not an option. So how can bats and hedgehogs do it? They're much thinner than we are. If it depended on layers of fat alone, we could all point out people who could hibernate for several winters on the trot. The trick is not the amount of stored fat *per se*, but the body's metabolic rate. Our rate of breathing and our heartbeat rate are indicators of how fast our metabolism is ticking over. And our bodies are ticking over very fast indeed. We need lots of food at regular intervals to keep going, as any parent of teenage boys can vouch for.

But if you could slow down the engine, the fuel would last much longer. Think of the car. A full tank of petrol would last ages if you were just idling the engine and listening to the radio. And this is what hibernating animals can do: they can slow down their metabolic rate phenomenally – to one heartbeat a minute, for example – and they can lower their body temperature, helping their supplies of fat last all winter. That is what hedgehogs do, and bats and frogs, and all those mated female insects.

And that is what squirrels don't do. Squirrels don't hibernate, I don't care what Enid Blyton says. Think about it. Why would they be collecting nuts and storing them away if they were going to be fast asleep all winter? You don't see hedgehogs collecting snails, or bats stashing away moths. They are truly asleep and food is of no interest.

But if you can't hibernate, what else could you do to get through the winter safely? You could go on your holidays to warmer climes – in a word, migrate. But you need some means of transport and, as we live on an island, our migrating creatures, the birds, depart by air. It hasn't always been clear where birds went in the wintertime. Several hundred years ago people were convinced that swallows dived down to the bottom of ponds and hibernated there. There is even written evidence of this, as people wrote of stories they'd heard from fishermen who had dragged up such hibernating swallows in their nets. Even then you couldn't believe everything you read in the papers.

Well, that was in the Middle Ages when we would not be surprised at such a lack of knowledge. But I remember giving a talk on wildlife to a public audience in north County Dublin in the mid-1970s. Among other things – many other things – I spoke of corncrakes and lamented the fact that, even then, fewer and fewer of them were getting here from Africa. And I was publicly corrected at the end of the lecture by a very knowledgeable man, who patronisingly pointed out that, while in the main the lecture was good, I couldn't surely be serious about corncrakes flying here from Africa. Sure didn't everyone know that corncrakes couldn't fly! And his companions in the hall nodded sagely in accord. What the eye don't see… and to be fair, corncrakes fly very little when they do get here in summer. The bird ringers have to resort to ground nets to catch them for ringing purposes. But they'd be a long time walking to Africa.

The swift must be at the other extreme. It cannot take off if it lands on the ground. So at home is it in the air, that it feeds, sleeps and mates on the wing. The only things you cannot do in the air if you are a swift is lay an egg and incubate it. So in they zoom to our urban eaves in mid-May, their screeches indicating that summer has finally arrived. They collect no nesting material but lay just two to three eggs on the soffit (which is under your eaves, in case you didn't know). It's a race against time to get the young one reared for the mid-August departure. If we have a wet, cold summer it's hard for the swift to collect enough food. Indeed, in bad weather they can go into a sort of torpor to conserve energy. This is a kind of mini-hibernation in summer and it saves energy until the weather improves and supplies of insects are available again.

There is actually an American bird called the poorwill which does indeed hibernate for the winter months in a hole in a tree. Ornithologists thought they were great to discover this and were somewhat taken aback to discover that the local Indian word for the bird meant 'the sleeper'. Imagine them thinking they could know more about local wildlife and its behaviour than the indigenous Indian tribes who had such respect for their environment!

The swiftlets that visit China and the Far East have the same sort of general lifestyle as our swifts. They too are aerial feeders but they do build nests. The building material is their own saliva, which hardens in contact with air, like dried egg-white and, indeed, like egg-white, the nests are mainly protein. This being the case, the thrifty Chinese harvest them when the birds have departed and they form the chief ingredient of bird's nest soup. So now you know, it's a real bird's nest in the soup in the finest Chinese establishments. I wonder who first thought of eating them?

The cuckoo, I suppose, is the most fascinating of all our migrating birds. In a world devoid of interesting and exciting events, the arrival of the cuckoo each April was especially welcomed by country people. Like most species of birds, it is only the male who sings, in this case making the characteristic cuckoo sound. (The female merely makes a not-very-loud bubbling sound.) The male cuckoo sings like this to attract a mate only, as cuckoos are not into property and don't hold territory or build a nest. And while cuckoos, as a species, can lay their eggs in the nests of several species of birds – meadow pipits, dunnocks, larks and robins have all been recorded – any particular cuckoo will only lay eggs in the nests of the species she herself was reared in. However, it may well be a tall order to find, say, nine meadow pipits' nests. If she can't find the 'correct' nest she will lay in the nest of another species. But as the cuckoo's egg tends to match that of the foster mother, the egg laid in the 'wrong' nest may be noticed by the nest's owners and the game will be up.

Timing too is important. Consider this dilemma. You are a cuckoo in Africa dependent, say, on meadow pipits to rear your young. You have to get to Ireland, mate and be ready to lay your eggs just as the meadow pipit has laid hers, so that it becomes part of the meadow pipit's life. If we have an early spring in Ireland, the meadow pipits will have a head start and the breeding situation will be far advanced early in the year. The cuckoo is too late coming with her eggs. On the other hand, if she arrives and spring is late, will the nests be ready when it is time to lay the eggs? How does the cuckoo get the timing right? After all, there are no weather forecasts of the spring situation in Ireland available to them in Africa. Do they come early just to be sure to be here on time? Not if the old rhyme is to be believed:

> *If the cuckoo sings on a bare thorn*
> *Sell your cow and buy some corn.*

This rhyme would seem to indicate that spring is normally well advanced by the time the cuckoo arrives and sings; and only in bad, late springs are they here before the leaves are on the trees.

When things go well and they do lay, perhaps one egg in each of nine nests, there is nothing more to detain the cuckoo here. So off they go, in July, the first migrants to depart – for them the summer is over. What, then, of the progeny? Well, the cuckoo's egg hatches fairly smartly and the first thing the baby does is heave out all the rest of the contents of the nest, in other words the legitimate offspring of the meadow pipit or whoever is the foster bird. The baby cuckoo has a special groove on its wing for doing this – if anything touches this, the baby is stimulated to heave it out of the nest.

And the odd thing, to us, is that the foster-parent birds don't seem to notice or care. They carefully and industriously slave away all summer feeding the monstrous offspring. Can't you just imagine them showing off when they meet other meadow pipits about how big their child is compared to theirs – and indeed the other meadow pipits smiling knowingly behind their backs. But, of course, birds are not people and we cannot know this. The Irish names for the meadow pipit – *banaltra na cuaiche* (the cuckoo's nurse) and *giolla na cuaiche* (the cuckoo's servant) – reflect the fact that it is the principal host species to cuckoos in Ireland.

It is really difficult to comprehend what happens next. Most youngsters, when they are reared, stretch their wings, declare the area to be a boring dump and fly away to the next parish. But what makes the baby cuckoo (who thinks he is a meadow pipit) decide to fly, not to the next parish, but to Africa? Uniquely of all our migrating birds, cuckoos do not return to Africa with their parents and other adult birds. They go on their own. How do they know where to go and indeed when they have arrived? We know that they are genetically programmed to do this, or hardwired if you like, but it is still incomprehensible.

Of course we also get winter migrants. Just as swallows and swifts leave a perfectly good Africa to breed in Ireland because the much longer day here in summer gives them more time to feed, other birds fly north to where there is light for twenty-four hours in mid-summer. Among these are the herbivorous geese and swans who cash in on the huge amounts of food available when the earth's deep freeze, the Arctic tundra, thaws out each summer. There is plenty of time to feed during the long, long days, but they need all this time to get the young fledged and away before the cold returns. In winter, when the days shorten alarmingly and the grass is covered with snow, the geese and the swans come back here with their new families.

This fact was observed long ago by astute country people sensitive to every change in their surroundings. But they wondered where the young came from. The geese headed out over the sea in April and came back in October with young. What land could there be out on the ocean? So, particularly in the case of the barnacle goose, people came up with an ingenious explanation: clearly, the young rose up out of the sea. This is not so far-fetched as might initially appear because, after all, the evidence was there for them to see on the beach after a severe storm. Timbers washed up from deep waters are often covered in black and white animals hanging down as it were by their heads from the timber itself. These animals are actually shellfish called goose barnacles. It didn't take much imagination for the people long ago to deduce that these grew up to be the black-and-white barnacle geese that arrived from over the ocean each year, and, of course, as the geese came from the sea, they were really fish and so could be eaten on the many days of abstinence from meat that were with us at the time. They were called the priest's fish – so interpret that any way you wish.

The Children of Lir were the migrating swans; probably the Whooper swans, given that they sang. Mute swans with orange bills do not migrate but breed here, and they do not sing either. They were eaten at great feasts, forming a dramatic centrepiece on the groaning food-laden tables, as the Tudor cookery books tell us. There are many myths and legends about swans – both in Ireland and in other European countries – inspired by their mysterious and, in those days, little-known migratory habits. It's a pity that we have to spoil these stories with the facts.

CHAPTER EIGHT

Bats in (and out of) the belfry

Can we blame Bram Stoker? Was it his book *Dracula* that gave bats such a bad name or had they it already? The way that bats emerge only when darkness has fallen and the skill that they have flying effortlessly in pitch darkness through heavily wooded areas without mishap must have seemed supernatural to our ancestors. Add to that the fact that they emerge from crypts, belfries, disused buildings and ruined castles, and really *Dracula* was only the icing on the cake for a creature with a sinister-seeming lifestyle already. But where did the expression 'as blind as a bat' come from? Catching moths at high speed in a woodland in pitch darkness is not the action of a blind creature! And did they ever fly into anyone's hair?

Bats are fascinating animals – the only true flying mammals. They can be divided into three groups based on their dining habits. There are the fruit-eating bats of the tropics, the insect-eating bats of the temperate regions and, yes, the blood-sucking bats of Central and South America. And they all work under the cover of darkness.

Our insect-eating bats are true hibernators. They spend the winter in secure roosts where the temperature never reaches freezing, so places such as underground caves and basements and crypts are perfect. When spring is well established and insect populations are sufficiently large to provide a continuous series of meals, the bats wake up and move quarters. What was fine for sleeping through the worst of winter won't do at all for summer – particularly for the females, who now require maternity quarters. The attics of our inhabited dwelling houses are good places for this. They get nice and warm during the day and, quite often, suitable attics are surrounded by trees or located by a river where lots of insects can live. Oftentimes, however, these nice suitable attics are parts of buildings whose lower floors are inhabited by householders who manifest an absurd fear of these creatures and ring radio programmes imploring us to tell them how to get rid of them. Would they really prefer clouds of midges and mosquitoes and moths (all of which are eaten by bats) whose caterpillars wreak havoc on their crops and vegetables? Apparently they do. But all our bat species are protected by law, and wilfully destroying them is an offence under the Wildlife Act.

Bats give birth to one young per year, after what appears to us to be a bizarre courtship. Some females can mate with several different males (that's not the bizarre bit) and can keep the sperm of each separate inside. She can then decide which sperm she will use to fertilise her egg when ovulation takes place, and it is not necessarily the first one. This has all been discovered by using genetic fingerprinting to determine the father of the child. Not that he hangs around to mind the youngster. The maternity ward – your attic – is a mother-and-baby unit only, with the babies home alone while the mother goes out to feed – or else she carries them with her.

Bats can catch moths in the blackest of moonless nights in the same way as sonar was used by the Americans to detect submarines at sea during the Second World War – in other words echo-location. The bat emits a sound at a very high frequency, inaudible to our ears. This then bounces off solid objects and is reflected back to the bat at a slightly lower pitch. The bat is able to build up a picture of the surroundings from the changes in sound. Moths and other nocturnal insects are detected in this way and the bat can ascertain where the insect is and whether it is coming or going. A swift swoop and another mouthful of food for the bat. Is it likely that such a creature, who hunts in swarms and never crashes into another bat, is likely to get entrapped in your hair? (Unless, of course, it is festooned with moths or your head is completely empty, so that the sound waves pass through uninterrupted.)

But all such reason vanishes when a bat enters a room. At a public function I attended where such an event took place, the hysteria was mighty. I remember getting a phone call not so long ago from the principal of a girls' school. She was in a state. A bat had come into the corridor overnight and was there next day when the girls came in. What would she do? It was at present resting on the wall high up at the window, but who knew, it could wake up and fly into somebody's hair at any minute. No amount of reassuring her that this would not happen had any effect. So, more to get rid of her than anything else, I suggested that perhaps it could be gently encouraged out of the open window with a tennis racquet. She said that she would get the male member of staff on the job and hung up. Fifteen minutes later she was back. He was afraid and wouldn't do it. So I suggested closing the corridor for the day if they must, leaving the window open and that the bat would fly out again when darkness came. When I heard her voice again on the phone the next day I nearly had a weakness, but it was just to thank me most profusely for the advice – the bat was gone. Never, never again would a window be left open overnight.

Tropical fruit bats are dull creatures by comparison. They don't hibernate because their food supplies never dry up – there is always fruit available in the forest all year round. And they don't use echo-location because they are herbivores – they eat plants, which cannot escape and don't have to be hunted down. They also drink nectar from night-opening flowers. For example, they leave footprints in the form of black marks on bananas as they stand on the fruit to drink the nectar from the next row of opening flowers. These bats fulfil an important role in pollination and seed dispersal in the windless tropical jungles, but we are such fastidious consumers that we won't buy bananas with bats' footprints, and so growers have to cover the fruit with bags while they are still on the plant to keep the bats from marking them.

But, I suppose, the blood-sucking bats are the most fascinating of all. Yes, they do exist, in Central and South America, and they feed on the blood of mammals, such as cattle and goats. Very silent in flight and light in weight, they land upon the victim and inflict a painless bite into a vein and lap up the blood. Needless to say, they don't attack humans – needless to say because, of course, you won't believe me. The *Dracula* story is much more fascinating.

CHAPTER NINE

Wildlife isn't only for children

Sometimes I feel a certain empathy with whoever said, 'I like children, but I wouldn't eat a whole one.' This is when well-meaning folk dismiss wildlife matters with the remark, 'Wouldn't it be great for children to hear this?' As if that was all it was – entertainment for children. When pressed, they say that children will have a love of wildlife when they grow up if exposed to it as a child, and then drag them along on a cold, windy, wet day on a field trip arranged for adults. And of course, for the child, it is often boring. Children are fed on a diet of wildlife programmes on television and, as in every other aspect of life, what you see on television bears no resemblance to reality. I have long suspected this, looking at the BBC extravaganzas, but having been involved in making a series called *Creature Feature* I am now sure. On television you can always see the creature in great detail – no quick glimpse against the sunlight here. This is because it is illuminated to perfection by a lighting operator whose job it is to do just that. In the real world, you are often peering into a gloomy hedge or getting a fleeting glance at creepy-crawlies scuttling away from under a stone you have just upturned.

And did you ever notice that the animals on television always do things as you watch? The butterfly opens and closes her wings, the bee packs pollen into the pollen sacs on her legs, the bird returns to the nest with a mouthful of worms, the dragonflies mate at that very instant. These are the edited highlights of hours and hours of filming, when for much of the time nothing at all happens. What you are likely to encounter on your field trip is a spider running away rather than one in the act of eating her husband, having just mated with him. No wonder the kids feel short-changed.

And how do they get all these lovely close-up shots of bluebottles or wasps? I'll tell you how: they use cameras the size of a biro and they keep the insects in the fridge. Insects move very slowly when they are cold. The minute they look like warming up and taking off, it's straight back into the fridge. A five-minute *Creature Feature* can take all day to shoot if the creature is alternating between the bright lights and the fridge and there's only one camera to cover all the angles. Not quite what the young *Creature Feature* fan expects when he is lured out on a field trip.

It's the grown-ups who urgently need the wildlife information. After all, who puts the nonsense into children's heads? Who tells them that worms are yucky and screams inexplicably at spiders, which any self-respecting infant in a pram would catch and examine as part of the rich kaleidoscope of life? Who thinks that earwigs go in your ear and that wasps' only aim in life is to sting us? Who thinks wildflowers are weeds and should be replaced with big showy aliens from the other side of the world? Adults, that's who!

So when I hear 'Wouldn't the childer love this?' I know what is really meant is that it is the adults who feel that they are only learning now what they should have learnt as children. The main target audience for wildlife programmes in this country should be adults between the ages of forty and seventy. For, unless they learnt it elsewhere or taught themselves, they received no environmental education through state schooling. We did have nature study on the national school curriculum that we inherited from the British at independence. And this stayed on the curriculum until the 1930s, when de Valera came into power with Fianna Fáil. He wanted much more Irish taught in schools and, for all practical purposes, got the extra time for it at the expense of nature study. It was still nominally on the curriculum, but low in the hierarchy of the subjects it was considered important to teach. It was to be 1971 and the *Curaclam Nua* (the first one) before environmental studies became mainstream in Irish primary schools again. So, if you were born around 1930, you went to school too late for nature study. Or if you had left primary school by 1971 (having been born around 1960), you emerged unburdened by any knowledge learned at school about the creepy-crawlies that inhabit the world with us.

By and large, who makes decisions about the country we live in? What is the average age of TDs, county councillors, city managers, chief planners, town engineers, ministers for the environment, fisheries, forestry, arts, heritage, agriculture? What age group has the most wealth and puts the most demands on our environment? I would bet they are mostly people who went to school in that nature-studyless period between about 1930 and 1971. No wonder they say kids should learn about the environment, as they certainly know little enough about it themselves. But the reality is that schoolchildren are learning about environmental matters and have been doing so in some fashion since 1971. They are gaining even more awareness now with the revised curriculum for primary schools and with biology being by far the most popular science subject among Leaving Cert students.

It's not just kids' stuff. It is very much all our business.

CHAPTER TEN

Adventure on Lambay Island

Having an interest in wildlife opens doors where, ordinarily, we would have no business knocking. When I was in college, I did postgraduate research on, among other things, salt marshes. There was one plant species, rock sea lavender, that occurred in considerable abundance on Malahide Island in north County Dublin and was part of the salt marsh community there. It seemed to occur rarely anywhere else on the east coast, according to the literature. However, there was an old record for it from Lambay Island, where it was reported as occurring on the sea cliffs. With the brashness of youth, I wondered could the Victorian botanist who described it mean the same species exactly as occurred on Malahide salt marsh? If so, why did it grow on a cliff instead of a muddy substrate? Maybe it was a different subspecies at least.

Lambay Island was then, and is still, privately owned. In the early 1970s, it belonged to Rupert Baring, Lord Revelstoke. To examine rock sea lavender on Lambay Island, I would have to get permission from him. No better woman. I wrote asking him if I could come to Lambay to further my academic studies on this plant. To my amazement, he had his secretary write back to say that I could come and that he would send his boat to Rogerstown to collect me and bring me out. As it happened, there was other business to be conducted that day, as I discovered when I met the local garda sergeant at Rogerstown. It was at the beginning of the revival of the Troubles in Northern Ireland and all guns were being taken in. Revelstoke, a man in his late sixties, duly arrived in the boat with his gun and collected me (and a horse, which had also appeared with a minder) from Rogerstown pier. On the way over, my flapping raincoat startled the horse, which looked for a moment as if it was going to jump overboard, causing consternation among the crew and the handler. But not Revelstoke, who continued to talk to me above the noise as if nothing was happening and it hadn't all been caused by my being too silly to do up my coat in the first place.

Upon arrival on the island, Revelstoke had business with the boat and told me to come up to the house in due course. The western side of the island, where the boat had landed, was all agricultural land – more of the good market-gardening soil of the adjacent mainland of Rush and Lusk – not much of botanical interest for me there. The cliffs were on the eastern side and on my way to them I passed the entrance to the house, which looked to me like a grey gothic pile. Upon knocking on the door, I was admitted by an elderly housekeeper of at least eighty years of age and brought in to his lordship, who was now in the library. I felt that I should tell him about the rock sea lavender which, after all, was why I was there.

He was more interested in telling me about the house, which was designed by Lutyens, he of the Memorial Garden to World War I in Islandbridge. He told me this between sorties out of the library and back in again for no apparent reason that I could see. What was I to do? I hadn't been asked to sit down, never mind offered a cup of tea. Surely as his invited guest... I then heard him asking me, upon his return from yet another unexplained short absence, if I would go upstairs with him to see the engraving on the fireplace in the bedroom, and off he went, leading the way, before I could consider my position. And, gentle reader, I went, believing his story about the fireplace, down the corridor, past the table with the bottle of Black and White and a half-filled glass, out of which he had another gulp as he passed (which explained the disappearances from the library). Up the superbly designed stairs to the bedroom. And there was a fireplace, a large white marble one, and on it engraved in Latin were words to the effect that in this room Calypso Baring – his sister, he informed me – was born. Then, without any further ado, we repaired downstairs again to the library.

I felt that I should leave at this point, while I was ahead, saying that I had to search the cliffs for the rock sea lavender before the boat took me back (or didn't take me back at all, it being his private boat). His parting words were that I probably wouldn't find it.

I didn't. The ecology of the place had changed since the plant was recorded and an enormous colony of herring and black-backed gulls covered all the grassy areas between me and the cliffs – a population explosion caused by the abundant feeding available directly inland at Baleally and Dunsink tipheads. They were not amused at being disturbed, and retaliated by dive-bombing me incessantly. Surveying the scene from a safe distance, I realised that the guano from the colony had changed the flora of the cliffs. Gone, too, was the reported puffin colony, forced out by the gulls, and, I concluded sadly, gone also was any possible site for the rock sea lavender. Revelstoke was right. But why had he let me come when he knew this?

I spent the afternoon looking at the rest of the island and talking to the farm staff who lived in houses that could have come straight out of a Thomas Hardy novel. They only got to go ashore at his lordship's pleasure – usually once a month when they got paid. He wouldn't let them go any oftener because they got drunk and were difficult to get back. Talk about the pot calling the kettle black! He made sure that he had supplies of his own tipple on the island.

It mustn't have been payday, as I made the return trip to Rogerstown unaccompanied by any farm worker and hungry enough to eat a passing seagull on a bed of rock sea lavender.

CHAPTER ELEVEN

Introducing the crow family

Observing and recognising the things around us requires a certain amount of interest, I suppose. Observant schoolchildren in parts of Dublin's inner city will be able to tell me the colour and make of the car I've arrived in and probably its number plate as well. The names of dinosaurs or Pokémon characters or pogs – remember pogs? – present no difficulties to the average eight-year-old obsessed with collecting them all (at his parents' expense). Why, then, when I ask them to look out the window and identify the very few species of birds visiting their school grounds, do they proclaim with great dismissiveness, 'crows'? When I ask which crow, I am looked at as if I wasn't all there and told that they are black crows (as if there was the possibility of white, blue or yellow ones as well).

We have seven different species of crow in this country and four of them in particular are well known to us all. The magpie is indeed a crow, which now seems to be ubiquitous, particularly in suburban areas. Hard to believe that it is a fairly recent visitor to Ireland, having arrived here only in the 1670s. A party of them were blown over in a storm from Wales and landed on the Wexford coast. At that time the country was reeling from the ravages of Cromwell and the Cromwellian plantation, and this new bird was associated with the hard times resulting from his campaigns here. Therefore it was considered exceedingly unlucky to see one, and that is believed, in this country, to be the origin of the rhyme, 'One for sorrow, two for joy, three for a girl and four for a boy' (although in fact that rhyme is also found in Britain, so it is unlikely that Cromwell's invasion of Ireland really had anything to do with it). They have increased and multiplied very successfully over the years and indeed it is very rare now to see just one.

Magpies are extremely clever birds and are able to adjust very well to new circumstances. They observe what is going on around them and exploit what they see to their own advantage. They eat a wide range of food and are always on the lookout for new sources of supply. In the old days, when people got their milk delivered in glass bottles, the magpies used to watch the blue tits hopping up on the bottles, piercing the foil cap and having a sup of milk. So they had a go too. Berating the milkman one payday for the fact that my milk bottles were overturned and spilled by the time I got up to take them in, he informed me that it was the magpies who were to blame. Being clumsier and heavier than the blue tits, they managed to make bigger holes in the cap and to upset the bottle during the milk-stealing proceedings. In any event, the matter resolved itself as milk bottles vanished (too costly, no demand, and so on). As I can hardly open their replacement, the tetrapak, without getting covered in milk, I would welcome an enterprising magpie who could pierce it with a swift jab of the beak, but so far evolution has not moved that fast.

Magpies are ever vigilant for sources of food. Looking out the upstairs window recently, I beheld a magpie's bottom on the outside window ledge. It was for all the world as if the magpie was mooning at me. It walked along the sill and then bent over, tail up, presenting me with a view of its well-feathered bottom. What could it be at? I went outside to look. There was the magpie bending over the edge of the windowsill to pick out the snails and other creepy-crawlies that were sheltering under the window while waiting for nightfall to launch further raids on the garden. The magpie was picking them off one by one and crunching them, shell and all. The thieving magpie indeed!

Do they steal rings and shiny objects and bring them back to their nest? Personally, I don't know – their nests are mainly inaccessible, built out of sticks high up in the trees. They have that reputation, certainly, but no shiny objects have been scientifically recorded in their nests. Magpies build early in the year so that their nestlings will be hatched out and ready for feeding with the eggs of the later-nesting songbirds in the area. But whatever about hiding away shiny objects, what about making your nest entirely out of shiny objects? The magpie that nested on the Georgian balcony of the INTO headquarters in Parnell Square in Dublin did just that.

It wasn't remarkable enough that the nest was built on a third-floor balcony instead of in a tall tree but, even more bizarrely, the nest was built out of wire coat-hangers with only the odd twig interspersed. The magpies must have found a source of discarded hangers, which were asking to be recycled. But – lack of observation again – no one had ever seen the magpies arrive with the hangers. Did they carry them in their beaks or on their feet? Did they carry one between two? Were there any dresses attached? However they got them, they must have provided a mighty uncomfortable seat for Mrs Magpie as she sat on the eggs to hatch them. But hatch them she did and the parents successfully bred and fledged several offspring in such an unlikely place. The occupiers of the building grew quite fond of them and missed them when they finally departed.

The problem with magpies really is their lack of sneakiness. They attack in the open in full voice and their killing of our baby songbirds is heart-rending to observe. Mind you, your own over-indulged cat can inflict even worse casualties on the bird population of your garden. They do it in a covert, sneaky fashion and just for the hell of it, as we know from television advertisements (which are never wrong) that nine out of ten cats prefer a particular variety of cat-food and so could not be hunting out of need and hunger at all.

The next two crows that we commonly see are the so-called 'black crows', the jackdaws and the rooks. People had no trouble distinguishing between them in the old days: *préachán* is a jackdaw and *cág* is a rook. It seems to be the English word 'rook' that we have difficulty with, because, on being pressed, people do remember that jackdaws nest in chimneys and that it is the 'crows' that nest in trees. It's hard to be a jackdaw with a need to find a chimney to nest in, these days. Long ago, when fires were the only form of heating, the jackdaw had to know which chimney to select. Of course, the active everyday chimney pots were very recognisable and no sane jackdaw would try to build a nest in a smoking chimney. But how were they to know when the odd fire would be lit in the parlour, or when somebody would be sick and have a fire lit in the bedroom? It's not any easier nowadays, even though we rarely light fires at all, because now the chimney pots are guarded with wire 'witches' hats' to keep the jackdaws from nesting. And when they do find a suitable chimney pot, in a disused outhouse or wherever, their troubles are only beginning.

Think of it. Imagine trying to build a nest in a chimney pot – a circle with a ten-foot drop. You have to get just the right-sized stick to jam athwart the chimney opening, to act as a base for the nest. You must select this stick without any tape to measure it, find just the right one by chance (you've no tools to cut and shape it), and then carry it to the chimney and insert it in just the right position, all with no hands. The large bundle of sticks below in the fireplace is evidence of their enduring patience, as again and again the stick is not jammed at the right angle and it falls down below. The wonder of it is not that there are so many jackdaws' nests in chimneys, but that there are any at all.

I lived in a bedsitter once, in the 1970s, at the top of a house in Dublin. The big room had been converted into a kitchen, sitting room and bedroom all in one. The fireplace was blocked up, the heating being provided by a one-bar electric fire on a meter. I woke up with a start at three o'clock in the morning in the dead of winter to hear a knocking coming from the fireplace. I put on the light and looked. Yes, definitely there was something on the other side of that piece of plywood blocking up the fireplace, which was knocking intermittently on the wood. And of course, as in all good horror stories, outside the rain fell and the wind blew in gusts. At three in the morning, all reason departs. Memories of that scene in *Wuthering Heights*, when Catherine Earnshaw comes back to haunt the narrator with knockings on the window, came flooding back. And, yes, I got up and dressed in a hurry and left in terror to join a friend in another bedsitter, who let me in and reassured me – a friend in need is surely a pest. Next morning, of course, courage had returned and back I marched to the bedsitter and removed the plywood, an action uncontemplatable alone at three in the morning. And what was there? Nothing but a huge collection of sticks from jackdaws' nests over the years. The waste pipe from the kitchen sink had been routed through the wall of the disused fireplace and the wind blew through the poorly sealed hole that the pipe went through, rattling the sticks. We'd had an easterly wind – an unusual one for Dublin – the previous night and the gusts rattled the sticks intermittently. Did I feel a right eejit? It never bothered me after that. I was able to be an expert, without even going outdoors, on when the east wind blew. I'm still waiting to meet a real ghost.

We got a wonderful insight into the life of breeding jackdaws when a very small camera was placed in a chimney to record a breeding season for the programme *Jackie and Daw*. This camera, placed so that it focused on the nest itself, recorded all that happened over a season. Three eggs were laid; two hatched out one day and the third one on the following day. Thus it was that two of the nestlings were bigger than the third and managed to attract most of the feeding. We watched a situation that was totally the opposite to that in a human situation, in which the two strong ones got most of the food and the small youngest one, who could not reach up as far in the nest, got less food. In a human situation, the small delicate child would receive extra care from the parents, who would not allow the siblings to bully it to the extent of depriving it of food. But nature is red in tooth and claw and eventually the smallest one died. At least the others didn't eat it, although they did eat a dead chaffinch brought in by the adults some days earlier. It was finally removed by one of the adults. The other two grew stronger and livelier and we could see them testing their wings and leg muscles. Then one day they just flew away and never came back. As it was a fixed camera, it didn't follow them, so we never saw them again. With technical assistance from Vinnie Hyland of *Wild Ireland*, The programme, however, incorporating as it did radio, television and live Internet streaming, won a Prix Europa award for Derek Mooney, its producer and presenter, in Berlin that year.

Rooks start building their nests on the first of March, unless of course it falls on a Sunday, when, like good Christians, they wait until Monday. And indeed the busy sounds of the industrious rooks are one of the signs of spring. They repair last year's nests, not baulking at stealing repair material from their neighbours' nests while the owners are absent. This leads to terrible wars of possession and accounts for much of the noise made at rookeries.

Rooks are the farmer's friends. They enthusiastically follow the plough with jackdaws and gulls, feasting on the wireworms and leatherjackets in the soil turned over by the plough. These invertebrates are very partial to grass roots (should they be the emblems of Fianna Fáil?) and will inflict much damage on the farmer's cereal crops later in the year if not removed. So the farmer welcomes such vigilant pest removers. They also feed on earthworms and you often see them probing with their bills in grassy fields, playing pitches and indeed golf fairways and greens in pursuit of a snack. But they will eat food that we put in their way and, like magpies, are very clever at adapting to circumstances.

When I was at primary school, we ate our lunches out in the playground, discarding crusts and gristly bits of filling that we didn't like. At one o'clock, the master blew the whistle to summon us in and we lined up in an orderly fashion in the school yard. At the same time, the rooks (and indeed the jackdaws) heard the whistle and came flying in to line up on the school wall. They had learnt that there would be uninterrupted snacks available when we were all marched in. Active recycling. And they still do this, though nowadays they respond to the school bell rather than the whistle (and no doubt they are wise to the fact that schools, having reached such a state of excellence as to be awarded the coveted Green Flag, are no good for a snack, for such schools would not dream of discarding unwanted pieces of lunch in the playground).

It's easy to distinguish rooks from jackdaws when they are together. The rooks are bigger with pale faces and big bills and glossy black feathers, whereas jackdaws are the smaller ones and they look really neat, as though they had just combed their feathers. In adult jackdaws, the back of the head is a greyish colour. Rooks have black eyes, but those of the jackdaw are pale white or pale blue, contributing to the characteristic personality of the bird. Two different species, both crows.

The other common crow is so well known that it has several familiar English names: the scald-crow, the grey crow, the hooded crow. This large bird is definitely a baddy in the eyes of sheep farmers whose sheep lamb out on the mountains, and it gives all other crows a bad name. Grey crows love mountains, the sea coast, rubbish dumps – in fact anywhere they can find a dead animal or offal lying about. They are well able to exploit the terrain and its occupants for food, most appallingly in some instances. These birds are carrion feeders, scavengers. They will eat dead things that they have not killed themselves, so they peck at lambs that have died of exposure and they eat the afterbirths of ewes discarded on the hillside after lambing. They will eat road kill. So, fair enough, they have a role in nature – waste disposal – revolting as it might seem to some of us.

But they don't stop at this. They attack sheep if the animal is lying on its back and helpless. They can pick out the eyes of living animals, leaving the distressed blind sheep to die of starvation. They can even poke holes in a sheep's abdomen and pull out its intestines and eat them while the sheep is stranded on its back. No wonder it is not protected under the Wildlife Act, although you do need a licence to get a gun to shoot it.

The raven, another of our crows, is a much more majestic bird. It resides too in uplands and mountainsides, but it is much scarcer than the hooded crow. Its Irish name, *fiach dubh*, has been incorporated into many placenames (as indeed has that of the golden eagle – *iolar* – another former resident of wild mountainy places). Ravens are the first birds of the year to nest, seemingly stimulated into courting behaviour by the lengthening day after the winter solstice. And these ravens do not court their sweethearts with mere dawn birdsong, or flashing plumage. No, ravens put on dramatic aerial displays in the sky over large tracts of mountainside, to show would-be mates what masters of the sky they are. And when a suitably impressed female joins in the aerial antics, he is stimulated to even greater feats, flying upside down and passing food to his potential bride.

Ravens are beautiful glossy birds with such black plumage that their name has been given to a particular colour of hair on humans. And this raven-black hair was a sign of great beauty in Irish folk tales, as was skin as white as snow and lips as red as blood. It sounds like a vampire to me, but then I never met Naoise, the lover of Deirdre of the Sorrows, who was described in these terms to Deirdre, before she had even met him. This picture was conjured up when herself and her wise woman encountered a raven one snowy morning eating something from which blood trickled on to the snow. Yuck.

Ravens were also considered to be birds of ill omen. Like the hooded crows, they feed on dead animals. Noah's one never came back to the ark after being sent out to see if the flood was over – too busy, no doubt, feasting on drowned non-ark occupants. Cú Chulainn was so ferocious a warrior that even when he was finally killed in battle his enemies could not be sure he was dead and were afraid to go near him. (It didn't help that he had tied himself to a pillar when he felt death approaching so that he would die standing, facing his enemies.) So who would approach him first? Even on his last legs Cú Chulainn was to be feared. It was only when the ultra-cautious raven landed on his shoulder that his enemies knew he was definitely dead. And so Cú Chulainn is depicted in the famous statue in the GPO in Dublin, upright, tied to a pillar with a raven perched on his shoulder. It sure beats a death mask anyway.

Our two other crows are much less well known, because the habitat where they live is uncommon. Jays are denizens of deciduous woodland. Much of our woodland fauna can be found in hedgerows but not the jay, whose distribution declined with deforestation. They are particularly fond of acorns and so are to be found in oak woods and large parks where there is plentiful tree cover. They are like a small magpie in design, but are a completely different colour. They are mainly brown but with a most brilliant flash of blue on their wings. Their 'song' is one of the most raucous in the woodland.

The chough is probably the least well known of all our crows, confined as it is to coastal areas in the south and west of Ireland. Its Irish name is much more descriptive, *cág cos-dearg*, the red-legged crow. Choughs are about as big as jackdaws and have bright-red legs and bills. They are particularly well adapted to *machair* – uncommon flat sand dunes in the west of Ireland with close-cropped swards. These they probe with their bills for invertebrates of all sorts. If you want to see them, they nest, among other places, in that beached ship thrown up on the coast of Innisheer in the Aran Islands, well known for appearing in the opening shots of the *Father Ted* series as Craggy Island. Approach with extreme caution, because the wreck is there since the 1970s and is falling apart with rust. The choughs nest inside and if you stand well away and watch during the nesting season you will see them.

So there you are – seven species of crows and not one of them a blackbird. Blackbirds belong to another family entirely, the thrushes, and share no characteristics other than perhaps colour with the crows. But confusingly in the rhyme 'Sing a song of sixpence', it is rooks that are meant by 'four-and-twenty blackbirds baked in a pie', not blackbirds. According to one of my cookery books, young rooks shot on leaving the nest are tender enough, but adult rooks should be treated like elderly pigeons for cooking purposes. I'll spare you the details of the recipes.

CHAPTER TWELVE

Strange but true – bugs and their idiosyncrasies

'Strange but true' was the title of a section in the comics I used to read *fadó, fadó*. It described weird and wonderful creatures that lived in places I was never likely to visit. What I didn't know was that we have our own strange-but-true heroes at home, if only we had eyes to look.

Consider, for example, the cuckoo spit. This spit-like object appears on twigs and grass stems in the month of June. The cuckoo is also heard in the month of June. Therefore the excrescence on the twigs is the spit of the cuckoo clearing his throat before singing and between calls. QED.

But it's not, you know. Where did this ridiculous story start? Did anyone ever see the cuckoo coughing up golliers? Any cursory examination of the 'spit' will reveal that it is no such thing. It is more like froth or suds, and if you probe it sufficiently with your fingers you will discover that it contains a small green insect with beautiful brown eyes that will walk slowly on your outstretched digit. This is an infant froghopper and is a perfect example of camouflage.

The froth is produced by the nymph froghopper itself, by blowing air into a liquid it exudes from its own body, to prevent it from drying out. Even more importantly, the froth disguises it from the all-seeing eyes of the ever-hungry birds who would consider the hapless young froghopper a very tasty morsel indeed. Birds don't read books (or listen to the radio), so they have never copped on really to this source of food. They don't seem to realise that the 'spit' contains an insect.

The insect continues its life cycle unchecked and, upon reaching adulthood, is able to acquire food by sucking the sap of leaves through its piercing mouth parts. A sudden shake of a well-leaved branch into a carefully held open upside-down umbrella will dislodge the adults feeding on the leaves and you can observe their jumping ability for yourself by poking their hindquarters with a judicious finger.

Enthusiastic shaking of well-leaved deciduous trees in summer may well also unseat shield bugs. These insects are so called because their backs resemble the Roman shields of long ago. Remember the rectangular ones, behind which the soldiers could shelter, shoulder to shoulder in a 'tortoise' position? Well, the shield bug has a hard back, complete with shoulders, and the species we have in Ireland are distinguished from each other by their different colours and the food plant on which they are found.

Another name for them is the stink bug, and this reflects a not very nice trait they exhibit – a form of selfishness, really. They are herbivores and feed on the leaves of trees, as do many other creepy-crawlies, as the contents of your umbrella/insect trap will reveal. But stink bugs are real '*mé féiners*' and instead of sharing their leaf with all comers, they secrete a foul-smelling scent all over it before commencing to dine, to deter any others from sharing the feast. Rather like a greedy child who licks all the buns on the plate before they can be stopped, so that nobody else will want one and they can have them all to themselves.

Maybugs are another interesting group of insects. The most dramatic of them is the cockchafer, a large brown insect that flies in the month of May – hence its name. It is the most frequent occupant of our postbag at that time of the year, as it seems to strike fear and terror into its beholders. Now, I will accept that it is quite a large insect, almost 3.5cm long, and that the males in particular have extraordinary antennae: they would put the old-fashioned chimney-top television aerials in the shade. But I don't think that it is its appearance alone that causes the terror. Its totally awkward way of flying also contributes to its bad impression. It comes out at night and blunders into houses through open windows and then it proceeds to crash into objects in its way, drawing unnecessary attention to itself. One mangled specimen I received came with the note, 'This got caught in the washing-up brush and somehow it died' – of shock, perhaps, at being at close quarters with the washing up. Or, more likely, it was bludgeoned to death by the same washing-up brush as a distraction from the dreary washing up.

But it was the cockchafer that provided us with one of our best answering-machine missions for the radio programme. This is a slot whereby a listener phones in with a query and leaves details on the answering machine. In return, they are rewarded with a visit from me to pronounce on the situation. On this occasion, the caller wanted a jumping egg identified – an insect egg all of 5mm long and shaped like a rugby ball that seemingly jumped of its own volition. Well, I jumped to it and went off to investigate immediately. The small, grey egg had been found under a hedge. It was the jumping that brought it to the observer's attention. It was now nestling in a plastic lunch box and was still jumping around. What was it – and why was it jumping?

Well 5mm, while quite small, is huge for an Irish insect egg. General insect books deal only with the adult insect, so descriptions of earlier stages in the life cycle are rarely accompanied by pictures. There were really only two likely suspects – one of the larger hawk-moths or our friend the maybug. The larger hawk-moths do lay eggs up to 5mm in size, but these are spherical rather than rugby ball-shaped and are mainly green anyway. The only one to lay a grey egg hasn't been recorded for Ireland. No, the cockchafer was the more likely. It lays grey, oval eggs. Inside, the infant insect develops into a comma-shaped larva with a brown head, which hatches out of the egg. It was the struggles of this larva to hatch that was causing the egg to leap about. The energy was in the creature inside – it wasn't the discovery of perpetual motion.

'Leave it to hatch and let me know what emerges,' I advised. When I hadn't heard for a fortnight I rang. Tragedy. The egg had stopped jumping and hadn't hatched. Once more a lightening dash to the house. Yes, the egg was well and truly still. So we got a very sharp knife and cut the egg in half, and boy had it a tough shell! Inside, sure enough, was the white larva of the cockchafer. But whether it was the temperature of the plastic box or the toughness of that particular shell, or its brief five seconds of fame on the wireless that halted the hatching process, we shall never know.

Cockchafer grubs do a lot of harm to garden plants, eating the roots, so the demise of one was no great catastrophe in the greater order of things. Still, I couldn't help feeling vaguely disappointed.

CHAPTER THIRTEEN

Badgers and other carnivores

The most common wild animal in Ireland is the badger, while rats and mice scarcely exist. This is the picture you would come away with, if you were gleaning your information on Irish mammals from the distribution maps produced by me in the Biological Records Centre in the 1980s. These maps were mainly composed of records sent in by observers, and often told more about the recorders than they did about the distribution of the animal species they were meant to be delineating.

In the case of the badger, observers felt that this was a wild animal worthy of reporting. They were all capable of identifying it correctly and indeed many of the records were of corpses killed on the road. Rats and mice, on the other hand, were not considered wild animals worthy of recording. Although I was sure that they were common and widespread throughout the country, I could not print distribution maps without records, and so the maps were very thinly populated indeed with dots indicating where they had been recorded.

The badger has been a resident species here since the last Ice Age ended and its ubiquity is reflected in the many placenames that contain its Irish name, *broc*. Badger setts in woodlands or under large hedges can have been there for many generations and reflect continued occupation in an area for many years. Badgers are creatures of habit and carry out the same actions day after day. They emerge from their setts after dusk slowly and cautiously, sniffing the wind carefully to avoid detection. They are omnivores, feeding on both vegetable and animal material. A favourite item in their diet is the earthworm and it has been reckoned that up to 40 per cent of their diet at times can be earthworms. The appearance of holes in gardens, lawns, fairways and greens, reported to us on the radio by irate gardeners and golfers, can often be ascribed to badgers on nightly forays for worms, but explaining who does it and why does not necessarily placate the owner of the garden with the holes dug out of it.

Badgers travel the same trails to and from their setts – trails that may have been used by many badger generations. They are also very brave animals, in our eyes at any rate, and will stand and fight any aggressor, as owners of dogs used for badger-baiting often learned to their cost. But travelling the same tracks and standing to face your enemy is not a good survival strategy if suddenly a new motorway is built over your nightly trail. And standing to face your enemy is unwise if the enemy with the shining eyes is a 10-tonne truck travelling at speed. No wonder so many of them are killed on the road. Thus, it is one small advance that, on new motorways that cross established badger territory (discovered during the Environmental Impact Study carried out before the site for the road is finally selected), underpasses are now being built to enable badgers to proceed on their way unmolested.

There are some improbable tales about badgers. Old people speak of two types of badger – the dog badger, which is a carnivore, and the pig badger, which is a herbivore and has a pink nose. The pig badger is the one to locate if the woman of the house has just given birth. In the old days, when confinements were at home, the mother took to her bed for a fortnight after the birth to recover – probably the only holiday she got, and the *fear an tí* had to cope with household duties as well as everything else. The way to restore herself to health was to get a pig badger (with the pink nose) and kill and butcher it. This was boiled with cabbage for several hours (can you imagine the smell?) and then served to the patient in the bed. After this, her health was restored and she got up and resumed her duties. I'd say you would too, after a feed like that.

People re-affirmed this story to us on the radio programme. Nobody who rang in, of course, ever ate badger themselves, or actually saw it being cooked. As usual, they had it on reliable authority from someone who had it from someone else – the normal unsatisfactory situation with fabulous stories like this.

However, two years ago I visited a primary school in Waterford city to take the pupils out on a field trip. Never was there so much rain. The field trip was impossible – time for plan B. I just happened to have a stuffed badger in the boot of the car, which I had borrowed from Dúchas for a different occasion, and was about to return it. I brought this in with me to show to sixth class. Two boys in the class were particularly animated at the sight of it and were dying to tell me what they knew about badgers. It turned out that they were Travellers and they told me, and the rest of the class, about being out one most exciting night with their uncles on the West Cork hills catching badgers. Why, I asked them, were they catching badgers? I was fixed with a pitying glance – what did I know? 'To eat of course,' was the answer. So now.

The badger isn't the only mammal to have unusual beliefs associated with it. The pine marten has too. This rare and elusive native Irish species lives in wooded habitats and never successfully made a transition to other habitat types when our woods were cut down. This is why it is so rare, the headquarters of its distribution being in County Clare and southeast Galway. It is a carnivore, killing for food. Its Irish name – *cat crainn* – indicates that it is an arboreal dweller, and indeed it was reputed once to have had squirrel on the menu.

Anyway, I wasn't long in the Biological Records Centre in the mid-1970s when I got a phone call from a man in County Sligo, who wanted to report a record of a pine marten. This pine marten had come into his shed and he had beaten it to death with his shovel. It was sufficiently unusual for him to go in and call his wife out to see it. And by the time he arrived back out with the wife to the shed where the dead pine marten lay, the nail in the tail was gone.

'What nail?' says I.

'What nail?' says he. 'Do yous know nothing up there in Dublin?'

Apparently pine martens have a six-inch iron nail stuck through their tails and this is why they are such ferocious killers. If you could get hold of this, you would have a powerful good-luck talisman. But they are very difficult to get hold of, as the pine marten reabsorbs it after it dies, unless you get it immediately. He had wasted time going in for the wife and by the time he got to examine the pine marten, the nail was gone – wouldn't you know! I accepted the record for my maps even though the animal no longer had a nail. It is, of course, illegal to kill pine martens now, under the Wildlife Act, and I've never heard from anyone who actually has a pine marten's nail in their possession.

Stoats are another mysterious lot. We don't have weasels in Ireland: they never got here after the Ice Age, although they did get to Britain. Our stoat has been isolated from its European relatives for so long, it is considered to be a separate subspecies. Stoats turn completely white in wintertime, in countries where snow lies on the ground for considerable periods of time, and this white fur is known as ermine. It obviously gives them an advantage in the snow, when creeping up on prey and, in turn, helps them to evade detection from predators such as foxes and large birds of prey. Such a winter coat would be a positive disadvantage to the Irish stoat, as periods when snow lies on the ground are so rare here, particularly on the east coast, as to be declared a national emergency when they do occur. Any stoat with a tendency to go white in winter would starve to death, or be quickly gobbled up, so the survival of the fittest has ensured brown coats only.

Legends have grown up about the stoat, not because of the colour of its coat, but because of its behaviour. It does not know its place – it is not afraid of humans. Stoats are very curious and will watch people going about their business, cutting hedges, saving hay and so on. Being watched by a wild animal unnerves people and makes them tend to ascribe human motives to animal behaviour, never an altogether sound idea. So we have stoats' funerals, stoats' parliaments – interpretations put on behaviour patterns which are not understood by the watchers. Now, we do have people ringing in to the programme who have seen these displays of groups of stoats with their own eyes, but what the explanation of them is, is not altogether clear. Not that that stops our listeners from declaring *ex cathedra*.

Ireland is one of the European strongholds of otters. These fish-eating carnivores are residents of our rivers and coasts. It is the same species that fishes the freshwater rivers and the sea. They are top carnivores, and, if conditions are right for them, all is fine in the levels of the food chain beneath them. As they are fish eaters, if there are otters in the rivers, there must be fish and enough food for the fish and enough dissolved oxygen in the water for all. So they are biological indicators of good water quality.

Otters dig burrows known as holts in the riverbank, which are entered underwater from the river. Here they sleep and breed. Holts are difficult to create, because they are burrowed right into the riverbank. Like digging a mine, there must be scaffolding in the shaft to prevent collapse. Otters use the roots of riverside trees as support for their holts, and they will only breed in an area where there are enough trees to provide this support. This, in turn, means that you only find otters in areas where there is a good environment.

Just how good Ireland is for otters was graphically brought home to me when I learnt the results of an otter survey carried out by the Vincent Wildlife Trust, a wildlife charity based in London. They employed two people – a husband and wife – to survey these islands in 1980–81 to ascertain the status of the otter. They divided the area into 10-kilometre squares and chose a representative sample (one in two) in each of the four countries to survey for otters. They looked in each square until they found evidence that otters lived there and then moved on to the next square. In England, they found evidence of otter in only 6 per cent of squares sampled. They found positive evidence in 20 per cent of Welsh squares, 73 per cent of Scottish squares and in Ireland they found positive evidence of otters in 92 per cent of the squares they surveyed. Twenty years or so on, we are still a stronghold of otters, a species which is now considered endangered in Europe.

I was amazed at the high turnout in Ireland and asked them how easy was it to see otters and how often did they encounter them. To my astonishment, they said that they had only seen otters once or twice, that all their records had come from otter spraints – otter droppings, in other words. These are very distinctive – tarry, with a characteristic smell, containing fish bones – and are deposited by the otter in prominent positions as territorial markings. I looked at the researcher as she told me this, with her elegant blonde hair and her beautifully manicured varnished nails, and tried to picture her poking through droppings for fish bones or bending close to get the characteristic whiff. I must confess my mind boggled. I wondered what she told people at parties she did for a living?

We are obliged under European directives, as well as under our own Wildlife Act, to protect otters. How then are they coping with the recent establishment of mink in the wild? The mink is an American species that was bred in Ireland from the 1950s as a source of fur for the clothing trade. Although the first mink farms were established in 1950–53, it was not necessary to have a licence for such farms until 1965. Following the introduction of this requirement, the number of such farms declined, although the size of those remaining increased. More recently, the collapse of the fur trade has spelt the death knell for mink farms. However, mink have been escaping from such farms into the wild since 1961, when the first recorded escape occurred in Omagh in County Tyrone.

Mink in captivity are bred for their pelts, which are maintained by breeding as the pinky-brown colour so beloved of the fur trade. After a few generations in the wild, the colour reverts to the normal black colour, not desired at all by the fashion-conscious, so you can't even make a collar out of the one you catch marauding in the chicken house.

In the wild, the mink is a ferocious creature. There have been multiple escapes since 1961 and they are now established in all our major waterways. Not only do they eat fish but they also feed on freshwater crayfish, water birds and their eggs, frogs and rats. They are not averse to leaving the water altogether and visiting riverside farms to dine on chickens and ducks and they have even been known to eat rabbits. And, of course, they have no natural enemies here. None of their natural enemies in Canada were introduced here, nor indeed would we want any of them.

Because they have such a varied diet, they do not seem to have a negative effect on otter numbers. Their depredations are most keenly felt among water birds, which can be almost exterminated in an area heavily occupied by mink. Owners of fish farms and gamebird rearers (unnatural practices in themselves from nature's point of view – all those animals cooped up and fed with food brought in rather than produced in the area inhabited by them) can be particularly pestered by mink, who see the caged animals as a food source for themselves, and are very adept at getting hold of them.

All this is yet another example of the upset done to an existing order by the introduction of a non-native species without the normal checks and balances.

CHAPTER FOURTEEN

Ageism – insect life cycles

Ageism is the latest politically correct concept. Employers cannot advertise for young, energetic employees, even if that is what they want and the work patently needs young people to do it. So how come publishers of books on insects have been allowed to get away with rampant ageism for years, albeit the other way round? Look up a mayfly in any popular insect book. Go on, do. What you will get is a picture of the adult mayfly, notwithstanding the fact that it may only be in this form for one or two days out of a life cycle that lasts for a whole year at least. What does it look like the rest of the time? Why are we not shown? It is the same with butterflies or bluebottles or daddy-long-legs: it is the adult form that appears in the general insect books and you have to buy a specialised book to see what they look like in the earlier stages of their life cycle.

A butterfly, for example, may only spend a small proportion of its life as the familiar butterfly-shaped insect we all recognise, but will you find caterpillars or eggs in the general guide? The female butterfly lays eggs, sometimes up to one hundred, on the food plant that is right for that species, say the cabbage in your garden in the case of the common large white or cabbage butterfly. These eggs are like tiny sculpted pats of butter. They quickly hatch out into small yellow caterpillars with dark heads and the first thing they do is eat their vacated egg shell. They then proceed to demolish the leaf upon which they have hatched. Caterpillars are just eating machines, they are neither male nor female, they exist solely to eat. Gender is determined later when they pupate into butterflies.

Children are sometimes told that if they don't stop eating they'll burst, but has anyone ever seen a burst child? The worst that happens is that they get sick. Well, caterpillars do burst. They eat and eat and get fatter and fatter, a process some of us are all too familiar with. But caterpillars are built differently to humans. We have our hard parts on the inside and our soft parts on the outside and the more we eat the bigger our soft parts can grow. Caterpillars, however, have their soft parts inside a hard outer coat like a corset, which cannot expand. When the strain from the ever-increasing inside soft parts becomes too much, the outer hard coat bursts and falls off. The inner, soft coat can then harden on exposure to the outside air. And the caterpillar merrily continues eating, no doubt having moved to another leaf at this stage. Again it fattens up, again its girdle is killing it and again it bursts, no doubt to its great relief. Butterflies can burst four times in all, each stage of development being darker and hairier than the stage before.

The bigger and hairier the caterpillar gets, the more distasteful it becomes to the birds who have been tipping away at the original hundred that were laid by the parent butterfly. Small juicy caterpillars are much beloved of blue tits, who time the hatching of their young to coincide with the first big flush of caterpillars in the year. So by the time the caterpillar gets to the hairy molly stage, it is one of ten rather than one of a hundred. Already it has changed shape and colour a few times – so you can see the difficulty for the book illustrator. It then leaves its leaf, climbs down off the plant, and crawls away to carry out the next stage of its life cycle, often over a footpath or a road, well away from the food plant where it has been gorging itself.

And it is at this stage that it is picked up by some curious passer-by and put in a matchbox and sent into the programme to be identified. And there we are, with this furry caterpillar found on a road with no food plant for a clue, half dead in a matchbox, and we are expected to identify it. The books only show the most exotic-looking caterpillars of the thirty-three butterfly species and over two thousand moth species we have here in Ireland. What to do? Well, if it is still alive because its packing was rigid enough, we can let it proceed to the next stage of its life cycle. Fortunately, it does not need any food for this. In fact, if it sees the food plant that it stuffed itself with ever again, it will be too soon. Whatever food it has taken on board has to sustain it now for the rest of its life. The eating part of its life is over. It has reached the end of the caterpillar stage and it must turn into a butterfly.

To do this it has to become a chrysalis first. It leaves the food plant and climbs up to a dry place. It is often found by curious humans, during its journey away from the food plant to a spot where it can form a chrysalis. I imagine this is because the caterpillar is no longer camouflaged against the food plant and its movement also attracts attention. However, it is now very furry and covered in distasteful hairs, so it is not attractive to birds, who couldn't fail to pounce on it if it was edible. So a hairy caterpillar moving purposefully and rapidly across open ground is definitely on the way to pupate. This can be on a twig, on a wall, under eaves; anywhere it can remain unmolested for as long as it takes to become a butterfly. It then attaches itself and begins to spin a silken cocoon around its caterpillar body.

It *is* a silken case too, although in most cases the silken thread is much too fine to be of any interest to us. This is not so, in the case of the silkworms. Silkworms are the caterpillars of a particular moth that is of great commercial interest. This caterpillar feeds on the leaves of the mulberry tree, a tree that can grow in Ireland but is generally cultivated in warmer countries than ours. When it has finished eating and is ready to change into a moth, this caterpillar is of particular interest. It spins such strong silk that it can be collected and spun into the silk fabric that is so beloved of lingerie makers and haute couturiers. Silkworms were cultivated in central France and southern Spain until the 20th century, but it isn't worth the effort in these places any more. Farming silkworms is a very exact business. They do not like strong smells or sudden changes in temperature. If a loud noise occurs while they are spinning their cocoons, they will stop and turn their heads, thus cutting the silken thread. Once the silken cocoon is spun, the silkworms are taken away so that the silk can be unravelled and spun, because otherwise the silkworm, like any other caterpillar, would continue its metamorphosis into an adult.

Inside their cases of silk, all caterpillars change completely. The butterfly (or moth) stem cells contained in the caterpillar body begin to develop and grow. The caterpillar cells that it no longer needs melt down to provide fuel for the growth of these butterfly cells. And the butterfly is a completely different looking creature from the caterpillar that crawled up the wall. It is developing four wings, in many cases of a completely different colour to the caterpillar. It is growing antennae on its head, and six proper legs. But most interestingly of all, the butterfly will have no digestive organs. It may take the odd drink of nectar as it flies about, but its eating days are over. Its abdomen contains its reproductive equipment, because this is what this highly mobile, brightly coloured stage is for – sex and reproduction.

When all is properly formed inside and the time is ripe, it will burst open the cocoon case and emerge as a butterfly. The wings will open and be pumped full of liquid to make them rigid. The beautiful colours, carried on tiny little scales on the surface of the wings, will appear. The butterfly is now dressed for the ball, and that is what the rest of its life consists of – one long ball, where it displays and shows off to others of its own species in the hope of attracting a mate. And, as indeed in all of our cases in these matters, luck plays an enormous role. Butterflies cannot fly in the rain, and strong winds do not help their cause either, so they are dependent on calm, sunny weather to meet their true love. Birds are not averse to a tasty butterfly for lunch (they strip off the wings first before swallowing them). A giddy, excited butterfly in the first dizzy rapture of love can easily blunder into a strategically placed spider's web, where with one well-placed bite it is quickly dispatched by the ever-watching spider. If we had to face such difficulties, we'd never go outside the door.

But when all goes well, when the sun shines on a calm, hot day, there is nothing so evocative of summer as a group of colourful butterflies in the air over a meadow full of wild flowers. And, for the successful ones, the reward is great: mating is quickly followed by egg-laying on the food plant that sustained it as a caterpillar and then, spent, the butterfly expires. Mind you, if they didn't mate and remained virginal instead, they would still expire, because, since they don't feed as adults, they all run out of fuel in the end.

We see no butterflies in the winter, so what happens then? Well, the general situation is that they overwinter as a chrysalis. Once they are safely in the cocoon, they can last like that for over six months. This doesn't help us to identify the creature sent in as a pupating caterpillar, as we will probably have lost the thing or be on a programme break by the time it hatches out. The brown hairstreak butterfly overwinters as an egg affixed to blackthorn twigs. The egg is laid next to the thorn on the twig and is quite unnoticeable. It stays there all winter, only hatching out the following year. The small tortoiseshell overwinters as an adult. It makes definite efforts to get into houses in the month of September, where it takes up residence in the hot press or, as was the case in our house when I was young, in the parlour curtains. When spring comes and the weather warms up and the sun shines, it sallies forth looking for action, one of the earliest butterflies to appear. Unless of course it was unfortunate enough to have picked our front room curtains to hibernate in. This was the 'good' room and we were never allowed in as children to mess it up. But at Christmas the room came into its own – the fire was lit, decorations were put up and the curtains were drawn. And the poor butterflies, who had never heard of Christmas, were kindly ushered out the window into the freezing cold, never to be seen again.

We do have several species of butterflies here who never heard of overwintering. These are the red admirals and the painted ladies, among others, summer migrants who arrive here by population expansion in July and August. Not that they fly here directly from Africa like the swallows and cuckoos. What happens is that, about the month of February, the adults lay eggs in the northern slopes of the Atlas Mountains in north Africa. The young hatch out, pupate, become butterflies fairly rapidly and then fly north across the Straits of Gibraltar in search of true love. They breed in southern Spain, their kids fly on to northern Spain, the next generation to France, and so on until, in the month of July, we receive the great-grandchildren of the first lot who bred in the Atlas Mountains in February. And, in a good summer, the population expansion may continue right up to northern Scotland. But like many a summer visitor, they don't know when to go home. They have no inbuilt mechanism to instruct them to fly south when the days begin to shorten. You'd think they'd notice one sunny day in October that there's no-one around only themselves – no cabbage whites, no meadow browns and definitely no tortoiseshells – and wonder what's up. But they don't, and one awful night, around Hallowe'en, the first frost comes and that is the end of them until next July. So in fact red admirals are usually the last butterflies we see on the wing in the year. Only in countries further south where there is no winter frost do they survive, poised to start the whole population expansion thing again next year.

Did you ever wonder where the name butterfly came from? Well, there is a yellow butterfly, the brimstone, that flies in the month of May. The male is deep yellow and it flies long distances looking for the paler coloured females.

This is a butterfly of limestone country, as buckthorn is its food plant. Good grass grows in limestone country, and, in the days when farming followed the seasons, cows out on the good grass produced enough milk for the churning season to begin. So it was that butter-making began in May, just at the time this large yellow, butter-coloured insect appeared, so what else could it be only the butterfly. The name subsequently spread to all such insects, regardless of their colour.

It is interesting that it is only in English that they are called after butter. They, along with moths, are *Lepidoptera* in Latin – which means scale-covered wings, *féileachán* in Irish, *papillon* in French, and *mariposa* in Spanish, none of which have anything to do with butter.

So the next time you see a picture of a butterfly in a book, remember that it looks like this for a very short period of its life. Much of the time it is in another state, of great interest to itself, if not to book publishers.

CHAPTER FIFTEEN

Rabbits and hares and their unspeakable habits

Zoologists have always been interested in establishing which mammals are native to Ireland and which have been introduced and when. Looking at bones that have been unearthed from caves, they know, for example, that the woolly mammoth, brown bear, spotted hyena, wolf, Arctic fox, Irish giant deer, reindeer, mountain hare, Norwegian lemming and Greenland lemming roamed the country 35,000 years ago. Obviously, it was much colder then than it is now. Another Ice Age came after that, and when it finally ended 10,000 years ago, the Irish giant deer was gone. Not only did it not come back to Ireland with the disappearance of the ice, it was gone altogether – extinct – as was the woolly mammoth. Reindeer passed through, moving northwards, as the tundra in which they lived moved northwards with the warming up of the region. The tundra is also home today to the lemmings and the Arctic fox. Bears and wolves re-established themselves here, as did the mountain hare, and they were joined by other species that moved up from further south with the deciduous woodlands.

So the mountain hare has had a very long history of being a native species: we can trace its presence back long before the arrival of man. It had the run of the country – no other hare species to compete with – and so it has made the whole country its habitat. It can live up in the mountains, as does its counterpart in Scotland. It also is equally at home in the flat lowlands, a habitat occupied by the brown hare across the water. It is a herbivore, which means it feeds on grasses, and, although hares have been recorded occasionally nesting underground, this is highly unusual – most hares live all their lives overground.

Its entire life is one of watchfulness. We were told as children that hares have no eyelashes and sleep with their eyes open, in a state of preparedness at all times to escape from danger – and boy is it able to run! To run like a hare is a common figure of speech: its turn of speed was obviously common knowledge. This is why it was considered a sport to hunt it, from the times of the Fianna to the present day. *Giorria* is the Irish name for the hare – a name that goes away back. I have sometimes wondered has this come from *gearr fhia* – short deer – in other words a substitute to hunt if deer was not available, a mini-version of the sport.

The hunting in the wild of a herbivore by a carnivore is a finely balanced affair. The carnivore has to estimate how much energy it will need to chase after the prey and what the chances of catching it are. Most of the hunting entails creeping up noiselessly, downwind of the unsuspecting prey and making a last-minute dash at great speed to catch it. In the wild, predators do not chase their prey for hours: the energy expended would not be worth it. If it is not caught in that sudden quick dash at the end, the predator cuts its losses and sneaks up on something else. So can hunting with a well-fed pack of hounds for a long period of time be said to be a natural practice? Can chasing a hare, an animal of open areas, in an enclosed course be fair and equitable, the so-called 'sport' of coursing? Why not call it what it is and stop trying to excuse it as part of what happens naturally in the wild – the hunter and the hunted. Hares would not have survived as long as they have if nature had stacked the survival odds so heavily against them.

We have other sayings that involve hares – as mad as a March hare being one. And, indeed, if you look at hares during the month of March, they do appear to be behaving in a completely deranged fashion. They seem to be having boxing matches with each other and then chasing around the field and sparring again. Of course, this is nothing more than courting behaviour and is no more mad in the eyes of the hare than our frenetic gyrating to ear-splitting 'music' is to us. Males spar and caffle with females, box and fight for real with other males and chase less lucky males around the field – much like many of our own social gatherings in a way! Females can have two or three litters a year with two or three in each litter, so it is a measure of how much predation there is on them from all sources that we are not overrun by them.

In the old days, people thought it was unlucky for a woman to meet a hare when she was pregnant, for she would then give birth to a child with a 'harelip' – a disfiguring deformity where the upper lip and sometimes the palate itself is cleft. This deformity occurs in one in 870 babies – in some cases there is an inheritance factor, in others it is purely random – but, of course, it has nothing to do with meeting a hare. Nowadays this condition is readily fixed by surgery.

Our hares do not turn white in the winter time as do the Scottish ones. They are both the same species *Lepus timidus*, but ours has been separated from the Scottish one for so long that any tendency it may once have had to do this has long since vanished. Thus we are considered to have a unique subspecies *Lepus timidus hibernicus*, found only in Ireland and distinguished from all others by staying brown in winter.

We do have another species of hare in Ireland – the brown hare. This hare is not native, but was introduced to Ireland during the second half of the 19th century. This is the lowland hare introduced to Great Britain, apparently by the Romans, and found in the flatter parts of that country (the higher ground being occupied by the mountain hare). Seemingly, it was introduced to Ireland for hunting, being fleeter of foot than the mountain hare. It never really got established here at all and has been recorded only in the north of the country, between Louth and Donegal. It is a different species to the native Irish hare but, in the field, the distinguishing feature is the black upper surface of its tail. Interestingly, it was the brown hare, as drawn by Percy Metcalfe, that was put on the threepenny bit when the Irish coinage was first minted in 1928. Like the hound on the sixpenny piece, it did not survive the change to decimal currency in the 1970s, still less the change to common euro currency in 2002.

Rabbits are not native to Ireland. They were introduced together with their name – *coinín* – by the Normans in the 12th century. The name *coinín* comes from the Latin *cuniculus* and, indeed, this animal is still known by that name in Denmark today. My brother, while working there during his time studying agriculture in college, was amazed to hear the continuous and unintelligible (to him) Danish being interrupted by a cry of *coinín, coinín*, as a rabbit bounded down the field. He hadn't been aware until then that they spoke Irish! The name travelled with the animal to America, and it is from the rabbit that Coney Island gets its name.

Rabbits were originally brought into Ireland as a source of food and became established in sand dune areas, where they could burrow easily. Such areas are often marked on old maps as warrens. Rabbits are very prolific and the term 'breeding like rabbits' has not crept into the vernacular by accident. Females can breed before they are a year old and can have up to seven litters a year, with about five babies in each litter. Rabbits rarely live longer than five years but, in that time, a female could have given birth to 150 young. No wonder they were eaten as food in olden times and, indeed, right up to the 1950s in Ireland.

Myxomatosis was the death knell really for rabbits as a general source of food. This is a viral disease that is carried by the rabbit flea and affects only rabbits. It was introduced to kill rabbits originally in Australia, where rabbits were causing terrible havoc, having been introduced by white people from Europe without any checks or predators. Myxomatosis was introduced to Ireland in the 1950s and decimated the rabbit population here. It is a particularly unpleasant disease for us to look at (and I am sure for the rabbits as well). The infected rabbit loses all sense of caution and wanders about in broad daylight with a horribly swollen head and practically blinded. People quickly lost all appetite for rabbit pie, in case they were eating early stages of myxomatosis that were not yet manifest. This disease only affects rabbits, not humans, but the public relations exercise was deadly. Rabbits have a certain immunity to the disease now, although it still flares up from time to time.

Foxes are great predators of rabbits and the huge decline in rabbits in the 1950s led to a decline in foxes too in certain parts of the country – proof of the ever-quoted dictum in textbooks that it is the prey who controls the predator, not vice versa.

Rabbits differ from hares in that they always live in burrows and rapidly scamper down them at the first sign of trouble. They communicate to each other by thumping their back legs off the ground and all grazing rabbits heed the warning and vanish – not much sport for hunting there. Links golfers hate them, as they burrow all over the golf course and the unwary golfer can easily twist an ankle in a burrow while in search of an errant ball.

Like hares, rabbits practise coprophagy. This interesting-sounding occupation means eating their own droppings. They feed on grass, which contains large amounts of cellulose, which is difficult to digest. Digestion takes place as the grass moves along the animal's intestine, but it reaches the end and is expelled before all the food value has been absorbed. So, in order not to waste good food, the rabbit eats these first droppings and runs them through again. Naturally each rabbit eats its own droppings – straight from the anus (there wouldn't want to be the slightest confusion about ownership!). The second time the call of nature comes, the rabbit emerges from its burrow and deposits the characteristically dried grass pellets around the entrance. There is not a calorie of food value left in them at this stage.

Rabbits are considered with a certain affection by people who do not have to accommodate them in the wild. The Easter bunny was originally a hare and the whole idea of chocolate Easter eggs being delivered by a rabbit is a complete travesty of the original fertility symbol that the egg at Easter is meant to represent. Or, considering the potential fertility of any given rabbit, maybe it's not.

CHAPTER SIXTEEN

Our own personal fauna

Some years ago, I did a programme in the *Habitats* series with Derek Mooney on the human body as a habitat for wildlife – it was received with a mixture of fascination and horror. It was repeated on several occasions and now, in my *Creature Feature* series on Den TV, the one on the head lice is the one I'm asked most about. Where did I get the head lice? Do they really look like that? There was no question but that the audience were familiar with them: head lice have never gone away, even if other denizens of our bodies, such as fleas and bedbugs, are less commonly encountered, in our civilisation at any rate.

Head lice are insects that have evolved to live on the human scalp and nowhere else. They are flat and wingless and they hold on to hair with the claws they have at the ends of their six legs. They have a really tight grip, so that scratching or combing with an ordinary comb does not dislodge them. Washing does not drown them and soapy shampoos do not bother them at all. They live on human blood, which they suck from our scalps. They pierce the scalp with their specially modified mouth-parts and then suck up the blood into their bodies. Both males and females live in the hair and when they are big enough and the mood takes them, they mate. The female then lays fifty to a hundred eggs over a period of days, which she cements to the hair close to the scalp. These hatch out in seven days or so and continue the process. Each louse lives and feeds for up to several weeks so your head can be 'walking' after a few weeks if nothing is done.

Because they get all they need from a human head, they don't need to be able to see very well, so they have poor eyesight. They don't need to be able to fly, so they have no wings. They can walk, of course, and if a nice, clean habitat is within walking distance they will quickly walk from one head to another. They are adapted to a certain thickness of hair, so if they walk onto a head where the hair is coarse and thick, they cannot hold on properly and so do not become established. Our hair gets thicker as we get older, so adults are not as plagued with head lice as children are.

Adults, of course, sometimes get afflicted with a louse that lives in the hair, not on the head, but in areas further down on the body – *Phthirus pubis*, more familiarly known as the crabs. This louse only adheres to the much coarser body hair and is passed from body to body by close contact. Like the head louse it sucks blood and causes terrible itches as it does so.

There is a third type of louse that affects humans. This is a subspecies of the head louse – the body louse. It lives on clothing and only visits the body to feed. It thrives in conditions of poor hygiene where people have little chance to wash themselves or change their clothing. Like the other two lice, it causes terrible itches, but this one is even worse than that. It also carries disease, most notably typhus and relapsing fever. In wartime conditions or after disasters, such as earthquakes and floods or during famine, much death is caused by lice-borne disease, often more so than by the disaster itself. During the Great Famine in Ireland in the 1840s, over a million people died, one-eighth of the population. Many of these died from epidemic typhus caused by bacteria-type organisms spread by body lice. The organisms are carried in the creature's faeces, which are deposited on the skin of the unfortunate human, who then scratches himself violently and introduces the disease into his blood stream. The patient suffers horribly from delirium, high fever and a rash and, without treatment, dies.

So maybe we shouldn't be so hard on the head louse, who at least doesn't carry fever. But how to get rid of it is the problem? Insecticides in the form of smelly shampoos are the usual treatment, together with horrible fine-combing to get rid of the bodies. But as this only kills adults, not eggs, it has to be administered twice – once to kill the adults present, and then a week later to kill the newly hatched-out creatures. People often don't bother with the second treatment because they feel so much better after the first and, as a result, two things happen. One, the hatched-out lot go on to rebuild a population in the hair and a month later your head is walking again and you're complaining that the shampoo didn't work. Two, by not carrying out the treatment properly and killing all the head lice with two doses of shampoo in the first place, you have allowed some that were nearly hatched out to survive the first dose and so go on to become resistant to the insecticide in your shampoo. So the next time you use the same treatment, it won't work because your particular population of head lice were already exposed to one sub-lethal dose and are now resistant to it. You have to try another brand of shampoo and insecticide.

The situation has now arisen whereby there are insecticide-resistant head lice doing the rounds. And head lice are always doing the rounds because they are not treated properly in the first place, with two doses a week apart. So if your children are head lice-free at the moment, try and keep them that way by making their hair unattractive to head lice. They don't like the smell of tea tree oil, although it smells fine to us. So a drop of that when rinsing washed hair ensures that they give your child's head the skip.

As well as our own special lice that attack us and no other species, we also have our own personal flea species – *Pulex irritans*, the human flea. Like many insects, this one has a whole life cycle of different stages and it is only the adult stage that bites us and sucks our blood. Fleas differ from lice in that they are compressed from side to side (as if they got squeezed in something) and they can leap. A human flea, which is about 3mm long, can leap 30cm, the equivalent of a 6-foot adult leaping 600ft.

So an adult flea leaps on us, bites us, sucks our blood and then is ready to lay eggs. Mind you, a female lays several lots of eggs (several hundred altogether), and needs a feed of blood before each laying session. The good news is that the small pearly eggs are not laid on our person but in furnishing materials, or mattresses, or blankets that happen to be nearby. They hatch within a week or two and produce worm-like larvae. These live by eating dust and skin cells and whatever else it finds on the surface it is on, and don't bother us at all. They thrive and grow big, bursting twice along the way, and after about three weeks are finished with this stage and are ready to move on to the next. They spin a silken cocoon and change to an adult inside. Now comes the clever bit: there is no point in coming out of the cocoon unless a nice juicy adult host is nearby to provide a meal, so they stay there, sometimes for months, until they feel passing vibrations. Then they quickly emerge, leap on the passing host, and dinner is assured. So stories of houses which have not been lived in for some time coming alive with fleas when people take up residence in them again are quite true.

While we have our own personal species, other species of flea are not averse to having a go at us. Cats and dogs have a species each, but both of these species will have a bite of us if we get too close to a flea-infested pet. Mind you, they would know after the meal of our blood that we were the wrong species (oops, sorry) but we still get an itchy lump all the same.

Our own flea is quite benign, really. It only wants a meal and leaves an itch, not like the rabbit flea, which carries myxomatosis, with fatal consequences, from one rabbit to another. The problem for us with fleas, really, is being bitten by the flea of another species, which carries a disease harmful to us. And the main culprit here is the rat. Plague is a rat disease, carried by the rat flea. It is in fact a fatal rat disease – so that's OK by us: the more that catch the plague and die the better. Alas, not so! When the rat dies, its fleas no longer have a living host and so they leave pretty sharpish. In olden times, when hygiene standards for waste and sewage in cities were non-existent, rats were an enormous problem. The pictures illustrating the story of the pied piper of Hamelin never show the piles of waste and filth on the streets that caused the rat problem in the first place. And inevitably, as happens in places of such squalor, some rat will have fleas with the plague and will pass it on to other rats. And, of course, some moidered and confused rat flea, whose host has died, will sample a taste of human blood if a handy human is nearby and start an epidemic of plague.

The bubonic plague in the Middle Ages in Europe killed 25 million people – one-third of the population of Europe at that time. It even got as far as Ireland, where people died of it in the 14th century – a punishment sent by God, it was felt, for wrongdoing. It was known as the Black Death because, when affected, the buboes – as the lymph nodes were known then – swelled up and bled into the skin, resulting in black patches, and death quickly followed. Bubonic plague is very rare in the world nowadays, but has not been completely eradicated in third-world countries.

An interesting aside on the Black Death is that we still carry the affects of it in our population 600 years later. Cystic fibrosis is a disease caused by a defective gene. This is what is known as a recessive gene, which means that, in order to have the condition, a person must inherit the defective gene from both parents. If a person only has one dose of the gene, they will be a carrier but will have no symptoms. This gene arises spontaneously by mutation in human populations. Statisticians can calculate the rate at which this mutation occurs and forecast how frequently it should be found. The figures hold true for Asian and African populations. However, among Caucasians, the incidence of this gene is much higher: one in twenty-five people are carriers. Geneticists tell us that a mutation that arises spontaneously (as this one does) would not be favoured unless it confers an advantage on the carrier. What possible advantage could the cystic fibrosis gene confer, when, especially until the 1930s, the disease was fatal and sufferers died in early childhood? It annoyed the scientists. They hate having their theories upset by the evidence. Eventually, in the last ten years they cracked it. It turns out that carriers of cystic fibrosis (and I suppose sufferers from it too, for all the good it did them in those days when their life expectancy was very short anyway) were immune to bubonic plague back then and the gene confers immunity to this day. When the plague hit Europe 600 years ago, a large proportion of those who survived did so because they had the cystic fibrosis gene and, as a result, even nowadays it occurs with above average frequency in Caucasian people.

If our own specialised lice and fleas were not enough to annoy us, we are also molested by a third specialised insect – the bedbug. Again we have our own personal species – *Cimex lectularius*. Bedbugs belong to a family of blood-sucking bugs that parasitise birds and mammals. House martins and bats, for example, have their own personal species too. Our creature does not remain attached to man, but hides away among clothing during the day and comes out at night for a meal of blood. While its bite can be very annoying, the good news is that it has not been found to transmit any disease.

All these blood-sucking parasites of humans are much less common nowadays, thanks to the invention of synthetic insecticides – organochlorines and organophosphates. Imagine what it must have been like to live in Viking Dublin, say. All those combs that turn up in digs would have been used for removing lice from the hair. But, of course, they would remove the adults only. And a night on the tiles might bring home more personal livestock than you went out with. So the next time you see the chimps grooming each other, you know exactly what they are up to and why. It was probably a form of entertainment we indulged in ourselves in the days before electricity and DDT.

However, it is not only the insects that prey on us. When John Donne wrote 'No man is an island', he could have added the adjective 'uninhabited' and given his poem a whole new meaning! You'll be riveted to know that members of the arachnid, fluke and flatworm families beset us as well, although hopefully not all at the same time. Scabies is a most itchy skin infection caused by the mite *Sarcoptes scabiei*, which burrows into our skin and lays eggs. The burrows become inflamed and sore and itchy. The eggs hatch out into new mites, leave by the same burrows and infect the nearest person. A whole household can be infected very easily. The solution, nowadays, is to paint on an insecticide solution. God knows what they did long ago.

A veritable tribe of worms can live in our insides. Tapeworms and roundworms choose our intestines, while another group live in our lymphatic vessels. Threadworms are the most common roundworms we see in this part of the world. Their eggs live in soil and humans become infested from sucking fingers with dirty nails. Once in the body, the eggs reach the intestine and hatch out into white adult threadworms. And here they live quite happily, emerging only to lay eggs at night, causing a terrible itch in the lower regions of the back passage. Scratching and then sucking the fingers that have been used to scratch re-infects the patient, who is usually a child. Otherwise these worms cause no harm. It is patently untrue that eating sugar gives you worms: it does no such thing.

Dogs that have not been de-wormed can have a threadworm of their own, which behaves in the same way in the dog's intestine. However, if humans are unlucky enough to ingest this one, they may acquire a disease called toxocariasis. This may cause only a mild fever but, in severe cases, can cause pneumonia or, if a larva enters the eye, loss of vision. This is why it is vital to keep your dog wormed and to wash your hands and nails after playing with him.

The really dramatic worm that can infect our bodies belongs to the tapeworm family. These tapeworms can grow up to 9m long inside the intestine, having been acquired by eating undercooked infected beef or pork where the worm was encysted as a larva in the muscle of the animal. Amazingly, these enormous worms rarely cause any symptoms except the odd mild abdominal discomfort that could be caused by any number of reasons – a bad pint, the bag of chips you had on the way home, the box of chocolates you finished all by yourself. You'll be glad to know that such infestations very, very rarely occur here because we have proper meat inspection and adequate sanitary disposal of sewage – haven't we?

Worms can cause very exotic-sounding diseases in far-flung places. Guinea worm disease is caused by a worm ingested by drinking infected water. It makes its way to the skin after a year's incubation in the infected person. There it creates an inflamed blister that bursts, exposing the end of the worm, all poised to lay its eggs. The only way to get rid of it is to wind the worm gently from the skin using a small stick – no task for the faint-hearted, when you consider that the worm can be more than a metre long.

Hookworms are a nasty lot as well. They live in water and enter the body through the feet – washerwomen are particularly prone to them. They really know their way around the body. They burrow into the feet and enter the bloodstream. They then go to the lungs where they leave the bloodstream and get coughed up. Swallowing the sputum introduces them to the stomach and intestines. Here they live on the blood of the unfortunate host – enough of them can cause anaemia. Eggs are excreted by the human host, perhaps into water if unsanitary conditions prevail in the area, to hatch into larvae and wait for the next unsuspecting person to walk on them and let them in again. No wonder we are told not to drink the water in places where sanitary conditions are unknown!

Not that worms are the only thing you can acquire from infected water. There is another disease called bilharzia that occurs in most tropical countries and afflicts over 200 million people worldwide. This is caused by a creature that rejoices in the name of the fluke. Flukes have a particularly complicated life cycle, involving freshwater snails, human bloodstreams (which they enter through the skin of someone wading or swimming in the infested fresh water), bladders and intestines (of the infected human) and the fresh water where the excreted eggs hatch out and enter another unwary snail. And the terrible thing is, there is no vaccine against the disease, which can progress in serious cases to liver cirrhosis and kidney failure. Fresh water in tropical countries should be treated with great caution and neither entered nor drunk lightly. Discretion is the better part of valour here.

Modern science has made great advances in the areas of sanitary disposal of sewage, thus making it possible to have clean water. At much less cost than armaments and war, these arrangements could prevail worldwide. Similarly, insecticides and other chemicals that kill the parasites mentioned above are quickly produced and administered if someone from the first world returns with more livestock on board than they went trekking or backpacking with – natives in those countries do not find such services made available to them. A lifetime of itch and misery from such unwanted human fauna is most often their lot. Napoleon (in *Animal Farm*) was right – some animals are more equal than others.

CHAPTER SEVENTEEN

What'll it do to you?

I am constantly amazed, although goodness knows I should be used to it by now, at the attitude people have to creepy-crawlies, to those in particular that are unknown to them. Having come across a large black beetle, say, or a harmless aul' shield bug, they want to know what is it and what will it do to them? The arrogance of the second part of the question! As if creepy-crawlies sat around all day thinking of us and scheming for our demise. The truth of the matter is that very few things, either plant or animal in this country, do us any harm. We must live in the safest country in the world.

We have got rid of the wolf through constant persecution and trapping, although there is no scientific evidence that a non-rabid wolf ever harmed anyone in Ireland, and our present mammals are much more afraid of us – and with due cause – than we ever need be afraid of them. The occasional one that has a bad reputation such as 'the cornered rat' is actually put into that position by us. If we left it alone, it would quickly slink off. No mammal in Ireland will attack us (as, say, rhinos or elephants or lions or tigers or polar bears would). We only have one reptile – the viviparous lizard – no snakes, no alligators or crocodiles, no komodo dragon. We don't need to check our shoes before putting them on in the morning or make loud noises to warn unwanted visitors in the coal shed of our approach. The only danger in our rivers is the submerged supermarket trolley or the odd bike.

We have no vultures circling overhead as their potential meal is in its death throes down below. (It took months of training and special effects to get the crows to appear so menacing in the film *The Birds* – they don't actually dive-bomb in real life at all.) Gulls and terns only dive-bomb us if we deliberately walk through their nesting colony during the breeding season, and they give us plenty of warning first. Swans have an undeserved reputation for being fierce, so much so that fine, hefty gardaí, who wouldn't think a pin of wringing the necks of a turkey or two at Christmas, send for our swan expert Richard Collins if any grounded swans have to be dealt with. Yet male swans are only defending the wife and kids when they bristle up and hiss alarmingly, and we are well warned of their intentions. In fact, we have made aul' mollies out of some swans, feeding them bread and making them dependent on this. There was a court case in Dublin recently where a swan feeder claimed that she had been attacked by a swan. What probably happened was that the swan, who felt he had been short-changed in the sliced-pan department, chased the feeder who had run out of bread before he'd had enough, whereupon the fleeing feeder fell and broke a wrist. If children in buggies do not let go of the crust they are offering the swan, the bird, which can't actually see in close to its bill, simply grabs in the direction of the bread. This can sometimes appear as if the swan is biting the child's hand, but it is not. These occasions can hardly be described as vicious attacks by savage swans. Frank Kelly's 'Twelve Days of Christmas' it is not.

Our fish are docile too. No flesh-eating piranhas shoal in our rivers. The waters are too cold (so far anyway) around our coasts for sharks to attack in these waters. The worst our largest shark can do to you is give you a heart attack when you see the size of him – 15m, as big as a double decker bus – swimming past you. But these basking sharks are vegetarian and only eat plankton. If you really are looking for thrills, you need to dive in warm waters with sharks, as I did once in the Red Sea with nurse and hammerhead sharks. That provided an adrenalin rush all right – for me at least, whatever about the sharks.

No, wild animals are guilt-free when it comes to unprovoked attacks on humans. Dogs, man's best friend, can be another matter, but I keep myself firmly out of the pet department.

When it comes to creatures that'll do things to you, we seem to be dealing with invertebrates – creepy-crawlies. Which of these actively seeks us out to attack us? Well, the main culprits seem to be Diptera – members of the fly family – and chief among these must be the mosquito. Yes, we do have mosquitoes in Ireland and always have had, long before global warming was ever heard of. We have up to twenty different species here. They lay their eggs in stagnant water and these hatch out into larvae that feed on small particles in the stagnant water. I grew them inadvertently one summer in my city back garden by not emptying the flowerpot containers of the rainfall that filled them on a continuous basis that whole summer. (They subsequently starred in the *Creature Feature* episode on mosquitoes.) After a suitable length of time as a larva, they develop into fully mature adults with two wings and the long straggly legs and the whine (like a Mig fighter plane) that we are unfortunately so familiar with. The females need a feed of blood after mating before they can lay fertile eggs. The males are an altogether more likeable lot, who feed entirely on nectar and plant juices. They do not even have the biting mouthpieces to draw blood.

But the females are well equipped in the biting department. They only fly at night and seem well able to detect where a vein is near the skin. They concentrate on ankles, wrists and faces, landing softly and piercing the skin, injecting anticoagulants into the wound, so that they can sip up enough blood before the blood clots. They can inflict a whole line of bites if they are allowed to work uninterrupted, so that you can wake up looking as if a sewing machine ran over your forehead or cheek.

The good news is that mosquitoes in Ireland no longer carry malaria or another disease known in the old days as the ague and have not done so in general since the 17th century. (Although there was a short-lived outbreak in Cork in the 1850s, caused by soldiers returning from the Crimean War.) The climate in Ireland was much warmer from the Middle Ages till the 1600s, and the malaria parasite was able to live and develop inside the mosquitoes here at that time. In fact, the last person of note to die of malaria in these islands was Oliver Cromwell, although whether he picked it up on his Irish campaign is not recorded. After his time, we entered a little Ice Age, as is most notably described by Charles Dickens who describes skating on the Thames, and the malaria parasite, though not the mosquito, was wiped out. The climate is warming up again, so I suppose there is always the chance that malaria will get back into our mosquito population again, particularly with the amount of foreign travel everyone seems to be doing.

Other members of the fly family that actively seek us out to bite are the midges. Anyone who ever worked on a bog is familiar with the midge, which emerges in swarms when the wind drops and bites our hairline and neck. There are actually two types of midges, both equally abundant I'm sorry to say. The Chironomids are non-biting midges, while the Ceratopogonids are the biting ones. The huge swarms dancing over the bog pools at dusk are really disco scenes where adult midges meet in order to mate. When the Chironomids have mated, the females go off to lay their eggs in the water, either on vegetation or in the water itself. The spent male meantime becomes food for a hungry fish, as indeed does the female when the eggs are laid. So would you begrudge them their few happy moments at the disco?

The Ceratopogonids are a different story altogether. Like mosquitoes, the females must have a feed of blood in order to be able to lay eggs, so this is their next task. Luckily, only a few of our more than one hundred species bite humans: the rest concentrate on birds, mammals or other insects. They don't actually bite their prey; they pierce their skin with their sharp mouthpiece and suck out the blood. Even though each midge is very small, no longer than 5mm, the bite is intensely irritating. This is because the midge injects its victim with a substance that prevents the blood from clotting so that it can extract enough to enable it to lay its eggs. It is this substance that causes us the pain and the itch and the lumps if we persist in scratching it. Once the female has secured her meal of blood, off she goes to lay her eggs in the water, where in summer the life cycle from egg to adult is only three weeks. No wonder there are so many of them!

In nature's scheme of things, both of these groups of insects are important consumers of detritus in water – in other words they are dustbin men. They are also a major food source for all carnivorous animals in fresh water. So maybe the fishing wouldn't be so good if our thoughts that they should all immediately become extinct materialised.

How do you keep them away from the back of your neck? There are all sorts of patented and expensive insect repellents that your pharmacist will happily sell to you. Others swear that smoking cigarettes will keep them away. (Well, I suppose if you want to kill yourself to avoid being bitten, why not?) But a tried and true remedy that the old people used, and they were no fools, was a sprig of bog myrtle in your hat. Flies and midges of all sorts hate it and will keep well away from you.

The other nasty member of the fly family is the cleg or horsefly. This must be one of the most obnoxious of insects. Unlike many flies that are noisy in flight, this one flies in complete silence, selects a suitable expanse of skin, lands without us feeling it and then sinks its mouthparts into our flesh. The pain of the bite is the first indication we have of its presence. They are large, stout flies and make a right big bite, which can hurt and itch for ages afterwards. Clegs are not called horseflies for nothing – they inflict painful bites on horses and cattle too, driving them mad in the summer months.

And that's it. Most of the rest of the creatures that we think of as being 'out to get us' only attack us because they think we have attacked them first or we have got in their way. Bees and wasps do not set out to sting us. In fact, in the case of bees, this is the equivalent of *hara kiri*, as the sting gets stuck in our skin and tears away part of the bee's abdomen and she dies later. Bees are not suicide warriors – they only sting as a last resort.

Wasps don't die when they sting, but they don't do it for fun either. However, if you poke a wasps' nest with a stick, what do you expect? If you smell like a flower or you are eating sweet things in September or October, you mustn't be amazed if a hungry wasp comes to investigate a possible source of sugar. And if you flick her away, can you be surprised if she stings?

Jellyfish have stings in their tentacles to stun small creatures swimming beneath them, which can then be hoovered up into their mouths as food. The whole action is a passive one. Jellyfish may have a lot of power, but they don't know how to use it. So anything coming in contact with the tentacles will be stung, regardless of whether it is of any use as food for the jellyfish or not. The tentacles still sting when they are severed from the jellyfish, as sometimes happens with boat propellers, or when the jellyfish is washed up on the beach. If you touch them, you will get stung. They don't actively seek us out to sting us, any more than we actively seek out mice, rats, badgers and hedgehogs to kill as we drive along the roads.

CHAPTER EIGHTEEN

The water police

What is clean water? Is it water in which absolutely nothing grows, or is it water that supports a thriving population of fish, mayflies, damselflies, water shrimps and so on? The latter, you might be inclined to think, but you'd be on to your local authority in a flash if you turned on the tap and a nice wriggling stonefly larva came out and swam around in your glass. So our view of what 'clean' water is depends on what we want the water for.

Drinking water must be completely free of all creepy-crawlies, both visible and invisible, it must not smell and it must be crystal clear. In order to have it like this, all life must be filtered and poisoned out of it, and indeed enough residual treatment left in it so that nothing creeps into it on its journey from the water treatment plant to our kitchen tap. If you leave a glass jug of tap water on the table overnight, you can see the bubbles of chlorine sticking to the insides of the glass the next day. And if you doubt chlorine's efficacy as a water steriliser, try adding neat tap water to your prized tropical fish, or even your average goldfish. They won't thank you for it, even if they don't die on the spot. Water that has been left to stand or, at a pinch, is drawn from the tank in the attic, say through the cold tap in the bath, is much better for them.

Getting and maintaining water at this level of cleanliness is not easy (or cheap), yet all the water that comes into our houses is to this standard, even though most of it is used for flushing the loo, or washing clothes and dishes, or bathing and showering in. We actually consume only a very small quantity of this expensively cleaned water. We don't measure how much we use or pay as we go, so of course we are very *flaithiúlach* in our use of it. It would be a different story if we had to carry it back to the house in jars on our heads – then we'd appreciate the ease of turning on a tap.

In fact, all we do in our houses is turn clean water into dirty water and send it off again, hopefully to be cleaned by the local authorities before it becomes a source of pollution. And, indeed, this in the main, is what happens, or at least in the mains. The local authorities, with the help of some very useful wildlife indeed, clean dirty water before releasing it to rivers, lakes or the sea.

What are these useful wildlife? Bacteria, that's what they are – germs. These very primitive forms of life are able to break down all the organic waste that we put into our dirty water and turn it into carbon dioxide and water. All they need is plenty of oxygen to do the job, and this is supplied to them in the waste-water plants where our dirty water ends up. That is if you are on the mains in the first place. If you send all your waste-water to your septic tank, then you are depending on your own bacteria and the myriad of surfaces with air on them throughout the sand in the soak-away area, to do the trick – which it will, if you have not been conned by the advertising that urges you to kill all known germs dead. If you pour strong bleaches and other antibacterial products down the loo, how do you think your septic tank is going to work? Where are the bacteria that should be stuffing themselves in your soak-away pit? Dead, that's where they are, along with all the unknown germs. Your dirty water emerges still dirty at the other end, which may well be the groundwater that feeds your neighbour's well, or indeed your own well, or it may be the local river.

There is a very strict hierarchy of life in a river. Clean, unpolluted rivers will follow this exactly. All animal life needs oxygen to live and, in rivers, the oxygen available to the fauna is that which is dissolved in the water; so it is in short supply compared to the oxygen available to land-living animals. A clean river will have the full quota of oxygen in it and will support a full complement of animals. So we can tell by looking at the wildlife in a river whether it is healthy or not. Where do you find the creatures in a flowing river? Well, unless they have some strategy for staying in one place we'll find them all in a heap at the mouth of the river, washed down by the flowing current. This not being the case, what are the strategies?

One strategy is to swim very strongly and keep your place against the current. This is what fish do, but if you plunge into your local stream, pinkeen net in hand, you might be forgiven for thinking your river is in its death throes, for all the fish you find. Not surprisingly, an animal that depends on detecting flows and water currents to stay in its habitat is going to be immediately aware of clumsy, floundering you in the water and give you and your net a wide berth. A pity because, if you could definitely establish that there were fish in your stream, you could rest easy about the water quality. Fish are near the top of the food chain, so if they are present, then there is enough oxygen for them and the lesser creatures that they feed on. You could hang around quietly for a while and see if any fishermen in the form of herons or kingfishers appear. They wouldn't waste their time hanging around a polluted river, so seeing them about the river is nearly as good as seeing the fish with your own eyes.

But if you can't be quiet or patient, is there any quick way of establishing if the water is clean or not? Well, there is: you can look for creatures that employ the second strategy for life in a river, that is to hold on for dear life to any fixed surface in the water. If you pick up submerged stones or plants from the river and examine what you see, you can quickly tell, not only whether the water is clean or dirty, but exactly what state it is in.

There are some very sensitive souls clinging to stones or rocks. They need the full complement of dissolved oxygen to be able to thrive. These are the very well-known dragonflies, damselflies and mayflies. We are mainly familiar with them as adults flying in the air in their short mating period, but they can spend up to two years as nymphs in the water itself and they are easy to identify once you get the hang of it. Find these and the water quality is ace. Further down the class system that prevails in rivers, we have a group of less sensitive souls who need less oxygen to survive and will be found in somewhat iffy water. Caddis flies and stoneflies are in this category.

What makes rivers polluted in the first place? In great industrial countries like Germany, rivers, such as the Rhine and the Ruhr, are polluted by chemicals from their industrial zones. These poison the rivers by directly killing the life in them. So if you go boating on the Rhine, the water will look perfectly clear, there will be no obnoxious smell, but the river is dead, poisoned. Only now, in the 21st century, are they getting round to making life tolerable for the fish.

Something to keep in mind the next time we hear some German tourist giving out about environmental conditions in Ireland.

On the other hand, we pollute our rivers here by putting in too much organic material – sewage and animal slurries in other words. This is perfectly good food for the decomposers in the food chain and they set to with gusto availing of this free food. However, they need oxygen to carry out this decomposing work and, in the order of things, they are able to lay first claim to the dissolved oxygen in the water and to hell with the fish and the mayflies and the dragonflies. The oxygen grabbers par excellence are the bacteria and, if levels of organic pollution are high enough, the bacteria will reign supreme, with no dissolved oxygen for anything else.

If the pollution levels are not so high, the invertebrate decomposers get a chance. In somewhat polluted waters, we will find lots of water lice and water shrimps working away on the food source and reproducing in big numbers. We will also find leeches, lots of them. These are only a pale imitation of the ones that had their fifteen minutes of fame in the picture starring Katherine Hepburn, *The African Queen*. Those ones were as long and as thick as a little finger and required massive amounts of blood to keep them going. Our leeches are tiny thin things, interested in snails and passing fish. They can't bite us or suck our blood – their jaws are not remotely in that league.

Interestingly, the big African leeches are now proving very useful from a medical point of view. As they need to suck blood for a long time from the small wound they have made in their host, it is of great importance to them that the blood they are imbibing doesn't scab over or clot before they have had enough. Accordingly, they inject an anti-clotting agent into the wound to keep the blood flowing freely. They are now being used in anti-clotting treatments for people who are prone to blood clots, either in their entirety (the entirety of the leeches, that is!), or if that is too off-putting, extracts from their chopped up bodies are used. It doesn't do to be too squeamish.

If the water is so full of organic matter that it is entirely the domain of the bacteria, that doesn't mean that there are no invertebrates there at all. Bloodworms, red wriggly creatures, have a form of haemoglobin in their blood, like we do ourselves, and this is able to store oxygen and keep the bloodworm going. And finally there is the charmingly named rat-tailed maggot. This creature sticks a part of its body up into the air and breathes through that as though it were a snorkel. It is thus independent of water conditions.

So in a perfect river we would expect the whole range from the mayflies right down to the rat-tailed maggots. There should be some of the good, the bad and the ugly there. But if we find, on a cursory examination of half a dozen stones, that the top end of the quality scale of creatures is missing, then we need no lab tests or elaborate water analyses to tell us that something is depriving the sensitive dwellers of their essential oxygen – and no prizes for guessing what it is.

The Water Pollution Act allows for water polluters to be fined heavily and it is fairly easy to find a source of pollution, downstream of which water quality deteriorates drastically, and fine accordingly. But that's not the only way rivers get polluted. As mentioned before, Irish lakes and rivers are polluted by fertilisers and slurries, which, when in the water, not only increase the growth of the oxygen-loving bacteria, but have another string to their bow, as it were. Farmers and gardeners know very well that they can get more plants to grow, quicker and stronger, by applying fertiliser to the soil where they grow. Well, it's the same with rivers and indeed lakes: if we apply fertiliser to them, the plants there will grow with great enthusiasm. So fertilisers sprayed on fields just before rain may well be washed into local water bodies, as may much of the slurry that is spread on farmland. The phosphate, in particular, in these slurries is like Christmas and their birthdays together to the green algae in the water and they grow and grow until the whole thing can turn into green algal soup.

So what? You might say – aren't these fellows plants, with the magic chlorophyll aboard, able to photosynthesise and fix carbon dioxide and give off oxygen? Surely they are adding to the oxygen in the water? Yes, but – there's always a but – they only do it during daylight when there is sunlight to give them energy. At night, like every other living creature, they need oxygen to keep going and, with the bacteria, they are first in line for any that's going. (The removal of flowers from sick rooms at night is not just because of an old wives' tale, although you'd probably want to have the Botanic Gardens in your room before it would be a matter of life and death.) Just before dawn, oxygen levels are at their lowest in water bodies. Not much point saying to the fish and the mayflies, hang in there for an hour or two and you'll be grand. And as more and more phosphates enter our water bodies (from our own profligate use of phosphate-containing washing powders as well as everything else), the number of rivers and lakes of pristine quality gets smaller every year. But we, of course, have to wait until there's nothing left but rat-tailed maggots and bloodworms everywhere before we take action.

Is there nothing in nature that will clean our water bodies? Well there is, actually: they are called zebra mussels, and they just love green algae. Once in a water body full of green algae they grow rapidly, eating the algae and cleaning the water. But these are foreign invaders. They came here originally on the bottoms of freshwater boats from the Caspian Sea, and are completely out of balance with our ecosystems. They grow like the clappers and block up water pipes, foul ropes and boats and generally cause more problems than they solve. They don't eat themselves out of house and home, because there is no shortage of phosphates being washed into our rivers and lakes, and so no shortage of green algae for them to eat. Now, if only we could invent something to feed on them!

CHAPTER NINETEEN

An Dúlra Blasta – edible wildlife

There is a genre of television – and indeed radio – programmes where people are cast adrift, as it were, into the environment and told to fend for themselves, living off nature, with none of the inventions of the modern age. They are to become hunter-gatherers for a week or a fortnight, and our entertainment is seeing what kind of a fist they make of it. It is 5,000 years since people lived in Ireland as hunter-gatherers, and there have been such phenomenal changes to the landscape in the intervening millennia, that Mesolithic man would be hard-pressed to recognise the place, never mind live here for a fortnight.

Farming has been devoted to ridding the environment of 'useless' wildlife and replacing it with carefully selected, high food-yielding plants and animals. Eighty-five per cent of our land belongs to the farmers, so there are really very few places for wildlife, edible or otherwise to live. Notwithstanding this, I made a series of six television programmes for TG4 called *An Dúlra Blasta* – the tasty environment. In this series, a guest and I visited an area and prepared a meal, the main ingredients of which came from the wild. It wasn't a survival programme or anything like that – it was just a way of drawing attention to the many wild things we still have that are edible.

The seashore was a magnet to our Mesolithic forebears and, not surprisingly, we based three of the six programmes there. The easiest things to find were the shellfish that clung to the rocks – that is, if you had found a suitable rocky shore in the first place. It couldn't be too exposed, or the shellfish would be dashed off the rocks, and it had to be free from any possible threat of sewage, as shellfish are, in the main, filter feeders and take in whatever is in the water.

There are lots of shellfish that cling to rocks, some much more desirable than others. Mussels are top of the league, followed by periwinkles. Limpets are edible too, but only the inner half of the animal. The kitchen midden on Omey Island, which is 5,000 years old, held shells of these same species. A midden is Mesolithic man's rubbish dump, and it was interesting to compare the size of the periwinkle shells found there with modern periwinkle shells – they were much bigger then. The midden also included oyster shells, obviously long since eradicated by gathering from the lower shore where they could be found at low tide. They occur now in deeper waters, or more likely in oyster farms.

There is a shellfish called a topshell, which looks like a rounded periwinkle, but it causes vomiting, so we left it alone. Of course, there were more of these than of any of the others, so obviously we weren't the only ones to know this. The rock pools, when the tide was out, yielded food too. Several sorts of seaweed can be eaten – *duileasc* (called 'dulse' in English) and carrageen moss – but most of the seaweeds could not: they were thick, coarse things. There were small, little prawns and shrimps running round the pools and little crabs, but they were easier to see than to catch. All in all, you'd be hard pressed to gather enough food for a family in the time between the tides when the lower, food-bearing part of the shore was exposed.

A muddy shore at the head of an estuary also proved to be a source of food. Many species of shellfish bury themselves in the mud when the tide is out, so by looking for telltale holes in the muddy sand and acting swiftly to dig out the occupants, we were able to get cockles, razor shells and gapers. Again, a lot of hard work for quite rubbery food.

Did prehistoric man ever eat any vegetables? Well, actually, many of our garden vegetables were originally seashore plants which, by careful plant breeding over the millennia, have turned into the mild-tasting vegetables we now enjoy. Their wild forebears were a rougher, tougher bunch. Sea rocket grows on the strandline and is hot and peppery to the power of ten. Sea kale and sea beet are both sandy shore plants (not that we gathered sea kale – it is now so rare as to be protected under the Wildlife Act). Sea beet is the same species as sugar beet and should be the real reason why we object to the genetic modification of sugar beet. As you will remember, there were trials of sugar beet, which had been genetically altered so as to be immune to weedkiller. Fields planted with the genetically modified crop could be sprayed with weedkiller as the beet grew, thus reducing competition with the weeds and producing a better crop. Now, the sugar we get from sugar beet is a chemical – $C^6H^{12}O^6$. There are no plant cells or chromosomes, altered or otherwise, in our sugar bowls. So in this case, it makes no difference to us if the plant is genetically altered (as opposed to genetically modified maize or soya, where we actually eat the plant cells). So what good reason could there be to objecting to it?

Well, genetic modification means that the change is carried from one generation to the next, so the sugar beet's pollen would have the changed formula. If this modified beet grew near the sea, its pollen could fertilise sea beet, its wild forebear, and the genetic modifications would enter the wild plant. And then we would have super weeds, immune to weedkiller, and the modification would have escaped from a controlled situation into the wild. And that, in my book, is bad.

For one programme, we made a quiche with the sea beet in it and it wasn't too bad at all. We also collected glasswort – small individual plants that grow in the mud near the water's edge which are supposed to taste like asparagus. In a pig's eye it does – it tasted like boiled string.

Collecting bigger food that might provide you with a decent bite required equipment. Crabs, lobsters, shoals of mackerel, all come into shallow waters but, unless we had a boat and fishing lines or lobster pots and all day and half the night, these things were not attainable. As it happened, TG4's budget rose to these things and we feasted sumptuously, but if you were poor and starving and only walking along the seashore, with no fishing equipment – tough.

It was much more difficult to find food away from the seashore. We needed woodlands, or at least decent hedgerows, and it had to be autumn. Naturally we contrived this for the programme and collected blackberries, sloes, haws, crab apples, rowanberries and elderberries. But with the exception of the blackberries, you'd be in a poor way without sugar. No wonder beekeeping was such an important occupation of the monks in Christian times. Mesolithic man hadn't the luxury of a sweet tooth. Woodlands in autumn are also full of mushrooms and, with experts advising us every step of the way, we cooked a most exotic-looking mushroom stew. DO NOT TRY THIS AT HOME! There are several mushrooms in this country that can kill you stone dead and, unless you know what you are at, desist.

This abundance of food is good for animals too, so we could have had a juicy pigeon or rook fresh from the stubble fields. Deer and hares are also well nourished at this time of year, but we contented ourselves with a rabbit (not, of course, a contemporary of our hunter-gatherer forebears, but introduced a mere thousand years ago by the Danes), washed down with elderberry wine that we had, in the tradition of televised cookery programmes, 'made earlier'.

The whole experience was a salutary one and it certainly stopped me for a while making disparaging remarks about farming and gardening practices. Hunter-gatherer is a full time occupation and you could see how the diet could be boring and monotonous, with periods of shortage and scarcity. Interesting to think that all wildlife, with the exception of us, are in fact hunter-gatherers. No wonder they congregate when a large supply of food is found! How are they supposed to know that it is your field of wheat, or your goldfish pond?

CHAPTER TWENTY

Your home as a wildlife habitat

You should not be at all surprised to realise that you share your home with an abundance of other wildlife. The really surprising thing would be if you had actually succeeded in keeping everything out – you would have to be living in a sterile bubble. The thing is, how much can you tolerate? Can you live and let live? Would you rather not know what shares your house with you? Does it really matter, anyway? Will it affect your physical health or just your nerves?

Well, the creatures that share our homes vary from the visible and obvious to things you'd never know were there. Mammals, I suppose, are in the first category. Whoever coined the phrase 'as quiet as a mouse' must never have lain awake in the dead of night listening to the racket made by mice scurrying across wooden spaces – between the ceiling and the floor above or behind the wainscoting. Or never heard the nibbling and rustling as it mooches behind the sideboard or the wardrobe or the chest of drawers. Field mice and house mice are both guilty of such behaviour and their numbers and nightly shenanigans increase as the weather gets cold for winter. Someone recently sent me what they described as a hibernating mouse. You wish! It was as dead as a doornail because, of course, mice don't hibernate and this one was dead and not sleeping. Ultrasonic sound seems to be the latest way of convincing them to leave your house. I've seen it work myself and equally I have heard perfectly true complaints that the mice gather and dance around the plug – perhaps those were deaf (as opposed to blind) mice. There's a lot to be said for the old food chain. A cat or terrier with proper instincts should keep the house free from such unwelcome visitors.

Bats seem to terrorise some people who have them as summer residents in their attic. A dose of positive thinking is needed here. These animals are carnivores that come out at night and eat nocturnal flying insects – so think, no more biting midges or mosquitoes, no more daddy-long-legs or big, hairy moths flying in the window when you open it to get a bit of air on a sultry August night – and no, the bats won't fly into the room. Only very inexperienced ones do that and they will fly out again if you put off the light and leave them be. Anyway, you might as well make a virtue out of necessity, because all our bat species are protected under the Wildlife Act and you'd be a criminal if you damaged them or interfered with their habitat while they were there, even if you think it is your roof space.

Mind you, people have complained to us of having other mammals living in their homes. One woman who owned a shop had a grey squirrel in residence in the attic. It used to descend after hours and eat the chocolate bars, leaving papers around the place and reducing the profits. She didn't want to wall it up in the attic and she could never nab it in the shop. Short of cleaning out the shop and leaving only one bar in a live cage trap (so that it could be released far away from the sweet shop), I couldn't think of anything else to do. I did suggest it might draw curious wildlife-lovers to the shop, but she wanted less attention rather than more!

And then there was the other couple, who were doing up an old house in County Clare and encountered a pine marten living in the roof space. Now, this was a big animal, with lots of droppings and smells, and they didn't really want to share with him. Pine martens are so rare that the local wildlife ranger was happy to come to the rescue and take the animal to another part of Clare, from whence it could not home back to its attic.

Foxes occasionally come indoors and, again, if startled, can get themselves into places from where they can withstand a siege – under floorboards, in attics. One such fox starred on *The Joe Duffy Show*, for weeks as it seemed. So mammals show no mercy, and you only have yourself to blame if you get behind with the house repairs.

But some stowaways in the house do not wait for holes and cracks to appear to get in. Your latest bargain at the auction house may already have residents *in situ*, who are only delighted to spread to unoccupied furniture once safely installed in the parlour. I speak, of course, of woodworm who are not actually worms at all, but beetles – the common furniture beetle to give them their full title. People are perfectly right when they say that woodworm do not attack highly polished good furniture. They cannot lay eggs on this. What the adult beetle is looking for is rough, unplaned wood such as you get on the cheap plywood backs of furniture or as drawer bottoms. The eggs can adhere here and when the larvae hatch out a month later, they burrow straight down into the timber. Again, the rule about fine furniture made from polished hardwood obtains. The larvae can only eat sapwood, which they do with a vengeance, making tunnels in the softer parts of your furniture for up to three years, safely inside, hidden from your eyes. After this time, it forms a chamber near the surface – amazing how it knows where the surface is – and pupates. The adult beetle cuts its way up and flies up to the ceiling leaving behind the characteristic woodworm hole and a trail of sawdust. So by the time you see the hole, the deed is done, and the adults are having a merry fling on the ceiling, before starting the same procedure all over again. Now they have the run of your house and can infest your wooden floor or any pine furniture they may find. They don't like really dry houses so keeping the place warm and dry is one way round them.

Of course, if you have a stately ancestral home, you won't be worried about mere woodworm. You'll have an altogether better class of pest – the deathwatch beetle. These beetles only infest damp hardwood, so if you've lost a few slates off the oak roof beams, you are a likely candidate. These are the original head-bangers. It can be quite difficult up there in the dark, trying to attract a mate, and after the ten long years you have spent as a larva, eating tunnels in the timber, you are quite desperate. So what the sexually mature, adult deathwatch beetle does (and the female is just as brazen as the male in this respect) is to attract attention by banging its head against the timber on which it stands. This brings them running and the cycle can begin again. The story goes that if this beetle is heard in the house, someone is going to die. You'd have to be very quiet in the stillness of the night to hear these sounds, particularly in a big, old house – which you would be if you were up keeping watch over someone very ill. But why spoil a good story with the facts?

Bedrooms are good places for creatures who live in fabrics, such as wool blankets, feather pillows and carpets. Chief among this tribe are the clothes moths. People used to live in fear and dread of them and every October you'd be asphyxiated in church by the mothball smell off the winter coats and jackets that had just had their first outing in six months. Mothballs contain naphthalene, which deters female moths from laying eggs in garments that reek of it. And, of course, it's only the caterpillars that do the eating – the brown clothes moth that we sometimes see flying out of a rarely opened wardrobe doesn't eat any more.

There are different species of clothes moths, but one that inspires a particularly awful fascination is the case-bearing clothes moth. No, this does not come with a suitcase in which to pack the clothes it wants to eat; what it does is worse than that. The larva, when it hatches out from the egg, begins to make a case or cocoon around itself from pieces of the fabric it finds itself in and nibbles away at this. As it grows, it makes its case bigger and bigger. Of course, it is the same colour and texture as the carpet it is destroying, and it is only noticed when extensive spring-cleaning or the like is being carried out. Carpet beetles can also reside in the carpet and they can make a fine old job of it as well. They have voracious cigar-shaped larvae with a tuft of hair at the rear end.

All of these diners on fabrics originated in the nests of birds and rodents and lived on feathers and rodent fur. They have much more abundant food in an Aran jumper or a stored blanket than they ever got off a mangy rat. However, modern-day fabrics are too much for them. They cannot eat the man-made fibres that come from oil, such as nylon, polyester and dralon and so, as we move more and more to these fabrics, particularly in our soft furnishings, times are becoming tough for the clothes moth. Soon we won't understand the expression 'that's been mothballed for years' – or worse, think it means something else altogether.

Another creature that can make its presence felt in our homes, although we may never actually lay eyes on it, is the mite. There are several species of these and they are at maximum about a millimetre long, about the size of a full stop. The dust mite lives in large numbers in the dust of mattresses and carpets. It grows by shedding its skin, which it leaves carelessly lying around. This is even smaller than the mite itself and can be inhaled by us as we lie in bed. What we don't know, doesn't trouble us – unless we are allergic to it. If we are, however, it brings on an attack of asthma, just as breathing in pollen gives an attack of asthma to those who are allergic to that.

There is also a house mite that lives in damp houses and feeds on the green and black mouldy patches that develop on the wallpaper in such dwellings. Drying out the house and changing the wallpaper usually persuades it to leave.

There are other mites which live in our food cupboards. Did you ever find an old half-used bag of flour and discover that the thing was moving when you looked inside – or, worse, when you had poured it out on to the weighing scales? Well that was the flour mite, which doesn't just confine itself to flour but can spread all around the food cupboard, eating anything it can get into. We are always getting samples of these in to the programme, wrapped in napkins and tissues, with pleas for help. At least I think we are: they are usually so small and decomposed that I have to assume so from the description of their depredations (not being a forensic scientist used to dealing with minute evidence). In any event, the remedy is the same – clean out the food cupboard, put opened bags of stuff into sealed boxes and eat it up fairly smartly. Why do you think 'best-by' dates were invented?

Mind you, flour mites are not the only things you might find crawling round your food cupboard. There is a whole collection of beetles that think the food you buy in the supermarket is specially for them and they particularly like the dry food that comes in packets such as flour, biscuits, spaghetti, dried fruit and even chocolate. The story is the same in each case – the packet has a tear in it or has been opened, then left unused for some time. The female lays her eggs on the food and the larvae hatch out and do the damage. The biscuit beetle, for example, was traditionally the beetle that affected ships' biscuits – really hard tack that had to do the sailors until they next took on supplies in port. No point in being squeamish here. You took the precaution of tapping the biscuit sharply on the table before eating it, to knock the larvae out – unless, of course, you wanted a mouthful of protein with your carbohydrate. They're not unknown on land either. One listener sent in a sample (visible this time, because beetles are bigger than mites) of a beetle she found in a group on the inside of her window. She was not at all fascinated to learn that it was a biscuit beetle and time for a major clean-out and disinfecting of her pantry.

The confused flour beetle has a great name. It's not all that confused when it is selecting your bag of self-raising to devour. The name comes from the way it behaves when disturbed. It runs around until it finds shelter and then it stops, unlike the grain weevil say, which runs around when disturbed and doesn't stop. Now, if I was naming them on their running behaviour, I would be inclined to think that the flour one has a great deal of savvy to stop running when it reaches shelter – perhaps it's the observer that gets confused.

There's also a collection of meat-eating beetles with names like the bacon beetle, the leather beetle and the museum beetle. With the advent of fridges and the disappearance of flitches of bacon from the chimney breast, they are no longer common in houses. They are still around, though, doing the work nature intended them to do, eating carrion and cleaning up the place.

So, bad and all as you may feel your house is, with uninvited guests, the remedy is in your hands. Remove their source of food and – eureka – they'll be gone. This is much more effective than spraying the house willy-nilly with poison, which indeed you may inadvertently ingest yourself – or, worse, paying a pest removal company vast sums of money to poison it for you.

CHAPTER TWENTY-ONE

Teaching teachers

I began work in 1974 in An Foras Forbartha as head of the Biological Records Centre. This was a grand title indeed because I was not only the head, but the body, arms and legs as well – in fact the sole member. I was employed to make distribution maps of our animals and plants so that we would know where everything was and, I suppose, make planning decisions accordingly. However, I had to depend on others to send in records of the Irish flora and fauna, as I could not be out covering the country recording everything and inside making maps at the same time. As environmental studies had only been introduced into primary schools in 1971, public knowledge of wildlife was not great. And people had to be able to know and recognise wildlife before they could send in records of it – so how could I ensure a supply of reliable records?

One way of teaching the public to recognise wild creatures was to run courses for teachers and they, in turn, would pass it on to their pupils. There was a scheme in vogue in the 1970s whereby primary school teachers gave up some of their holidays to undergo training to become better teachers. They did this voluntarily, at their own expense, and in return they could claim three days' leave during the school year – three days' discretionary leave for the five days' holidays that they had given up. And when they took these three days' leave during the school year, no paid substitute was provided – their class was taught by their colleagues in addition to their own pupils for no extra charge. Nice one, Department of Education! What other employer could get their employees to undergo staff development at their own expense during their holidays? This was the story in the 1970s and the remarkable thing is that it is still the case. If a teacher wants to attend a funeral or a wedding or have a day off for any personal reason, or even take delivery of a washing machine, the only way is to have the three days squirrelled away.

So by organising a course that met with Department of Education approval, I could get teachers to come along and learn about Irish wildlife. Teachers, particularly primary teachers, are a unique constituency. Firstly they are a most tolerant audience. Technical hitches – such as projectors breaking down, rooms which cannot be darkened, power failures, non-appearances of guest lecturers, rain – all are understood and forgiven. All, that is, except a problem with tea breaks. Once tea and coffee (however dire) can be provided at the promised times on the schedules, all is well.

Secondly, it seems that the primary school day is the model for all work done by teachers. This leads to the situation whereby lunchtime on a teachers' course is half an hour only and happens between 12.00 and 12.30 while the whole day ends at 2.30, just as a school day would. As they are paying for this out of their own pocket and attending during their holidays you can't really blame them for applying the maxim, 'He who pays the piper calls the tune.' But it doesn't suit bird life in particular – birds tend to doze and be quiet in the middle of the day after the dawn frenzy.

Providing a teachers' course certainly is an effective way of acquainting teachers with their environment. It gives them confidence to be reassured that knowing the names of creepy-crawlies is not the be-all and the end-all of everything – after all, spiders and squirrels and earwigs do not know their own names but they function perfectly well in spite of this. And, indeed, recognising a species is not a matter of divine inspiration. One does not wake up one morning, knowing the names of all wildlife. They have to be learned painstakingly, one by one. As the names have been imposed on them by us, it actually has been done according to an overall plan, not willy-nilly. Explaining this and showing how a totally unknown flower, say, can actually be named using an identification key is very satisfying – provided, of course, that you have chosen the correct flower, one that obeys the rules and is not the exception. Keys work very well in theory, but there are always some species that are identified more easily than others and some, sad to relate, that are downright exceptions. One of the tricks teachers like to learn is which to choose when showing off to their pupils how proficient they are.

The real problem with teachers' courses is the time of year when they happen. Teachers collapse into a course in the first week of July, exhausted after a hard year's work, delighted to let someone else do the talking, but by the time they get back to school in September, the details of what they have learnt have faded somewhat. I used to think that a course the last week of August would be the business, and I see now that they are beginning to happen in the last year or so.

Ah, yes, a breed apart, primary teachers. Delaying your holidays is one thing, but cutting them short (however long they may seem) and returning to work early and voluntarily is bordering surely on the masochistic.

CHAPTER TWENTY-TWO

Things that sting and things that don't – wasps, bees and ants

Right, before we start, let's get one thing straight. People sometimes find it hard to tell the difference between a honeybee, a bumblebee and a wasp. So here is the definitive statement. Wasps are shiny, not hairy, and have yellow and black stripes. Bumblebees are large and hairy and have stripes of colour, mainly yellow, on their backs. Honeybees are about the same size as wasps but they are easy to recognise – they have a dark brown or black body, thinly covered with beige hairs. There is no yellow on them and you couldn't mistake them for the shiny, stripey, yellow-and-black wasps if you look at them at all.

I must nail my colours to the mast at the outset and state that I am on the side of wasps. They are the victims of bad propaganda, much of which is entirely undeserved. Honeybees are the goody-goodies – symbols of industry and harmony, working away busily making honey for our delectation, pollinating flowers as a sideline and doing all this with harmonious sounds. Yeats's 'bee-loud glade' was part of the idyllic scene immortalised in the poem 'The Lake Isle of Innisfree'.

Well, let me put the case for the wasp. Like many of our insect species, wasps overwinter as fertile females, or queens. Only queen wasps survive the winter – all the drones and the workers die off during the first frosts. Come a fine, sunny day in spring, the queen hibernating down her mousehole or wherever she is escaping the winter frosts, wakes up and emerges into the sunlight. She has to get the show on the road by herself, so she needs first of all to find somewhere to live – somewhere suitable where she can rear a large family. She needs space and food.

The ceiling of your garden shed seems ideal, or the hole behind the fascia board, where she can gain access to the attic – anywhere she can attach a nest to some exposed wood, because wood is vital for making the nest. She scrapes off some dead wood, either from your rafters or an outside post or a rotting tree, chews it to a pulp and spreads the pulp in a spherical shape, which she attaches to the ceiling of the nesting site. It resembles nothing more than a paper golf ball stuck to the ceiling with a hole in the underside. Wasps were, in fact, the first paper makers, and the nest is made from paper woven in the most fantastic shapes. Construction continues and eight hexagonal cells are formed inside. An egg is laid in each one and the queen is then very busy collecting food to feed the hatching grubs.

And what does she feed them with? Sugar? – wrong. Nectar? – wrong. What do all baby wasps dine solely on? Insects, that's what. The queen is busily scouring your back garden for greenfly, whitefly, blackfly, anything small enough to be collected and brought back to the ravenous young.

They quickly grow up and develop wings but never become sexually mature, so they are no threat to the queen, although they are all female. They take over the building and feeding duties and the queen then goes into the egg-laying business full-time. Bit by bit, the nest is built up and the queen lays in each new cell provided. Every grub that hatches out has to be fed greenflies, whiteflies and so on from your garden. The queen can lay up to 40,000 eggs in a season. That's a lot of provisioning – and a lot of garden pests got rid of for us.

But what do the grown-up worker wasps eat themselves? No more than ourselves, they are not into baby food. The greenflies *et al* are all right for the young-uns, but adult wasps, like ourselves, have a sweet tooth that must be satisfied. The solution is ingenious and a model of sustainability – they eat the saliva of the larvae. Baby wasps produce very sweet saliva and it gives the worker wasps all the nourishment they need.

Any particular batch of wasps lives six weeks from egg to death in old age and there are many generations in the nest over the summer months. The queen lives for a twelve-month period, hibernating as soon as she is mated and then spending all the next summer laying eggs. By the end of the summer, as you might imagine, she is worn out and her supply of eggs is coming to an end. Time to think of the future. She is able to produce male eggs at this time, which hatch out into stingless male wasps (only the females sting). Some carefully selected female eggs are reared to queenhood. And then, of course, the inevitable happens. The new queens disport themselves shamefully, they are pursued by the males, mating takes place outside the nest, males from other nests are involved too, and next year's supply of wasps is assured. None of the wanton creatures are readmitted to the nest after their high jinks. The males, having performed the one useful task of their lives, are now surplus to requirements and don't survive long. The mated queens find somewhere to hibernate, such as a disused mousehole.

But what of the old nest and the founder queen? Eventually she stops laying and dies of exhaustion, having provided one last egg round. The grubs which hatch out of this final round of eggs are fed, as is customary, by the previous generation and, in return, generously allow them to eat their dribble. But when they grow up they are the last of their tribe. There are no babies to feed – hurrah! – but no saliva to eat either and a lifetime of nearly six weeks stretching before them. They must find sweet food somewhere else.

Every September we become very aware of wasps. They come into our houses, they invade classrooms, they spoil picnics. They have short tongues, so they can get sweet nectar only from shallow flowers. They can feed as well, however, on fallen fruit oozing their sweet contents. And they are also very good at smelling out sweetness; leave an open jar of jam in the garden and you will attract hundreds within minutes. But if we send them the wrong signals, we must be prepared to take the consequences of our actions.

If we have fallen for slick advertising and are washing our hair with shampoo containing apricot essence, or wildflower scents or some such, how can we possibly blame the wasps for becoming confused? They smell the scent of fruit, they come to investigate, they buzz around our heads looking for the sweet food that we have so clearly indicated is there and what do we do? We try to beat them to death, with shrieks that we're being attacked. We go for them with rolled up newspapers, and whack them as hard as we can. And the wasp does what any self-respecting foraging wasp being attacked does – it stings the aggressor. Would you blame it?

Wasps have a sharp, pointed sting, for all the world like a hypodermic needle. Mind you, it's only the females that sting: the sting is a modified ovipositor or egg-laying canal. They can stick it into us, release some venom, withdraw and fly away to sting again. It doesn't take a feather out of them. The same cannot be said for us, the recipients of the stings. The stings are alkaline, so we should rub vinegar on them to neutralise them.

Some people are hypersensitive to wasp stings – having being sensitised by the first one they ever received. What happens is, the sting is seen by the body as a terrible invasion of foreign danger and it produces antibodies against it. When such a hypersensitive person is stung again, and it could indeed be years later, the body's antibodies 'remember' the foreign danger and immediately spring into action to get rid of it, but the antibodies in such a hypersensitive person react out of all proportion. They produce chemicals that can cause anaphylactic shock and kill. Such people may have to carry adrenalin injections (as an antidote) with them for such eventualities, but in the main they keep out of the way of wasps in the first place.

Wasps mainly get in our way in September and October, yet all wasps, at all times of the year, are tarnished with the same brush. As for the discovery of the nest in the attic – which usually seems to happen in autumn when it is the size of a football at least – this leads to apoplexy, to the calling out of expensive pest-removal companies and frantic calls to our wildlife programme. We get more calls about wasps than about any other creature. And in truth all you have to do is hang in there till the first frosts, when all the wasps in the nest die of cold. Wasps do not last in a paper nest in the attic from one year to the next. The old queen dies in September. Her last lot of offspring live six to eight weeks at the most. By Hallowe'en, never mind Christmas, in any half normal year, there will be no more wasps left alive in the nest. And that is the end of the wasps in that particular nest. It is a temporary little arrangement, as it were. Next year's queen will want to start a fresh new nest come spring, not set up home in a smelly second-hand nest. The nest is now all yours.

What you do then is spray it with hair spray to prevent it from breaking – wasp nests are very brittle – and take it down and admire the co-operative building skills of the wasp. Or, indeed, you can even leave it there. Mind you, if the nest is in a good site, plenty of food available in the garden, raw wood around for nest building – in other words a prime piece of real estate – next year's queen may build her nest next door. Really good untouched attics may have five or six wasps' nests hanging down from the beams, one for each year. They will all be empty except for the current model. So just think of the number of garden aphids that these helpful residents have removed from your garden plants over the years – and for free, with no poisoning of the food chain, as sprays would do. Fascinating creatures wasps – you couldn't prefer greenfly?

Bees are also social insects, which means that they too live together in a large, female commune bossed over by a queen. They too can sting, and do, but we have a much more benevolent attitude to them than we have to wasps. They are synonymous with quiet industry and happy summer days. I wonder how many of us realise, when we describe someone as being as busy as a bee, that bees actually die of exhaustion from all the work they do. Maybe their lives are not all sweetness and light.

Honeybees have always been prized by man because of the honey they produce. We only have the one species in this country, *Apis mellifera,* and it is almost entirely domesticated. Some do make a break for it and set up nests in chimneys or hollow trees or hay sheds, but they are one and the same species as the domestic bee, and any beekeeper will be glad to lay hands on them.

All summer long they visit flowers, making a noise not unlike a cat purring – *crónán na mbeach* it is called in Irish, which is more descriptive than merely calling it humming. (Why do bees hum? Because they don't know the words.)

They have the same general set-up as wasps. They have a queen, a fully mature female who does nothing else all day but lay eggs. These are all female and they hatch out to become worker bees. They have the potential to become queens but they are not fed long enough with the top-quality food while larvae, and so they have a stunted development, as it were. They are quite content to work for the good of the hive for the whole of their lives. Bees have several different areas of employment and they work in each of these departments during their lives.

Feeding the young is a very important part of the work of the hive. All larvae are fed a substance excreted from the salivary glands of the workers. This bee dribble is called royal jelly, no less. Ordinary potential workers are fed with pollen after this – which their older sisters collect from flowers and bring back in special baskets on their back thighs. This is a protein-rich food and it's good enough for the babies, who, after all, are going to grow up to be drudges like their older sisters. The older sisters, of course, can eat what they like and what they like is honey. But first it has to be made. This is the entire work of another group of the sisters, who are not on baby-feeding duties. They visit flowers to collect nectar, a sweet liquid deep within the flower, which they lap up with their long tongues. They bring this back to the hive in their tummies to concentrate and store in special cells as honey. As flowers of a particular species open at the same time, they can make varieties of honey depending on the time of year – heather honey, clover honey, apple blossom honey, and so on.

Like anyone else, bees can take short cuts if these are available to them. Beekeepers in Drogheda were amazed at the amounts of honey their bees were making, until they discovered that they were not making it at all but stealing it from Boyne Valley Honey, whose honey they were able to access. Needless to say, this loophole was quickly sealed off and the bees were back to hard graft.

Bees can communicate with each other where the best flowers are by means of a dance – different steps tell how far away the flowers are. I wonder how they told each other to abandon flowers altogether and head for the honey-packing company – and what the atmosphere was like at the dance afterwards, when they had been found out!

There are other jobs to be done in the hive as well. Cells have to be made out of beeswax, and the workers have special wax glands for this. They also have to repair the hive and seal up intruders. Mice, for example, can get into a hive and steal honey. Killing such a robber is no problem, particularly if you have a thousand angry sisters to help you sting it. Soon it lies dead on the floor of the hive. But how do you stop it stinking the place out? The bees cannot physically drag the mouse out, but they can embalm it. Collecting resins and glues from timber is another area of work that bees do, and they use what they collect to seal up the mouse so effectively that it never decomposes or causes further harm to the bees.

So in its lifetime, the bee progresses through all these activities. No wonder it dies of exhaustion after a few weeks, particularly in summer when bees work flat out! And, of course, should she drop dead in the hive, she'll be quickly carried out and discarded by her heartless sisters.

Another difference between wasps and honeybees is that, while wasps' nests only last for a year because, with wasps, the new queen founds a new nest and the old one dies off, bees' nests go on forever. We heard on the programme about a bees' nest found at the top of an old hay barn which had to be removed with the bucket of a tractor. It was so big because it had been there for many years.

Interestingly, the running of the hive is controlled by the worker bees. They make the cells for the queen to lay eggs in and, depending on the shape and size of the cell, the queen will lay male or female eggs. If she lays female eggs in the normal hexagonal small cell, they will be fed royal jelly for only three days and become workers. If the female eggs are laid in cone-shaped cells, they will be fed royal jelly for longer and develop into fully mature females – queens. If the cells are of normal shape but bigger, the queen will be stimulated by the shape to lay male eggs, which will hatch out into drones. How does the queen know in advance it's going to be a male egg? Elementary, my dear Watson! It's an unfertilised one. Although the queen was thoroughly fertilised on her wedding flight with all the sperm she was ever going to need, it didn't join up at the time with her eggs. She can choose whether or not to fertilise the eggs with that sperm as she lays them. Females come from fertilised eggs, males from unfertilised ones. The shape of the cell stimulates the process. And, as it is the workers who prepare all these cells for the queen to lay in, essentially it is they who control what happens in the hive.

If the workers feel that the colony is about to swarm, in other words, if they think the queen will do a runner with half the colony, they make sure that she lays in cone-shaped cells before she goes, and also puts down a supply of suitors. The first new queen to hatch out is instantly on the ball. Her first act is regicide – she visits all the other cone-shaped cells and stings the other queens to death. Effective, or what? She then makes sure the drones are aware of her presence and when she has them suitably aroused, flies off out of the hive up into the air on her marriage flight with the amorous males in hot pursuit, not only from her own hive but from nearby ones as well. The strongest, most daring, best flier and sharpest operator is the successful one, ensuring that the best male genes go forward to the next generation. Not exactly the survival of the fittest, as the poor drone loses his life in the process – as do the also-rans. The sisters are delighted to welcome back the new bride, who takes up where her runaway mother left off, in the same hive, but the door is firmly closed to returning drones who, disappointed in love, are now left to starve to death.

But what of the old queen who departed with her swarm? The sight of a swarm of bees is enough to strike terror into the stoutest of hearts. But apparently bees have no interest in stinging at this time. They stuff themselves with honey before they leave and are so full that it is difficult to bend their bodies to sting. But they will sting if forced to, to defend the queen. They accompany the queen who is looking for a likely site to set up a new home. Well-organised beekeepers have an open empty hive just waiting, but sometimes this is not the case and the swarm takes off. It may land in a tree or a shop front or somebody's porch or chimney, causing absolute panic. Beekeepers are very good about going out to such situations, not least because they usually get to keep the new swarm. The earlier in the year the bees swarm, the more time they will have in the new nest to build up a supply of honey before the winter – hence the rhyme:

A swarm of bees in May is worth a load of hay
A swarm of bees in June is worth a silver spoon
But a swarm of bees in July is seldom worth a fly.

Queens only swarm once, so when the swarmed queen is getting old and beginning to lose vigour, the sisters cop on and once more build the cone cells and encourage the queen to lay. The first new queen out this time not only commits regicide on the other potential rivals, but is a willing accomplice to the killing of her aged mother by the sisters when she comes back from her successful marriage flight. No retiring gracefully to the old bees' home, in spite of having had maybe 50,000 children!

When winter comes, honeybees, unlike wasps, do not die off. They cluster round the queen, feed on the honey they laid down during the good times and have a well-earned rest. Enough of the workers survive the winter to be able to attend to the queen when she starts laying again in spring.

Bees were very greatly valued in Ireland long ago. They provided people with their only source of sugar – there was no sugar cane or sugar beet here then

– and so they were very important. Monks, in particular, kept them in monasteries in straw hives, called skeps, and often there were special niches in monastery walls for these. Some of these niches have survived to this day. Of course, alcohol could be made from the honey, and some monasteries were famous for their well-made mead.

Is it true that bees will die if they sting? Well, they will if they sting us. Again, only female bees sting, and their sting is shaped like a fish hook. When they stick it into us, our skin is so tough that it gets caught, and they can't withdraw it – so it tears away from their body, leaving an open wound in their abdomen, from which they quickly die. If they sting softer things, they can withdraw the sting and escape intact. Queens don't die after stinging other queens, quite the reverse actually.

When we get stung by a bee we are left with the sting sticking up out of our skin. The thing not to do is to grasp it, trying to pull it out. This will only pump more of the poison venom in. You should scrape off the sting using a finger nail (or a new euro, if your nails are bitten to the quick). And these are acid stings, so bread soda is the old-fashioned antidote.

Honeybees, both queens and workers, live all the year round, an indication that, however long they have been here, they are not native to these latitudes. Only the mated queen survives in all our other groups of social bees and wasps, so honeybees must have evolved in regions where winter was not cold like here. It is thought that they were brought to these parts by man and were originally native to southeast Asia.

We do of course have native social bees – I refer, of course, to the bumblebees, or humble bees as they were once known. They are big, fat bees, black in colour, with bands of yellow and indeed other colours too, depending on species, across their bodies. They are very hairy and really couldn't be mistaken for either a wasp or a honeybee. These too are social insects. They live together in nests ruled over by a bossy super-female, the queen. Like wasps, they all die out every winter, with only the mated queens surviving. When spring comes, the emerging bumble queen is one of the earliest insects to appear – sometimes one can be seen on a sunny day in late February flying around seeking to get the show on the road. We have several different species of bumblebee here. The ones that most of us are familiar with build their nests in holes in the ground, say mouseholes. People often used to discover them in late summer when cutting hay. Bumblebees don't often sting people, but they can, as any haymaker who has accidentally chopped open a bumbles' nest can testify to.

The queen selects a suitable mousehole (one assumes that the mouse has already departed) and builds a nest out of dried grass and moss – she may even steal the former occupant's bedding. Then she visits what flowers are in bloom at this time of year and gathers nectar and pollen from these. She brings this back to her mossy nest and makes a concoction known as 'bee bread' from it. She spreads this in the centre of the nest, like a disc, and lays up to a dozen eggs on it. She then builds a wax wall, with wax from her wax glands, around the eggs and – wait for it! – she sits on the eggs to keep them warm. She's nothing if not versatile, our queen bumblebee, not like the spoilt queen honeybee who is waited on hand and foot.

Oh yes, and before she settles down to incubate the eggs, she runs up a little wax honey pot and fills it with honey to keep her going during her confinement. She could give lessons to single mothers. After five days, the eggs hatch and the larvae feed on the bee bread they have been so fortunately laid on. They pupate into worker female bees and – you've guessed it – they get lumbered with all the work, feeding all the other babies the queen produces. The bee bread was just a blind to start the operation. The queen does keep control by building the wax cells she needs to lay the eggs in – no being ordered around by bossy workers who decide what she must lay. And so it continues all summer. The honey is made by the workers, who store it in wax pots.

Bumblebees make nothing like the amount of honey that honeybees do – they don't need to, as they won't be overwintering on it. Towards the end of the summer, the queen lays eggs that become drones and new queens are produced by longer feeding with royal jelly. Mating takes place, again a frenzied affair up in the air with lots of suitors in hot pursuit (the flight of the bumblebee!), and then the new queens go off to hibernate for the winter. The old queen weakens and dies and the workers die away. The whole story must begin again the following spring.

A curious thing can happen to a bumblebee's nest. It can be invaded by a cuckoo bee, a different species of bee that looks very like the species she parasitises. Like cuckoos in the bird world, cuckoo bees do not build their own nest but seek out a nest of their chosen species of bumble. The queen cuckoo waits until the first round of workers are hatched out and then she enters the nest. She eats any eggs the bumble queen has laid, lays her eggs in their place, and the worker bumbles have to rear and feed them. Oh yes, and she kills the founding bumble queen. Of course, being a cuckoo bee, she has no pollen baskets on her legs, so she is dependent on the bumble workers to feed her. And, of course, all her children are fully mature males and females, no workers here. So there is really only one generation of them, as the whole set-up can only last as long as the enslaved bumble workers live to feed them. But they have really screwed up the happy bumble home and there is an unexpected empty place at the bottom of the hayfield when haymaking comes round.

Ants live in communes as well and all work for the good of the community. Ants originally had a good press. In the Aesop fable about the ant and the grasshopper, it was the grasshopper who was feckless, whiling away the summer as a guitar-playing layabout, while the good, industrious ant worked away to be prepared for the hard times ahead. This was seen as a good thing. People are not a bit positive towards ants nowadays, though, and seem to have a terrible aversion to them on their property or – God forbid – in their houses.

It all depends on your point of view. Let's hear it for the ant. The ant most commonly complained of to us is a perfectly harmless creature called the garden ant. Like all ants, this is dumbell-shaped insect with a large head and a large abdomen and a very narrow bit in between. It lives with the queen and all its worker sisters in a simple nest excavated in sandy soil. There are no structures in it as in, say, a bees' or wasps' nest. The ants live in a series of chambers and tunnels. The queen has a royal chamber, of course, where she lays the eggs. She can lay one every ten minutes at the height of her powers, when she really gets going, and she can keep this up for up to six years. The workers then reverentially remove the eggs and hatch them out elsewhere. The eggs get great attention from their worker sisters as they develop, being moved about the nest as they grow from eggs to larvae to pupae. They are even brought up to tunnels just under the surface on warm days so that they'll grow big and strong even quicker.

All these young need lots of food and the worker ants forage far and wide to gather it. Any particles that are small enough to be carried are painstakingly lugged back to the nest to feed the others. If a good source of food is found, the ants communicate this to each other and soon a whole line of them is on the way to collect more. All these ants live underground in small little tunnels, which are just big enough for them to move around in. At certain times in summer the queen lays eggs, which develop into sexually mature adults (unlike the poor workers which are always undeveloped females). Nests at this time of year become like primary schools long ago and are either *buachaillí* or *cailíní*, containing mainly male or mainly female mature adults. During certain weather conditions, these mature adults, all of which have wings, unlike the workers, erupt from the nests and have one glorious abandoned orgy in the air. As well as attracting the notice of hassled humans, all the aerial feeders in the bird world are attracted to the spot – swallows, swifts, even gulls – and there's sex and violence and gluttony and murder all going on at the same time.

Very few ants survive this. It doesn't really matter about the males: once they have done the business, they have no further role anyway. But the successfully mated queens who escape the depredations of the birds, fall to earth and the first thing they do is break off their wings, first one, then the other. You can easily observe this as you sit on your patio with your sundowner. They are then able to squeeze back underground and seal themselves up until spring. They can survive on the reserves supplied by the wing muscles that they no longer need. Good recycling, huh? When spring comes, the female ant starts a colony by laying the first batch of eggs and feeding them with her own saliva. When they hatch out, she has her workers, so she can go into the egg-laying business full time.

So why are people so exercised about them? Well, from the ants' point of view, people are very kind and have modified their homes and gardens to make life easier and better for them. In the first instance, they have removed the damp, heavy topsoil from a portion of the garden and replaced it with nice dry sand and roofed this sand with nice flat patio slabs. Perfect for tunnelling in and building nests – sand is so much easier to tunnel and build a nest in than soil, and the slab roof gets nice and warm, so good for the little growing larvae! And then, this sandy habitat is conveniently placed just beside the house itself, into which access has been much improved by the provision of nice glass double doors, particularly on those hot days when ants are always so starving. And there's always food to be found in the house, lots of tiny crumbs on the floor or on the worktop. Occasionally, the ants even hit the jackpot and find a food cupboard open with tears in the sugar bag, or no lid on the sugar bowl. They have to be careful not to wander into the fridge if it is left open. It gets very cold and dark in there when the door is closed and they cannot move for the cold, even when the door is opened again. Ants are sure that the humans must be grateful to them for carrying away all the things that they spill on the floor and the patio.

But the humans are not, they are so not grateful. They hoover up the poor industrious creatures, not caring how many babies are left to starve to death. They put down horrid ant poisons in the form of dusts sprinkled round the doors where they get in, not seeming to care if it blows on to their own food. And, all the time, they do not seem to realise that they brought the problem on themselves by constructing the sand-based patio that screamed 'come and live here' to the ants. And I am supposed to provide an instant solution to all this on the radio! These ants don't even sting, for heaven's sake – so what's the problem? We are lucky we don't live in Africa, where we could have to cope with army ants that can kill humans if enough of them sting together, or termites that could easily gobble up the expensive wooden decking that is such a feature in your garden. Nobody forced you to have the patio, get rid of it if you really can't abide the poor ants.

We do have other sorts of ants here too. If you examine your roses you may find that they are host to lots of greenflies, particularly now that we seem to be having such mild winters that they are not wiped out from one year to the next. If you just stand and gaze at the greenflies you may notice that there are ants walking up and down the rose stems as well. These are actually tending and minding the aphids like cowherds do in Africa – I kid you not. And what they get from the aphids is a sweet secretion, a delicious liquid pooh called honeydew. They feed on this, so it is in their interest to mind the aphids and keep nasty predators, such as ladybirds, away from them so that their dinner and tea are secured.

Remember the picnics we had by the seaside in the summers long ago, when the sun always shone? Well, do you remember sitting down on the nice soft grass on the back dunes in your togs to eat your food (or indeed do other things)? And you weren't there five minutes when you were attacked by pissmires – great big ants – and these fellows really stung. We should be grateful that this species hasn't taken up residence in our sandy patios – yet...

CHAPTER TWENTY-THREE

Maligned and misunderstood – who'd be an insect?

There are many creatures with which we are all familiar that have an undeservedly bad reputation. The wasp is a bit different: it's a victim of false advertising – our false advertising that is, luring it with smells of food that we don't deliver – but wasps can and do sting, so I suppose they do something to warrant their bad press.

But what did an earwig ever do to anyone? The very mention or sight of one causes people to shudder involuntarily. Yet the only crime, as far as I can see, that it commits is that it doesn't look too lovely to some of its beholders. I wonder what we must look like to an earwig? The nerve of us 'Johnny-come-latelys' in the evolutionary stakes, having the temerity to accuse a species that has been on this planet for millions of years longer than us, of not being good-looking enough to justify its existence! When did good looks ever come into it? Earwigs are exemplary mothers who look after their young – which is more than can be said for the much-admired feckless butterfly or dragonfly. Alas, such exemplary behaviour does not improve its lot in the affection stakes. Beauty is all.

The English name earwig is a corruption of an earlier English name. If you so much as give an earwig a passing glance, never mind examine it closely, you will notice that it has two appendages protruding from its rear end. These are not to pinch people with, but are a help in the mating process. These were considered to be a sort of wig that covered the lower abdomen of the insect, and so it was named, in the normal accepted English of the time, arsewig. (The wheatear, a bird of our uplands, was called, in the same vernacular, white-arse because of its white rump.) When prissiness overcame the official use of the word, 'arse' was changed to 'ear', thus giving us earwig (and white ear – later wheatear) instead.

But I digress. Earwigs are fastidious creatures. Their preferred food is flower petals. They are particularly fond of dahlias and have the unnerving habit of exiting from such flower arrangements across the white tablecloth, when guests are assembled at dinner. That is if they weren't in the tablecloth in the first place. They quite often come in on clothes from the line – the smell of Lever Brothers' products must convince them that the washed clothes are flowers.

How do they get on to the line? Why, they fly of course. Earwigs have wings, which they keep folded up under their wing cases. It has been reckoned that they have to be folded forty times to fit in there, and the earwig uses its abdominal forceps to help with the folding. It's obviously all a lot of trouble, because they don't fly very much.

Listeners to the radio programme have decided views on earwigs. Many are convinced that they go into your ears. One listener regaled us with a story of his summer holidays in the 1950s in a rented house by the sea in County Louth. It was idyllic and the sun shone the whole time as it always did in those days when we were young. It was all great, except for the cotton wool in your ears. Cotton wool, in your ears, on holiday by the sea? Why, of course, their mother put cotton wool dipped in Vaseline into their ears every night to keep out the earwigs. And it worked!

Where did such a belief come from? Why do many people think that earwigs will go into their ears and deafen them by biting their eardrums? Well, it is true that earwigs like tight spaces. They like to feel a surface on their back at the same time as beneath their feet. A good place to hunt for them is in the dead, hollow stalks of the hogweed in autumn. It is conceivable, I suppose, that if you lay on the ground with your ear correctly positioned one could come calling, but they would soon retreat from the average waxy, hairy ear hole. They certainly wouldn't bite your eardrum, or force their way into your skull –

unless, of course, you keep dahlia petals in there. But it is much more likely that the belief comes from the name, which, of course, as already explained, really has nothing to do with ears.

The sawfly is another misunderstood insect that graces our postbag in numerous matchboxes during August and September. Usually it comes with the words, 'What is this and how do you get rid of it?' Mind you, it does look ferocious. It is a large black-and-yellow stripy insect with a long needle-like ovipositor protruding from its bottom. It is about 3cm long and the horrified correspondent is usually convinced that it is a hornet.

We don't have hornets in this country and I must say the first time I saw a hornet, in France, I was quite disappointed. It was merely a large, reddish wasp – no terrifying protruding sting, no sudden savage attack. Mind you, I didn't provoke it.

The sawfly, or to give it its proper Latin name *Urocerus gigas*, really looks the business. However, the protruding needle from its abdomen is not a sting, but an egg-laying tube – an ovipositor – and it is long because it is a mini-fretsaw. It files a hole into timber and then lays its egg into the hole. The ones we get here in Ireland have a black ovipositor, which means that they are the northern European subspecies.

Usually it is people who have moved into new houses who find them. What happens is that the eggs are laid into the timber in Scandinavia. An egg hatches out and spends two to three years as a larva inside in the hole, eating the timber. After this it pupates and emerges as a fully mature sawfly – two wings, enormous eyes like any member of the fly family, the black-and-yellow stripes and, if it is female, the fearsome-looking ovipositor. Of course, by this stage, the timber has left Norway or Sweden and become the roof trusses of your new home. You have moved in and are just in time to welcome the emerging adult insects. Of course, they'll do you no harm – they don't sting – but here again appearances are everything and they are promptly dispatched, in a matchbox, and sent in for their five seconds of fame on the wireless. Don't do it! Admire the creature instead and open the window and let it off. (The fact that it finds itself in Ireland instead of in Sweden will be punishment enough for it.)

And while I'm at it, can I put in a word for the *deargadaol* – the rove beetle. Again, its various names indicate the odium with which it is regarded, the devil's coach horse being another of its common names. This large, black beetle comes out at night to hunt for smaller insects and indeed it is partial to the odd earwig or two. (That should improve its popularity stakes in certain quarters.) The rove beetle is a belligerent fellow and faces up to his enemies, no matter how large. It is a big beetle, maybe up to 5cm long, and it has the disconcerting habit of facing its perceived enemy and cocking up its tail over its back to make it look more fearsome. If you pick it up it is well able to nip your hand and cause you to release it pretty smartly.

In the old days in houses with flagstones or indeed earthen floors it commonly walked around houses at night. On suddenly being interrupted by us, instead of running away, it would face the perceived danger with its tail cocked over its back. It was considered to be the height of bad luck in certain parts of Mayo to see the *deargadaol* in this position. Mothers used to shield children's eyes from such sights. Devil's coach horses are still around and turn up occasionally in the postbag for identification. They can give you a nasty nip if they are still alive, as they quite often are when you empty them out of the matchbox. But they have well earned their place in your garden as a voracious feeder on slugs and other invertebrates, which, if left unpredated, would be feasting on your precious plants.

CHAPTER TWENTY-FOUR

Sex and the single plant

The aim of every living thing is to reproduce. If you don't reproduce and pass on your genetic information to the next generation, there's an end to all that talent that is uniquely you. Living things that don't reproduce become extinct. There are two blueprints for reproduction – sexual reproduction and asexual reproduction. Asexual reproduction isn't much fun. A piece of the adult breaks off and grows into an exact copy of the parent – cloning in other words. Sexual reproduction, on the other hand, requires that cells from two different parents fuse, producing slightly different offspring with genes from both. So the old joke is true – the essence of sex is the loss of genes! (Try saying it out loud if you don't get it.)

Plants have been reproducing successfully for millions of years, at least the ones we see today have. And they employ every trick in the book to make sure that this continues to happen successfully.

There are two major stages to effective reproduction, as anyone who ever gave birth to a baby knows. The first stage is getting pregnant, which itself requires particular skills and talents. The second is producing the healthy offspring, which will grow and flourish and, in turn, go on to reproduce.

It is exactly the same in the plant world. The first stage is called pollination and a plant 'gets pregnant' when the male pollen lands on the ripe female part of the flower and fertilises the egg. In the animal world, which includes us, this is easy enough (in theory anyway). Animals can move, so the two sexes can physically get to each other to do the deed. But plants can't move. Fertilising yourself is not a good idea from a genetic point of view, and – for this reason – usually the male and female parts of the same flower are not ready at the same time. So the male part has to get the pollen to go to a ripe female flower without being able to deliver it itself. (The human equivalent might be if, in order to continue the human race, men had to send sperm in the post to likely females and hope for the best.) The plants do in fact use postmen – at least some of them do – and the postmen they use are messengers from the insect world.

Now we all know that bees pollinate flowers, and some of us realise that flies, butterflies and moths do it as well. But they don't have a meeting every morning where they decide to go and pollinate a few flowers just for the hell of it. In fact, insects don't know they are pollinating flowers at all. They think they are going for a drink, just as if a flower was a pub and they were popping in for one. Most insects smell the perfume of the open blooms and visit the flowers to drink the nectar, which is cleverly stored in a little sac way down deep at the bottom of the flower. To get to it, the insect has to put its face right into the flower and stretch its tongue all the way down to the nectar. Of course, in doing so, it gets its face covered in pollen. It's not really much of a pub, it only has one drink to serve the customer, so off the insect goes again, on a pub crawl to the next flower, where it repeats the performance. In doing so, it introduces the pollen from the previous flower to this next one, where the female part may be ripe this time, and so pollination takes place. By the end of a long morning's flower-crawling, the insect will have a very dusty face and may have left behind some very satisfied flowers indeed.

The only insects that are interested in pollen *per se* are the pollen eaters, who collect it and bring it home in baskets on their legs – the bees. To all the others, it is a nuisance that gets between them and the drink. There are, of course, a few flowers that attract insects with more than just nice smells and sips of nectar. The arum lily smells horrible to our noses, because it promises feeds of raw meat to visiting meat-eating flies, in order to get pollen from one lily to another.

The bee orchid takes the performance a step further. The petals of this orchid are arranged so that it exactly resembles a certain species of bee. When the male bee sees the flowering bee orchid, it thinks it is a female of its own species. So it approaches and attempts to mate with it. As it gets into position, the pollen of the orchid is released in such a way as to stick on to the forehead of the amorous bee. Much disappointed at the lack of enthusiasm with which it is received, the bee flies off seeking another mate with the pollen fixed firmly on its head. At the next flower the pollen is in position for action if the female part of the orchid is ripe – never mind the bee and his desires. I suppose the bee must eventually find a female bee, not an orchid, or the whole thing would come to a sudden end. It is interesting, with such a complicated procedure in place, that these orchids are also self-fertilising. There must be a need for a default option.

Not all flowers have petals. After all, petals are only there so that the insects will notice the flowers and come calling. If you are not depending on insects to act as a go-between, then there's no need to spend all that energy getting dressed up in lovely petals. Many flowers that depend on the wind to pollinate them have no petals because, after all, the wind cannot see. The most obvious of the wind-pollinated flowers are the catkins that come on hazel, willow, poplar and birch early in spring, long before the leaves come on the trees to get in the way of proceedings. These catkins shamelessly flaunt their pollen on long, dangly catkins and the wind blows it away like yellow talcum powder. In a way, this is a profligate waste of resources: all this genetic material is just flung into the air in the hope that some of it will land on receptive female catkins. And the wonder of it is that it does. Grasses, rushes, sedges and such plants all go in for this kind of carry-on too, though a bit later in the year.

The problem, from our point of view, is that there is such an abundance of pollen around in May and June that we breathe it in as we walk through grassy areas. Pollen has a very hard silica coat and even though each grain is tiny, in some people's air passages the grains cause an irritation, which manifests itself as hay fever. The other thing about this pollen is that it goes everywhere as dust. If it lands in bogs, it becomes incorporated in the turf. So by looking through a microscope at turf of a known age – say 2,000 years old – we can see what pollen is there and thus know what wind-pollinated plants were growing at the time. This technique is called 'pollen analysis'.

Anyway, by whatever means, boy meets girl and the eggs are fertilised. This will enable them to swell to form seeds, and some plants may have many eggs and thus many seeds. These are all potential new plants. The aim of the parent plant – like many parents – is to get the seeds as far away as possible so that they can settle down and raise large families of their own. Thus there is no point in a hawthorn tree or a holly tree just dropping all the seeds on the ground underneath. There will be no space in the ground for them to put down roots, because it's all taken up already with the parent tree's roots. Also there will not be enough light under the tree for the seeds to send up leaves. So it's not a good idea to drop all your seeds on the ground around you if it's immortality you're after. You need to bribe someone to do the job. Insects and creepy-crawlies are a bit small for tree seeds – you couldn't imagine a bee or a butterfly flying off with a haw. No, the job specification is for the bigger boys – the birds and the mammals. And they have to be bribed into doing this, as they don't see themselves as foresters and gardeners.

So the trees giftwrap their precious seeds in a sweet, juicy coat and ensure that the coat is a bright shade that can easily be seen, such as red, or shiny black, or yellow. Think of a holly tree, or a blackthorn tree with sloes, or a mountain ash, with gleaming berries in autumn sunshine. The birds flock there and feast hungrily. And inside each berry they gobble whole is a hard seed. After a feed of ten or twelve berries, the seeds begin to accumulate rather uncomfortably in the bird's tummy. How to get them out? Think about it. Did you ever see a bird up a tree coughing up berry stones? No, they go right through and are voided at the other end, together with a handy bit of manure to help the seed on its way as it germinates and grows. And, of course, all this is accomplished well away from the parent tree. Every autumn some gourmet bird which feasts on elderberries in my locality perches on electric wires above where my car is parked and festoons the car with elder seeds and fertiliser in an effort to start an elder wood on the roof. But elder is a very common tree in all our hedgerows, so many of the seed-bearing poohs must in fact bear fruit.

So if the hedges are full of berries in autumn, it's not really a sign that there is a hard winter ahead and that provision is being made to feed the birds. Much more prosaically, it is just a reflection of the fact that the previous spring was a good time for pollination. The insects were on the ball, the wind blew enough pollen to the right places, and there was enough moisture and sunshine all summer long to swell and ripen the berries. But none of this can possibly indicate what winter will be like. If it's harsh, well, the hedge has a good supply of food for the birds, and if it is mild, sure the birds won't need the berries.

What about nuts? If a squirrel eats hazelnuts, or a jay gobbles up an acorn, surely that is the end of it. Nothing is going to grow from squirrel droppings. Surely this is a silly thing to do, making the seed itself the food, instead of wrapping it in food. Have trees such as beech, oak, hazel and chestnut lost the plot? Well, hardly, seeing as there's no shortage of them. They rely on the overproduction principle that so much wildlife subscribes to. Go out and look at an oak tree in autumn that's covered in acorns. If every single one of those grew into a new tree and did this every year for the lifetime of the oak, as did the acorns of all its offspring, we'd soon run out of space on the planet. Much is wasted from the tree's point of view, but enough nuts get to germinate all the same. The tree relies on creatures such as squirrels, field mice or jays and rooks collecting the nuts and taking them away to store for eating later. Perhaps they'll drop one, or forget where they put it, or even not survive the winter at all, leaving the cache untouched and ready to germinate when spring comes. Nut-bearing trees can afford to sacrifice most of their offspring for the common good, that of successfully passing on their genes to the next generation.

Of course, there's a collection of plants that can't be bothered with all this truck of bribery and fancy packaging. They are into aerodynamics. Put wings on the seeds and get the wind to blow them away for free. This works very well, as anyone who ever had to remove miniature sycamore trees from gutters and chimney pots will verify. Ash are masters of this method, as are lime, birch and most of the conifers, which have winged seeds inside their cones.

In fact, so good are plants in general at getting rid of their seeds and starting up new generations, that to take them on is a mug's game. Seeds will germinate in any bare patch of soil as gardeners and farmers know only too well. It's very hard to impose your own will on nature without taking mean advantage and poisoning it with weedkillers.

CHAPTER TWENTY-FIVE

Nature's weirdos – fungi

Mushrooms belong to a really weird group of organisms – the fungi. While these are definitely not animals, they are not plants as we know them either. They do not make their own food, but cadge it off other organisms. So they are usually not green in colour, as they contain no chlorophyll. That green patch of damp mould in the corner of the bathroom is a fungus all right, but the green colour comes from the spores, which are just ready to shoot off and colonise another nice damp piece of wallpaper.

Amazing to think that such unpromising material can be the source of so much pleasure. One fantastic thing that certain fungi can do is change sugar into alcohol. (All we can do, for all our sophistication, is change the alcohol into water!) Yeasts have been known to have this ability since the time of Noah. All they need is a sugar source – such as honey or grape juice, or less obvious ones like fermented grain – and drinks, such as mead or wine or beer, can be made from their endeavours. These yeasts float around freely in the air all the time, just looking for a sugar source to convert to alcohol.

One of the most exotic of tastes is said to be that of the truffle. It has been described as aphrodisiacal, food fit for the gods. Truffles are fungi that spend all their lives underground. They are associated with the roots of certain trees and can only be detected by smell. However were they discovered in the first place and who ever thought of eating them? Who but the French and the Italians! Black truffles are found in the Périgord region of France and white truffles in

Albi in Italy. People use poodles and pigs to sniff them out, and then sell them for astronomical prices in the local markets.

We are not known to have truffles in Ireland, so imagine our surprise one day when we got a call on the programme from a listener who had found a white egg-shaped truffle under the ground. Was it a first? Could it be a truffle? Truffles had never been recorded for Ireland, but maybe nobody had looked – we are not noted as a race for our adventurousness in eating wild food. We couldn't wait to get our hands on it.

A white egg-shaped thing duly arrived, cosseted and carefully wrapped. It was a fungus, definitely, but there certainly was no heavenly smell. There was really no smell off it at all. Eventually, having poked and prodded at it for a while, I cut it in half to see if this would help with the identification. According to the identification books, white truffles should be all white on the inside too. This one, however, had a dark green line forming a circle in its centre and it certainly didn't smell any more heavenly than it had in its entire state. In fact there was still no smell off it. Back again to the mushroom books and consultations with mushroom experts. The only truffle ever described for these islands was a thing called the summer truffle, which was green on the outside, white on the inside and had a warty skin and a sweet smell. Ours was white on the outside, with a green line on the inside and had a smooth skin and no smell. Sadly, not a truffle.

It actually turned out to be a baby stinkhorn, *Phallus impudus*, which looks like an egg in its youth, but quickly bursts forth from the egg to attain the shape so graphically described by its Latin name, and the smell which gives it its English name. The green line becomes a slimy spore-bearing cap on the top and its disgusting smell quickly attracts flies, who land on it and take off again with the spores on board to spread the fungus far and wide. A few of these in your garden and you would be convinced that your septic tank was acting up. Food of the gods? Heavenly aphrodisiac? Not on your Nellie!

Fungi will grow anywhere they can get a bite to eat and they are not particular in their dining habits. Athlete's foot, an annoying itchy and sore condition of the feet, is caused by a fungus that just loves sweaty shoes and smelly areas between toes. Ringworm is caused by a fungus which grows on the skin of the scalp and can cause bald patches. Fortunately, these conditions can now be treated with modern fungicides, but in the old days these conditions were much more common than they are now and 'cures' of all sorts were peddled. Thrush is also caused by a fungus, a bad yeast in this case, which loses the run of itself when the normal body bacteria that keep manners on it are destroyed by our use of antibiotics.

Our homes are havens for all sorts of fungi. Many species live in timber. After all, that is their job in the real world – breaking down dead timber and recycling the nutrients there. How are they to know that the timber in your window frames or rafters is off limits? One of the most spectacular fungi that can attack your timber is dry rot, although if you come across it in your house, you will hardly be in a mood to marvel at its growth patterns. It grows in massive sheets and splits the timber into squares as it goes, completely ruining any structural strength your timber had. It can even travel over masonry with no timber there at all to get to the next bit of timber. Getting rid of it requires ruthless amputation of all timber that's even adjacent to it. By comparison, wet rot lacks flamboyance. Oh, you wouldn't welcome that in either, but it is slower and less dramatic than dry rot and somehow doesn't strike such terror into the heart of the beholder.

Dead wood can host a great variety of fungi, all with the general aim of breaking down the timber by growing on its nutrients. One particular species, the honey tuft fungus, which grows inside hollow trees, is luminous and glows away as it spreads slowly through the softening timber. One can only speculate as to why it is luminous. (Is it afraid of the dark?) In a world without electricity and light pollution, when people travelled at night on foot or on horseback, such phenomena were noted and marvelled at. We tend not to travel in the pitch darkness nowadays and so are not really aware that luminous fungi exist.

So it was with complete incredulity that we listened to the tale of the luminous flying object seen by one of our listeners one dark night as he returned home in a completely sober condition. Seeing something like that would sober you up quickly, right enough. Piecing the story together and getting a description of the flying object, it became apparent what it was. It was an old owl, which spent its days asleep in a hollow tree obviously infected with honey tuft fungus. It had lived there so long that the fungus was all over its feathers, so when it came out at night it glowed in the dark. Our informant was obviously made of stern stuff. A lesser man could have dined out for months on tales of ghosts and banshees.

Fungi have also been implicated in deaths on a truly biblical scale. Ergot is a fungus that grows on rye. Its fruiting bodies replace the grains in the ripened rye and so can end up in the harvested grain. When bread is made from this, people end up eating ergot without being aware of what they have done and the results can be truly awful. One result is a condition known as gangrenous ergotism. After eating the infected bread, sometimes as soon as twenty-four hours later, the limbs become covered with swollen blisters, which soon develop into gangrene, and nails, thumbs, fingers, toes and even whole limbs become mummified and fall off. Death quickly follows. In another form of the disease, the first symptom is a tingling, burning sensation in the hands and feet. This was referred to as 'holy fire' in the 11th and 12th centuries. People then had no idea what caused these conditions, which could suddenly affect a whole parish, and they ascribed it to a plague sent by God as a punishment to sinners. It was particularly common in France, where rye was much grown for bread. The first account dates from AD 857, when 'a great plague of swollen blisters consumed the people by a loathsome rot, so that their limbs were loosened and fell off before death'. In 1722, Peter the Great of Russia could not undertake his planned campaign against Turkey because 20,000 of his cavalry died at Astrakhan after consuming ergot-contaminated rye bread. Nasty stuff.

Ergotism became much less common after 1772, when a failure of the crop led to a famine in France and they changed from growing rye to growing potatoes. You could say they jumped out of the frying pan into the fire, because the potato did not stay free of infection from fungus for long either. As we know only too well in this country, in 1845 a new fungal disease of potato was sweeping Europe – potato blight. This fungus, carried by the wind and thriving in the muggy, wet conditions of a typical Irish July, grew on the leaves of the potato plant, quickly reducing it to a black rotten mass. It didn't confine its attentions to the leaves, but rapidly invaded the whole plant, particularly the potato tubers, which rotted as they lay in the fields. People recognised it only too well, so they didn't eat the infested potatoes and get an awful disease as the people who ate the ergot-infested rye bread, did. They just had nothing to eat at all, because the potato was the only food they had, and one million of them died from hunger and famine-related disease during the ensuing Great Famine.

Mind you, horrible diseases weren't the only thing ergot in rye gave you. Clever women early in the middle ages recognised that judicious use of it would bring on labour pains and contractions and induce childbirth – surely a welcome potion in a world where pethidine and epidurals were unknown. I'm sure some of them were branded as witches and burnt at the stake for their efforts, particularly if they used the ergot to induce contractions at a very early stage in the pregnancy, causing abortions. Ergot, as we now know, contains a whole cocktail of drugs, one of which is closely related to LSD and could induce hallucinations. There are those who unkindly attribute the 'voices' that spoke to Joan of Arc and inspired her to lead the French against the British, to eating mouldy rye bread infected with ergot.

Other fungi are well known to contain hallucinogens, and some of these occur in Ireland. The fly agaric is a bright-scarlet mushroom that appears in late summer in areas where birch trees grow. It also grows commonly in Lapland and the Lapps noticed that when their reindeer ate it, it affected their central nervous system, causing them to be highly overactive and to make giant leaps up in the air. (Obviously Santa Claus keeps a supply for Rudolph and the rest of the team.) The Lapps further noticed that the urine of such reindeer was also hallucinogenic if drunk. (How do people discover such things? The mind boggles.) However, the fly agaric also contains other substances, which are poisonous to humans. These occur in varying amounts from one mushroom to another, so, while eating one might bring on elation and vivid dreams, a different one might induce a death-like sleep (maybe that's how people ended up being buried alive!), or in extremely unlucky cases death itself follows ingestion. Getting high on fly agaric isn't worth the risk unless you're Rudolph.

Magic mushrooms are the liberty caps that grow on lawns and pastures and which fruit in autumn. They are small toadstool-type mushrooms, yellowish brown in colour, which look not dissimilar to many other small grassland species. The problem really is being sure of your identification – getting the wrong one may hasten your demise. Mushrooms are one of the few categories of wildlife in this country that contain specimens that can kill you outright with no known antidote. It's not for nothing that some of the deadly *Amanita* species have names such as the death cap, panther cap and destroying angel. In fact, if you are trying out wild mushrooms, it's always a good idea to leave a sample of each on the mantelpiece for the state pathologist, to save him having to cut open your stomach to establish cause of death.

Still, I'd better not leave you with the impression that fungi are the enemy. Alexander Fleming was growing colonies of bacteria in a culture in a laboratory to study their characteristics. Some of them got contaminated with the green fungal moulds that are always floating about as spores in the atmosphere. Instead of sighing and throwing them out, he looked at them and noticed that anywhere the fungus was growing in the dish the bacterial colonies were kept back a considerable distance. It was as if the green fungal mould was causing the bacteria to retreat. And so it proved. He called the bacteria-destroying substance produced by the fungus 'penicillin', and modern medicine took a giant leap forward. We cannot imagine living without such antibiotics today and, despite there being a whole range of them available, penicillin is still of paramount importance.

Still, I don't recommend licking your green mouldy bathroom wallpaper if you have a sore throat. Better give the pharmacist his prescription fee.

CHAPTER TWENTY-SIX

The ones St Patrick missed – amphibians and reptiles

We have a very poor collection of wild amphibians and reptiles in Ireland – only three amphibians and one reptile are definitely on the list, with the possibility of another. It all goes back to the end of the last Ice Age, when Ireland became an island before many of these slow-moving creatures got as far as our shores. Reptiles in particular like warm, sunny climes, so they were in no hurry northwards. They wanted to be absolutely sure that the weather was going to last, so no snakes and only one lizard got here under their own steam. The amphibians were no speedier and we have only one definite native species – the smooth newt. A great deal of doubt is attached to the status of the other two, the frog and the natterjack toad.

But to begin at the beginning. What is an amphibian? It is a creature that can live in two domains – in water and on land. It is entirely dependent on water for reproduction. The eggs it lays have no protection against drying out and they hatch into gill-breathing, swimming tadpoles. But, as they develop and grow, they sprout legs and lungs, lose the gills and can leave the water and live on dry land. However, they do not lose their ability to live in water, and in winter can even hibernate for months at the bottom of ponds. Needless to say, the lungs are no good to them for breathing at this time, so they obviously have a further trick up their sleeves. They can also absorb oxygen through their skin, and this is actually more important than breathing through the lungs. On land they need the oxygen from both the lungs and that absorbed by the skin to keep them going; whereas in water, during hibernation, when their metabolic rate has slowed down, the skin alone is enough.

Amphibians are considered to be very primitive animals, one step up from fish. However, this was a vital step, because it enabled life to emerge from the sea and become established on dry land. They first emerged from the sea during the Devonian period – 400 million years ago – and have been around ever since. So think of that the next time you look at a frog. Humans are hardly three-quarters of a million years here on the planet and we behave as if we owned the place!

The most common amphibian in Ireland is the frog. This species is the common frog and it occurs in every county in Ireland. Although it is very abundant here, it is scarce enough on mainland Europe, and so it is protected under the Wildlife Act, which makes it an offence to interfere with it or destroy its habitat, and it can only be captured and bred under licence. This has led to the situation that, if a school wanted to put frogspawn into a fish tank to observe the emergence of tadpoles in the classroom, the teacher had to apply to Dúchas for a licence. So every spring Dúchas was deeved and demented with applications to keep frogspawn in classrooms around the country, when truth to tell, the species is under no threat here at all. Naturally, there has been an Irish solution to an Irish problem – a general licence to breed frogs in classrooms, but nowhere else – has been granted by Dúchas to the Department of Education and Science for schools. At least common sense prevails and the law is still respected.

Growing them in fish bowls and tanks is easy enough if a few points are remembered. The condition of the water affects their growth. After all, they don't know that they are in a fish bowl – all they can sense is that the water is getting stagnant, running out of food and waste products are increasing. No point in developing any further if there's going to be no grub. So, to keep the development moving smoothly along, the water should be changed regularly, preferably with water from the pond where the spawn was collected. Secondly, tadpoles are carnivores and eat the tiny animals in the water that surrounds them. They can be nasty little cannibals too and eat each other if times get hard.

Another reason for changing the water regularly, or you may end up one Monday morning with only one very fat tadpole with a smug, satisfied smile on his face.

Avid gardeners should make every effort to encourage frogs into the garden, as they are very partial to snails and slugs and, in some cases, these constitute a quarter of the diet. They also eat caterpillars, centipedes, woodlice, beetles and flies, so if you have a down on those levels of the food chain, get a frog or ten.

They, in turn, are part of the diet for lots of other animals such as hedgehogs, rats, stoats, otters and birds such as herons and grey crows. They are even part of the human diet but not, of course, of ours here in Ireland. In France and Belgium they regularly eat a different species which doesn't occur here – the edible frog. They are so addicted to the taste of the *grenouille* that they will eat the poor common frog in early spring when the edible one is still in hibernation. And by all accounts, you'd have to be a very specialised gourmet to tell the difference between the legs of the edible frog and those of the common frog when they are reclining on your plate in a pool of garlic butter.

Not every predator of frogs enjoys every morsel, and sometimes the leftovers from the frog feast are unrecognisable as ever having belonged to a frog. Sometimes in autumn people find a whitish jelly-like substance on the ground which they can't recognise. The old wives' explanation was that it was left behind by a shooting star, but the truth is much more prosaic. It is an uneaten part of a frog, which its bird predators don't like – the glands of the oviduct. These glands, on exposure to moisture, swell up and burst, and decompose into masses of jelly. As there will be no other trace at all of frog nearby, there is no clue as to where they came from. They must taste horrible if herons take such definite action to avoid them.

What colour is a frog and can you foretell the weather by looking at its colour? Well, only sort of. There are three different types of pigments in a frog's skin and each type makes a different colour: black, yellow/orange and white, and sometimes red as well, are all made by these pigment-making cells, and the colour of the frog on any one day is a result of which of these colour-making cells are being stimulated most. Moisture, darkness and low temperatures stimulate dark colours, while dryness, light and high temperatures favour light colours. So black frogs are a sign of rain, or at least reflect the fact that it has been cold, dark and raining for some time already. A period of bright, dry, sunny weather gives us yellow frogs. But as frogs can change their colour in two hours if conditions change, how can looking at a frog's colour tell us anything about the future? It only reflects past weather that we, of course, know already.

Interestingly for a species so common and so well adapted, the common frog is not thought to be native to this country. The story is that there is no Irish word for it, only frog. No less an authority than Pádraig Pearse pronounced this; yet in the dictionaries they give *loscán* as the word for a frog, and the oracle, De Bhaldraithe's dictionary, gives another word, *lispín*, which was commonly used for the frog in Sligo, when it was Irish-speaking. Of course, the frog wouldn't have to have been here since the Ice Age to have an Irish name. After all, the magpie, which arrived in 1676, is the *snag breac*, the hedgehog is the *gráinneog*, and the rat was called after those who brought it – *francach* (although whether these first rat-bearing strangers actually came from France itself cannot be scientifically proven – they hardly owned up to the crime).

Robert Lloyd Praeger, an eminent, Victorian, Irish naturalist, was particularly interested in the frog and its Irish status and he has gathered together the story in his book, *The Way That I Went*. Much of the history of animals in Ireland goes back to a researcher (if that is the word) from the 12th century, one Gerald of Wales, Giraldus Cambrensis, a gullible lackey of King John who came here, apparently on a fact-finding mission. He enquired about the status of Irish wildlife and dutifully wrote down and recorded everything he was told, apparently believing it all, as he enters no caveats. It would seem the more he wrote down, and thus gave importance to, the taller the tales he was spun. He thus reports verbatim the 'fact' that nothing venomous brought here from other lands could survive in Ireland. Serpents shipped over specially to Ireland were found to be dead and lifeless as soon as the middle of the Irish Sea was crossed (they would have been handy for the map-makers!). According to old Giraldus, when toads were deliberately brought here and put on Irish soil 'they immediately turned on their backs and bursting their bellies died, to the astonishment of many who witnessed it'. And we think it is only the English tabloids in Ireland that are given to exaggeration! Nevertheless, in Giraldus Cambrensis' time in Ireland, didn't a frog turn up near Waterford to the astonishment of all! Even though this was 1187 and the Normans had landed in 1169, the king of Ossory, who happened to be in Waterford at this time and beheld the frog, was able to 'forecast' that this previously unknown 'reptile' portended the coming of the English and the subjugation of the Irish nation.

There is no further account of frogs here at all until the end of the 17th century (being the portent of such gloomy news was obviously too much for the Waterford frog). At that time, some Trinity students, no doubt doing a baseline study, found that we had no frogs in Ireland and thought this was contrary to the order of things. So, to improve upon nature, they introduced the frog from England to a ditch in College Park, from whence frogs spread all over Ireland. So think of this the next time you behold a common frog – its ancestors were graduates of Trinity College, no less. Another thing to blame the reign of William of Orange for.

What is the truth in all of this? One way of verifying the authenticity of our native species is finding old bones in archaeological deposits. There was great excitement in 1979 when amphibian bones were found in a grave in a Megalithic cemetery in Carrowmore, County Sligo. Surely this was proof that the owner of the bones was around in Megalithic times, 5,000 years ago. Recent zoological studies on the bones established that they were the bones of the common frog, but radiocarbon dating puts them at only several hundred years old, not several thousand. The frogs were a recent visitor to the grave. And no frogs' bones more than several hundred years old have ever been found here, despite research in the area, so the old tales may well be true.

Certainly it is commonly accepted that it is a sign of bad luck if a frog comes into the house, and that one way of curing a toothache is to place a live frog in the mouth. I can't see too many dentists being put out of business by that practice and I can't really recommend it, as there are glands on the skin of frogs that are distasteful if not downright poisonous.

But what of toads? The common toad is abundant in Britain, but does not occur here. How would you know which was which? The common toad, when fully grown, is of a similar size to a fully grown frog, so size is no help. The majority of toads are brown and warty, but you can get brown warty frogs too. No, the simple difference is in the way they move. Frogs are marvellous hoppers, whereas toads can hardly hop at all and walk around the place looking for food. I think it might strike us as odd if we encountered walking 'frogs' – odd enough, at least, to phone up the radio programme. We get reports, after all, of red frogs or early frogs or late tadpoles, but never of a big, brown, warty, walking 'frog'. They only seem to be encountered by Irish people camping in France.

We do, however, have a species of toad in Ireland – the natterjack toad. This toad has a very distinct yellow line down the middle of its back and runs, very definitely runs, not walks or hops, but runs. It only occurs in west Kerry, and lately in The Raven in Wexford, so I think you'd probably recognise one if you saw it and not mistake it for a frog. Again, a mystery surrounds the origin of this creature in Ireland. It only lives in the wet areas of sand dunes by the sea – in dune slacks. It lives in burrows and so must have sandy soil which it can excavate and ponds where it can breed, both of which constitute a dune slack. Natterjacks were first recorded in 1836 in Kerry in Castlemaine harbour in the *Magazine of Natural History* by the naturalist Mackay, who had just then got around to recording the fact that he had first seen them there thirty-one years earlier. But just as Columbus didn't really discover America, since the Native Americans knew it was there all along, so too did the native Kerry peasantry (as the Victorian gentleman Mackay described them) know all along about the 'black frog' as they called it. At that time the natterjack toad only occurred in a circle around Dingle Bay from Inch to Rosbeigh, and the story went that a collection of them were brought here by a ship which discharged them on to the shore.

Before the mind begins to boggle at the thought of a group of natterjack toads booking a passage to Kerry, remember that, in those days, ships used loads of sand as ballast when they were sailing with a small amount of cargo, and dumped the sand when taking on a full load. So it is not inconceivable that a ship sailing into Dingle Bay to take on a large cargo could have rid itself of sand ballast taken on in another country where there were natterjack toads hibernating in burrows in the sand. The natterjack is a western European species, occurring in England, France, Spain and Portugal, and indeed further east in Belgium, Holland, Denmark and Germany as well. There could well have been trade from any of these countries to Dingle Bay.

These toads are habitat specialists and as the quality of their coastal habitats declines, because of drainage, erosion and invasion by sea water, so too do their numbers. At their height they were found well away from Dingle Bay near Cahirciveen and at Caherdaniel, but a careful survey carried out in 1971 failed to re-find them. They have since been introduced to State-owned properties at Derrynane near Caherdaniel and to The Raven in County Wexford, and the introductions have proved to be successful.

It is to the credit of the Castlegregory Golf Club that they appreciated the danger the toads on their golf course were in, when sea water breached their breeding ponds at the end of the 1980s. They created special breeding ponds for them in the vicinity of the ninth hole, and they have been thriving ever since. It's not often I find myself praising golf clubs for their sensitive approach to wildlife, but credit where credit is due.

The other amphibian we have is the newt. Is there any possible explanation for the expression 'as pissed as a newt'? It's no more appropriate than the expression 'drinking like a fish' (Fish do not gulp down great mouthfuls of water – you'd always have to be replenishing the fish tank if that were so. They take water into their mouths to pass out over their gills and not to drink, although it looks to us like drinking.) The species of newt we have in Ireland is the smooth newt. There are two others species as well in Britain, but only the smooth newt made it this far. It is like a small lizard in looks, as it is long and narrow and has a tail. In fact the Irish word *earc* is used for both species, the newt being the *earc sléibhe* (lizard of the mountain), while the lizard is *earc luachra* (which could be either the silver lizard or the lizard of rushy places).

Another name for the newt is the mancatcher, and it is implicated in Irish superstitions. It was thought that if you fell asleep out of doors with your mouth open such a creature could jump in and live in your insides. Indeed such a fate befell a king of Munster and the creature inside him caused him to have an enormous appetite, so that he caused famine wherever he went. In the end, a holy man had to be sent for and his remedy was to fry rashers of bacon and dangle them in front of the king's mouth. The creature, maddened by hunger, leapt out to get at the rasher, and then the king closed his mouth and the country was saved. (Great hunger can in fact be caused by large tapeworms in the intestines, so maybe this fanciful tale had its origins less romantically.)

The newt is widely distributed in Ireland and it can be seen on land or in water. It hibernates on land and returns to ponds to breed. The eggs are laid singly and are attached to vegetation or sticks in the water. They hatch out into newts, but they do not lose their tails like frog tadpoles do. They are able to grow a new tail or even a new limb or part of the head if they have the misfortune to be injured. Sometimes this regeneration process loses the run of itself and newts with two tails or extra legs are found. No wonder they feature in stories and myths!

Lizards are a different class of animal entirely. These are reptiles, a much more advanced group than the amphibians, and one which took over the world for millions of years in the form of dinosaurs. They quickly succeeded the amphibians in evolutionary terms, appearing on this earth a mere hundred million years after the amphibians evolved. They first appeared during the Carboniferous era, 300 million years ago, and have been around ever since. Dinosaurs, the most famous of all the reptiles, ruled the world from about 200 million years ago until 65 million years ago, when they got their comeuppance when the earth was struck by a meteorite plunging it into a nuclear winter. Reptiles, which are cold-blooded creatures needing the sun to warm them, were at a disadvantage in these conditions, and the warm-blooded groups – the birds and the mammals – had the opportunity they were waiting for. What the creatures of today's world would be like, if it were not struck by that meteorite, we can only postulate. We'd certainly look different anyway, if we were here at all.

This country is not noted for its extremely warm climate, so it is not a haven for reptiles. The only one that got here before Ireland parted company with mainland Europe was the viviparous lizard and it only got here because it had a nud in the race and got off to a flying start. The viviparous lizard doesn't lay eggs like most reptiles, which depend on the ambient temperature being high enough to hatch them out – some hope during wet, cold, Irish 'summers'. Instead, it keeps the eggs within its body until they hatch, because it would be too cold for them outside, and so seems to give birth to live young – hence the name, viviparous, which means having live young. It gets the heat it requires by sunbathing and basking in such sunshine as is available in what passes for a summer in this country (much as we do ourselves, indeed). As a result, this species has a greater tolerance of the cold than do egg-laying lizards, such as the sand lizard, which is confined in these islands to the very south of England. Our species, the viviparous lizard, occurs as far north as Lapland and Archangel in Russia.

This lizard has been recorded from all around Ireland. It has a coastal distribution where it occurs in warm, sandy areas, but it occurs inland quite extensively and has been known to breed in boggy areas. There is a certain amount of confusion between it and the newt, when seen on land. The lizard does not go swimming – trying to keep warm is what it is doing lazing about on rocks. It is bigger than a newt too – females can grow up to 17cm, whereas newts are put to the pin of their collars to reach 10cm. If seized roughly by the tail, the lizard can shed it and grow another, although the replacement will never be as fine as the original. It pays for its superior evolutionary status to the amphibians by confining its regeneration talents to tail replacement – no new legs or extra digits here.

But, in spite of being well aware that there are no snakes in Ireland, because St Patrick banished them, you may be taken aback some fine, sunny, summer's day down in the Burren to see what looks for all the world like a bronze-coloured snake sunning itself along with you on the rocks. Do not forswear blue smarties for life – your eyes do not deceive you: you are looking at a reptile called a slow worm. Mind you, it is neither slow nor a worm, nor indeed a snake; it is, in fact, a legless lizard. When disturbed it can move with considerable rapidity, gliding, almost flowing, along in a most amazing manner – but they are not snakes, honestly! They have eyelids, which snakes don't, and a broad, flat, feebly notched tongue and, of course, they can't bite and poison us. They are native to Britain and at some time in the 1960s they seem to have been introduced to the northeastern end of the Burren (no doubt causing St Patrick to spin in his grave). The slow worm was first noticed in the early 1970s and identified definitively in UCG (now NUIG) in 1977.

Although they can live in the wild for over thirty years, and in captivity for up to 60 years, we do know that they are increasing and multiplying in the Burren and that it's not the same one that is being seen over and over again. As long ago as 1988, a young one with two adults was seen, and by now they are colonising this wild rocky habitat, which apparently suits them. Their diet consists of worms, spiders and especially slugs, of which they are particularly fond and will eat in preference to any other food, all things being equal.

Someone else, playing God, introduced the green lizard to the Burren in 1958 when fifteen were released. But not having too good an idea of what they were at, they picked a most unsuitable species. These lizards are native to the countries adjoining the Mediterranean, and they must have got some shock the first summer they spent here! They struggled gamely on for a few years and were last seen in 1962, but they did not breed or become established here, probably because the summers were not hot and dry enough.

Introducing species that are not native into Ireland is not a good idea. They come here in isolation, without any of the checks and balances that prevail in the country they naturally colonised, and can cause great upset to the food chain. Mink, grey squirrels, zebra mussels, rhododendron, the salt-marsh grass *Spartina* – they have all been introduced here in recent times and have lost the run of themselves, to the disadvantage of the dispossessed, native species with which they were in direct conflict. It was the introduction of pigs and rats to the island of Mauritius that spelt the end for the poor dodo, who had had no such ground predators to cope with before. (So why is it that describing someone as a dodo somehow implies that they are stupid and won't move with the times when the real stupidity belongs to the humans who didn't know or care how the natural world works?)

CHAPTER TWENTY-SEVEN

Piseoga and folklore

Irish country people were well acquainted with the wildlife they shared their every day lives with – not surprising in a country that had such a large proportion of its population as rural dwellers engaged in agriculture. The people observed and understood a lot about the life around them, but there were many things that they observed for which they did not have an explanation, given the state of scientific knowledge at the time. So it is no wonder that supernatural explanations were offered to account for things that could not be understood.

Birds in particular feature in many of these explanations. After all, birds can fly, although they are heavier than air, and so can come and go as they please, obviously with their own agenda in mind. We know what we consider to be normal behaviour, so anything outside that is viewed with suspicion as it may indicate that they know something we don't.

Birds coming into the house are generally not welcomed. It is widely believed that if a robin comes in, then there will be a death in the family. If an owl comes in, it must be killed, no less, as it will otherwise fly away with the luck of the family. The bird most likely to come into the house is the jackdaw, which falls down chimneys from its nest. No supernatural bad luck is attached to this, apparently, as this is an understandable occurrence (although anyone who ever had to clean up a room after a jackdaw has been flying around it for some time, will have no doubt but that they have been visited with the height of hardship and bad luck).

There is much folklore attached to the robin and how it got its colouring. Christianity has got its version accepted, and stories abound that the red colour is caused by the blood of Christ. In one version, the robin (at that time, apparently, an entirely brown bird), attempted to help Jesus on the cross by plucking out a thorn. Jesus's blood splashed on the robin's breast, colouring it red. In another story, when the soldiers were chasing Jesus to catch him and kill him, drops of blood on the path marked the way Jesus had fled. The brown robin sat on each drop, mopping it up, as it were, and so the soldiers lost the trail, and the robin is red to this day.

There are also older stories about the robin's red colour. These refer to the robin as the bringer of fire, a valuable gift in very old times. The burning brand marked its breast, causing the red colour. In any event, the robin is a goody, and anything causing harm to it will itself suffer harm. Cats that kill robins may even lose a limb. Killing or even caging robins brings bad luck to the humans who do so, while boys who rob robins' nests will get sore hands.

On the other hand, the wren is not so highly regarded at all. Christian tradition labels it as the telltale, the one who betrayed St Stephen by flying in the face of the guard who was sleeping as Stephen tried to make his escape. So this is why it gets its comeuppance on St Stephen's Day. Indeed, Irish history continues to malign the wren. It bounced up and down on the drums of the Irish army when it was planning a sneak attack on Cromwell's soldiers, the story goes, thus alerting them in advance. In another version, it is the Williamite army that is being warned by the perfidious drumming of the wren, while yet a third version has it that it was the Danes who were so warned. Anyway, the wren was already known to be a sneaky bird from way back in the days when all the birds were having a competition to see who was the king. He who flew the highest should be king. The eagle, as we know, flew higher than all the rest and when he was exhausted and could fly no higher and was about to declare himself king, the wren, who had been hiding in the feathers of his back, flew up in the air above the eagle and claimed the kingship. In some versions of the story there was a rematch to see who could go the lowest and again the wren cheated by going down a mousehole.

In any event, there was a great tradition of hunting the 'wran' on St Stephen's Day in Ireland. A wren was captured and brought from house to house by a group of performers dressed in disguise. Originally, there were particular characters in the group: a man dressed as a woman, and a character called Jack Straw, and particular lines were chanted or sung. This visit by the wren-boys was welcomed and refreshments were given. At the end of the day, the wren was buried beside the house that treated the wren-boys best. Of course, there were variations on this all around the country but, in general, it was only men and boys who did it, not women. Interestingly, this custom only occurs south of a line from Dundalk to Donegal town. It is virtually absent in Ulster, where the houses were traditionally visited by mummers who came before Christmas, with no wren or any other bird. Apparently, as you might have guessed, the tradition is far older than Christianity and long pre-dates the death of poor St Stephen.

It goes way back to the days of celebrating the return of the sun after the winter solstice. It belongs to the category of rites which have as their object the banishment of evil. Allegedly it was brought to Ireland by Mesolithic people, who came from the Mediterranean through France and built gallery graves here. A different group of Mesolithic people settled in Ulster and built what are described as horned cairns. They had no wren folklore in their tradition – theirs was an eagle culture – and this accounts for the lack of wren-boy tradition in Ulster.

Mind you, wren stories are not the only ones which originate so far back. Swan traditions go back to the early Bronze Age. In those days, the swans that people would be familiar with were the migratory swans, the whooper and Bewick swans. These overwintered in Ireland, but left in spring to return in autumn with new families. It was thought that they embodied the souls of virtuous maidens and, indeed, that they could turn from swans into women. There are various stories about men finding beautiful women bathing in lakes. All going well, children may even be born, but the one thing the husband must take great care about is never to let her have her original cloak, the one she wasn't wearing when he found her bathing in the lake. Why the men in these legends never destroy the thing in the fire is beyond me, because invariably at some stage the woman finds the cloak, puts it on, turns into a swan and flies away.

Swans had beautiful singing voices and in many cases anyone who heard them fell under a magic spell when time passed with great rapidity. The Children of Lir were turned into swans by their jealous stepmother Aoife, but she left them beautiful singing voices. They lasted until the Christian era, in time to hear the Christian bell and to be baptised and go straight to heaven. Lots of stories based on Tara involve swans. King Eochaid wagered a hug (or something) with his wife Etaine in a game of chess against Midir and lost. When Midir came to Tara to claim his hug, there was great security around the whole place. Undaunted, Midir clasped Etaine to him and they both rose through the smoke hole and flew away as swans. It was nine years before Eochaid got her back (that learned him)! Etaine's grandson, Conor, not aware of the family story – or maybe only too aware of it – was into hunting swans, until one fine day a flock he was chasing landed and turned into armed men who told him that it was very wrong to kill birds. They also told him if he walked naked to Tara carrying only a sling and a stone he could become king. Which he did.

There are also various stories about Cú Chulainn and swans, mostly, I'm sorry to relate, about slaying them or tying them with silver chains.

The mute swan was considered a royal bird in Britain. They were very highly thought of as food, and the earliest record of ownership is for the year 966 when King Edgar gave the Abbots of Croyland rights over stray swans. This is taken to mean that the Crown was claiming ownership of swans by that date, because if strays could be distinguished, then swans must have been marked in some way. The first reference to the swan as the 'royal bird' is from 1186. By 1553 there were about 800 registered swan owners in the fens of East Anglia alone. They were given an individual swan mark to put on the bill of the swan signifying ownership. Anyone caught stealing a swan was in deep trouble, even stealing a swan's egg brought with it the punishment of a year and a day in jail as well as a fine.

Do they sing just before death – the swan song? The story goes back to Aristotle. The swans sing, according to him, not in grief but for joy that they are at last going to meet the god Apollo whose birds they are. But there is thought to be a basis in fact for swan song. Whooper swans have a very long, looped trachea which enables them to whoop. When they were shot, the air in the lungs and air sack would take a while to escape through the trachea and, in doing so, would generate some musical notes. But I wonder – they certainly didn't have guns in the time of Aristotle.

Another migratory bird, the swallow, has lots of fables told about it. Close up you can see that a swallow has red coloration under the chin and it too has been implicated in ancient tales of the arrival of fire. It apparently brought it from the heavens and the smoky dark blue of its plumage shows that it grabbed the burning brand from a fire. In Ireland they were called devil birds, as were swifts. The name comes from the fact that they fly around very fast and, in the case of swifts, shriek a lot and live in church steeples. They were of great use in medicine. In the belly of a swallow there was believed to be a stone which, if acquired from a swallow's nest at the August full moon, would cure epilepsy, blindness and stammering. A case of the twittering bird being used to cure diseases it resembled – sympathetic magic. There is a 1692 recipe which is a cure for falling sickness and sudden fits that calls for the following ingredients:

Fifty swallows bruised in a mortar, feathers and all
One ounce of caster powder
White wine vinegar
Sugar

The poor swallows! On the other hand it is great good luck to have house martins build nests on the outside of your house, and you must under no circumstances remove them.

The swallow is not the only bird to provide a cure for blindness. The owl, as you might imagine, with its keen sight, has a role to play there too. Eating owls' eggs cured blindness, particularly if they were charred and powdered. In ancient Greece the owl was the bird of Athene, the goddess of wisdom, and so some of the wisdom rubbed off on the bird, giving us the wise old owl. Athene's nemesis was Dionysius, the god of revelry and ecstasy. So it doesn't take long to figure out that excesses caused by following Dionysius can be cured by Athene's bird. Therefore owls' eggs dissolved in alcohol cure drunkenness and alcoholism, while salted owl flesh was a remedy for gout, a disease thought to have been brought on by too liberal a bending of the elbow.

In Ireland, we only have two resident species. The barn owl, white, ghostly silent, flying at night and with a terrible screech, is the progenitor of many ghost stories and indeed of the banshee herself. The long-eared owl, another night-flying species, spends its days standing still on a branch up against a tree trunk. It is well camouflaged because its plumage matches the tree trunk so exactly that it is very hard to spot. However, if you did see one and it was awake and saw you, you could get it to twist its own neck by walking round and round the tree. It would move its head to follow the movement and so wring its own neck. This species mustn't have passed the aptitude test when being chosen by the goddess Athene. The real explanation is that owls have binocular vision and so have very flexible necks. If you walk in a circle around an owl, its head will turn with you through 180 degrees. Then it will turn its neck back almost 360 degrees and resume watching you. It moves the head so fast that many people don't notice that it flicks its head around and they think that the bird will twist its head clean off.

Owls, because they came out at night, were also associated with witches, so an owl nailed over the barn door would protect from the evil eye.

Eagles have always featured in folklore. There are eagle gods in the legends of Babylon and ancient India, and the eagle was sacred to Zeus and Jove. Roman legions carried eagles on their standards. It is one of the four beasts of the Book of Revelations, which were assigned to the four evangelists. While Mark got the lion, Luke the calf and Matthew the beast with the man's head, the eagle went to John, and so it appears adorning the lectern in our churches from which the word of God is read.

Eagles were very common in Ireland in olden times, both the golden eagle and the sea eagle, and many placenames derive from them. Giraldus Cambrensis described them as being very numerous when he visited here at the end of the 12th century. They were disliked by farmers, who accused them of carrying away their lambs, and the numbers were decimated by poison and shooting. The story is told of the eagles that nested on Slieve League in County Donegal. They were known to be there and were tolerated by the locals until the time of the Great Famine. People were so starved then, that they died of hunger out in the fields looking for food. The Slieve League eagles, out scavenging for food, came across human corpses and took bits of them back to their nest to feed the young. One man was so disgusted at the sight of human limbs in the eagles' nest that he took a torch to them and burnt the nest. It was not bad enough that the poor unfortunate people had died of hunger, but the final indignity of ending up as food for eagles was a step too far. Eagles became extinct altogether in Ireland during the first two decades of the 20th century. They have been re-introduced to Glenveagh, in County Donegal, as a millennium project and five survived their first winter.

CHAPTER TWENTY-EIGHT

Why did God make rats?

At the end of a talk I gave once on the mammals of Ireland I asked, as usual, if there were any questions. I was quite taken aback to be asked, 'Why did God make rats? What good are they? What are they for?' The whole attitude was that anything that shared the planet with us had to confer some benefit on us by their presence and the questioner was at a loss to see any possible redeeming factor in the rat. The truth is that evolution has been such a ruthless selector that any species that isn't perfectly adapted to its surroundings is overcome and made extinct. The question should have been, 'What are humans for? What good are we?'

Rats, like any other animal, only do three things – they spend their time eating and drinking, resting and sleeping, and breeding. A plentiful supply of food and drink means that they can get on with the other two activities. The more food we make available for them – and they eat a very Catholic diet – the greater the numbers there will be. We were plagued with rats long ago because of our filthy habits, particularly because of carelessness in disposing of our waste in cities. The rats acted as dustbin men, the sewage disposers, the eaters of any food we had that was not carefully secured from them. That's why God made them – to punish us for our dirty habits!

Any animal population is controlled by the amount of food available to it. We do not have a million robins in our garden because we only have enough food for a pair. The infestation of bluebottles dies away when the jackdaw

191

carcass they are feeding on becomes picked clean. If you are a species that has only one food source, if that food runs out, you're snookered. Pandas could soon become extinct (there are only 200 of them left in the wild in China) because they can only eat bamboo and the bamboo forests are being cleared because the Chinese want the land for agriculture. Pandas can eat nothing else, so the future, as things stand, is grim. On the other hand, an adaptable species like the magpie can eat a whole range of food. If one thing runs short they can eat something else. They can adjust to the circumstances; they can survive environmental change.

Man is the supremely adaptable species. For much of our existence we were hunter-gatherers. We had to move around continually looking for food. There was no great plenty and our population was low, controlled by available food. When agriculture was first invented by humans 10,000 years ago, our world population was only between 2 and 20 million. There were more baboons on earth than people. We had taken maybe 500,000 years to reach that population level.

But being the only species that could make food appear for us gave us the edge over everything else. Eight thousand years later, by AD 1, we had between 200 and 300 million people on earth. In another 1,500 years, it had doubled again, to between 400 and 500 million. It took just over 300 years to double again, reaching 1 billion in 1820.

Growing enough food to feed everyone was working. People had huge families, one every year the mother was able to reproduce. But such large families suffered from disease and illness. Disease-carrying bacteria and viruses could wipe out whole communities. People died early, in their forties and fifties, from an accumulation of things that wore them out. But then we discovered how to cheat death, at least for a while. Great medical discoveries, such as vaccinations, antibiotics and sterile medical practices, enabled people to live longer. The world population began to rocket. If it took only 300 years to double from half a billion in 1500 to 1 billion in 1820, it took less than eighty years for another half billion of an increase. By 1900 we had 1.6 billion people on earth, by 1950, 2.5 billion, and by the year 2000 the world population had reached 6 billion. With no shortage of food overall (although not equally distributed in all parts of the earth) and with huge medical advances to prolong life, what is there to halt the continued increase? China, with its own population at over 1 billion, has tried a one-child policy, without a great deal of success or support from the rest of the world. No wonder there is no room for pandas!

Because of our own history, lack of food in the 19th century and of money to buy it in the first half of the 20th, our population is completely at odds with world trends. Our lowest population since the 1700s was reached in 1961, when we had merely 2.8 million people in Ireland. It had increased by 1 million by the end of the 20th century. Isolated as we are by our island status from world population movements, we somehow feel that the fact that the world's population has quadrupled in the last hundred years should not affect us.

Is it inevitable that, as we increase in numbers as a species on earth, we leave less and less space for other creatures, and begrudge them the space they do have. If we are so intelligent, is it beyond our wit to realise that this earth will not function with just one dominant species plus the thirty crop species and the fourteen animal species that, in the main, feed it?

It is estimated, from habitat studies, that we have between 5 and 15 million species on earth, not counting microorganisms – although, as we have only identified and named 1.8 million of these, we cannot be at all sure. One thing we are sure of is that we are making them extinct at a rate not seen since the time of the dinosaurs. Some estimates figure that we are making 25,000 species extinct annually. They are all here for a purpose, and the world won't work without them. So even if we don't like the look of some of them, even if we cannot work out what they are for or why they exist, it should be evident that they have a right to be here.

Adaptable species can adjust to a changing environment; those that can't adjust fast enough become extinct. This does not mean any particular animal scratching its head and deciding to become vegetarian because there are no rabbits around anymore. What it means is that there is so much variation in that species that somewhere there are one or two that are not so affected by the changing conditions. They can still reproduce and have offspring that are also suited to the new, changed conditions. It happens all the time among insect pests of crops. There are always a few that are hardy enough to survive the sprays and, over time, they build up numbers that are immune to the insecticide. We develop a new spray to get those and the procedure happens all over again. It is the same with bacteria that cause disease. We zap them with antibiotics. But, whether through not finishing courses of tablets, or taking them when we merely have a viral infection like a cold that can't respond to antibiotics anyway, we are now seeing the rise of antibiotic-resistant bacteria. It is interesting that, in spite of all these efforts, we have not succeeded in making extinct a single species of disease-causing organisms. (Even in the case of smallpox, which is said to be eradicated as a disease, we had to keep the bacteria in laboratories – and now we're worried it will fall into the hands of terrorists.) Yet, because of habitat destruction – another name for direct competition between man and wildlife for space and food – we have made more than 200 species of large mammals and birds extinct in the last two centuries, and unknown numbers of invertebrates.

We are changing our world all the time. We are damaging the ozone layer and letting in ultraviolet rays capable of causing cell mutation. We are causing global warming by increasing the amount of carbon dioxide and methane in the atmosphere. We are depriving water bodies of oxygen because of our careless disposal of organic waste. We are interfering with food chains everywhere by making certain species extinct. We are setting the scene for non-adaptable species to become extinct and for adaptable ones to mutate and change. How do we know that the ones that are left won't see us off too?

What to do? It's very simple really. Self-interest, if nothing else, should tell us. We have to leave a space for wildlife. We have to realise that all parts of the food chain are necessary. We cannot make life untenable for one section and then wonder what happened to the rest of it. We really have to believe that other creatures are entitled to be here. We have to realise that rarity indicates that the rare creature is just hanging in there and any further slight change will see it off. Roadways are not delayed because they cross the habitat of an endangered snail, just out of bloody-mindedness. The snail is rare and only occurs here and not in adjoining areas, because somehow this place has a little bit extra that the surroundings have lost. The motorway will obliterate all that. Is that so impossible to understand?

Or is it simply that we don't care if we send the environmental bill to our children (it may not even get as far as our grandchildren)? After all, what did posterity ever do for us?

CHAPTER TWENTY-NINE

Surrounded by water

My first dive ever was in Coliemore Harbour in Dalkey in Dublin Bay. A gang of nervous beginners, we followed Rory Corvin down to thirty feet and sat on fish boxes at the bottom of the harbour in a pale green light. And we took a deep breath through our regulators, which we had only ever used up to this in Tara Street baths. And lo and behold, we could breathe. The equipment worked. We could sit down there breathing and making ridiculous hand signals at each other. I was so excited, I scarcely missed not being able to talk. This dive marked the start of a few exciting years with the Irish Sub-Aqua Club, when I got to explore the Irish coastline underwater.

You could still dive in Dublin Bay in those days – the mid-1970s. You could be forty foot down at the back of the Muglins on a summer's evening by seven o'clock, having completed a day's work in the city, travelled out to Coliemore Harbour and covered the rest of the distance to the back of Dalkey Island in an inflatable. There was such life to be seen down there. Dublin Bay was famous in Molly Malone's time for its mussels and they were still here in abundance in the 1970s. Mussels are filter feeders. They suck lots of water through their bodies and any food in that water they absorb. They cannot pick and choose what they will absorb – it all goes in. There was lots of food in Dublin Bay in those days: our waste treatment system had seen to that. Wasn't Dublin Bay big enough to dilute all the waste that the population of Dublin produced? Maybe, but what happened to the diluted waste? To be strictly scientific about it, this was food eaten by us, but not, of course, completely digested and absorbed by us. The diluted organic mixture was food for others in the food chain and filter feeders, like the mussels, loved it. They drew it through their bodies and thrived on it. There was a carpet of blue-black mussels on the bottom, right across Dalkey Sound from the shore, right to the Island and round the back to the Muglins. These mussels were food for the next lot in the food chain – the starfish.

Ordinary starfish have five tentacles with an eye at the end of each tentacle so that they can see whether they are coming or going. They grab hold of the mussels with these tentacles and prise them open. And then they extrude their stomachs out through their mouths, which are at the centre of their bodies on the underside. They poke their tummies into the opened mussels and envelop the tasty morsel, the living mussel body, inside. They then restore the stomach and the mussel flesh through their mouths, back down into their lower regions again. Wouldn't you just love to go out for a meal with a bunch of starfish! They don't confine their attentions to mussels, but will happily eat other bivalves too, such as scallops. One of our diving companions who was partial to the odd scallop used to wage war on the starfish. Not being fully *au fait* with the body structure of the creature, he used to cut it with his knife. But starfish being such primitive creatures, they could grow back new tentacles, so he was actually increasing the population by his activities rather than the other way round.

You'd want an iron constitution to eat the mussels of Dublin Bay in those days. As well as second-hand (or something) food, they also filter the bacterial contents of our waste into their bodies as well. And while a light boiling until the shells open may cook the mussel flesh, it doesn't kill bacteria. You'd need to boil them for thirteen minutes to be sure that all the bacteria are dead. What would your average mussel look like after being boiled for thirteen minutes? A tiny bit of yellow chewy rubber – that's what. The fever that Molly Malone died of was typhoid fever, probably contracted from eating the mussels she had for sale. People who were already suffering from typhoid at that time would have excreted the bacteria with their waste into Dublin Bay, which would be absorbed by the filter-feeding mussels who lived there.

Or could the cockles have been to blame? These shellfish are also bivalves – that is they have two shells and they live buried in the mud in the very shallowest waters. When the tide is in and the mud is covered with water bearing lots of food, they stick up their filter, which is a long, tough white tube, and filter in the water. Any food in that water is theirs, and they expel the water again when they have absorbed it. So any baddies in the water – bacteria, poisons, heavy metals, whatever – will all be absorbed too. When the tide goes out, the mud flats lose their covering of water, so the cockles retreat down into the soft mud, pulling their feeding filter tube back into their shells. Walking over the mud at low tide, you can, with a practised eye, see the slight indentation they leave on the surface. Cockle-gatherers use rakes to comb the mud to dislodge the cockles, which do not bury themselves so very deep down. Cockle-gatherers have to work between the tides, often at night, and it can be a cold, thankless job. Many Irish people consider this type of food to be *bia bocht* – poor food eaten during famine times to ward off hunger – and have not much time for it now. It is much more popular in Britain and France than it is here.

The food chain is a wonderful thing. Diving in Dublin Bay in those days I was struck by the abundance and size of the crabs, particularly the edible crab. They were the size of dinner plates. I cod you not. And the wonderful thing about being a biologist diver was that you understood how the food chain worked. You couldn't risk eating the filter feeders, because the bacteria would get you. But you could eat whatever ate those, and crabs, and indeed lobsters, were at this level on the food chain. They ate the mussels, bacteria and all I suppose, but by absorbing this food into their own bodies they purified it. You could eat crabs with impunity out of Dublin Bay and lobsters too if you could find any. Crabs were given to walking along the bottom, feeding on the wall-to-wall mussels and you could select whichever one you wanted as you cruised slowly over them. Lobsters had the wit to hide in holes in the rocks and only emerge at night, so we didn't encounter too many of them at seven o'clock of a summer's evening.

Mind you, my greed was nearly the end of me one evening as I swam along selecting a crab for supper. I kept swapping the crab I was holding for an even bigger one, until eventually I was holding one as big as the dinner plate you'd be given in a fancy nouvelle cuisine restaurant. One holds a crab behind its front claws, as they cannot angle their claws back to get you. So, as I slowly finned back underwater, holding my crab up in my right hand, I began to notice that I could hardly draw any breath. Could I be out of air? No, the contents gauge reassuringly read quarter full. So why couldn't I breathe? Looking back at the air tube leading from my bottle to my breathing regulator, I saw to my horror that the crab had fastened one of its claws around the rubber tube and was closing in on it. And I had greedily selected such a large crab that I couldn't prise the claw back open. Had I just drawn my last breath?

You never ever dive alone: I had a buddy. I got the chance at long last to use the Terrible Emergency Altogether signal – a hand drawn across your throat. And my buddy didn't panic. One twist of the trusty diving knife in the claw and the crab thought better of throttling me. It gave me great pleasure to cook it that night, even though it wouldn't fit in my largest pot and I had to bake it in the oven (having first of all dispatched it of course). I don't think I am cut out to be a vegetarian.

CHAPTER THIRTY

Why you can't burn holes in the ozone layer from your back garden

Spring moves north across Europe at the same speed as a person walks. The arrival of spring is heralded by the opening of the leaves on the trees, so that if you could look at Europe from the air you would see this green wave starting in southern Europe in February and moving north at about four miles an hour. It reaches Ireland in early April and if you take a European holiday at this time you will always be struck by how different things look at your destination. It will be much greener if you go south, while if you go to Denmark, say, spring has not yet arrived at all. This has all been described recently from satellite images that are taken of our world from space. Climate scientists compare these images, one year against the next, and they have discovered that spring is starting its march earlier and earlier each year. Our climate is changing – rapidly – and we are all affected by it.

If there's one thing that seems to be utterly confused in people's minds, and indeed in the minds of some of those in authority, it is this whole concept of climate change and what is causing it. How many times have I been told that burning rubbish in your back garden will damage the ozone layer? It will do no such thing. It would want to be a bonfire eighteen kilometres high. Or, that all that rain was caused by a hole in the ozone layer, as if it were some sort of punctured umbrella. Or, indeed, that cows are affecting the ozone layer! The thing is that there are two completely different environmental problems here. We found out about both at the same time, and in some people's minds, they are inextricably mixed up.

Let not the readers of this book complain that I did not do everything in my power to address this confusion. Let us start with the ozone layer. This is a thin layer at the very outside of the atmosphere that surrounds the earth. It is about eighteen kilometres above the earth and up there it is very cold and the pressure is very low. The atmosphere anywhere around the world has about 20 per cent oxygen in it. Normally this oxygen is in the form of two oxygen atoms stuck together to form an oxygen molecule, which we call O_2. However, on the extreme rim of the atmosphere, where it is very cold and the pressure is very low, the oxygen atoms go round in gangs of three. We call this O_3, or ozone. The ozone molecule has a different shape from the normal O_2 molecule found everywhere else in the atmosphere, because in this case there are three atoms bound together rather than two. (Are you with me so far?)

This layer of ozone (O_3) is a wonderful shield around the world, because it protects us from the very harmful ultraviolet rays of the sun. These rays are full of energy and, if they struck our skin, would damage our cells and cause cancers. The ultraviolet rays can pass though normal-shaped oxygen molecules but not through the quare-shaped ozone ones. So by and large, the general population is protected from virulent skin cancers, as indeed are animals and crops, by the existence of the ozone layer. But, of course, we have discovered a way to damage this wonderful protective ozone. We didn't do it deliberately, we didn't even know we were doing it, but damage it we did. We invented a wonderful new gas called chlorofluorocarbon (CFC). This is for all the world like a three-piece jigsaw. Chemists looked at all the elements in the periodic table and picked three that would completely bond with each other, leaving no sticking-out sides as it were. These three all joined together like three jigsaw pieces and there were no grooves or promontories that could connect to any other jigsaw piece, or, in other words, to any other element. It was complete in itself – an inert gas – and would do no harm to anybody. It would not react with anything, or so the thinking went; it was just a neutral filler and could be made very cheaply.

So CFC filled bubblewrap; it was put into cans under pressure to act as aerosols; it was put into expanded polystyrene, which was used as insulation; it was put into fridges and air-conditioning systems as part of the cooling operation. We were delighted with all these useful things and used them liberally. What we didn't realise, what nobody realised, was there was one thing that would react with the chlorofluorocarbons and that was the ozone in the ozone layer. When the CFCs were released into the air, they were able to drift unchanged throughout the atmosphere because they reacted with nothing. However, when they got to the outer layers, the very edge of the atmosphere, they were able to react with the ozone. They broke up the gangs of three and turned them back into ordinary oxygen, O_2, which, you will remember, allows nasty, cancer-causing ultraviolet rays through. This happened fastest in the dark in extreme cold, and the darkest, coldest time and place was winter over the poles. So, at the beginning of spring every year, about March in the northern hemisphere and September in the southern hemisphere, the amount of ozone over the polar regions was greatly reduced – the so-called ozone hole.

And we didn't know anything about it. We continued on our merry way, spraying our backcombed beehives with hairspray as if there was no tomorrow. And there might not have been either, if the cold war between Russia and America hadn't ended. Now what was America to do with all their spy planes that had been keeping an eye on Russia? They deployed them on scientific work, collecting samples of the atmosphere from very high up. Only in the early 1980s did we discover the damage to the ozone layer. The cause was quickly determined, and at the Montreal Convention at the end of that decade, it was agreed to stop using CFCs. Other, non-dangerous substances could replace them, which they did.

But it isn't as simple as that. The CFCs are very long-lasting. They will be up there for at least another fifty years, attacking our ozone. Fridges are very long-lasting too. Lots of us still have ones that were manufactured in the 1980s. There are, of course, facilities for disposing of them safely, when they come to the end of their life or must be replaced by the latest colour and design. However, these facilities are not in the middle of bogs, or in quarries or in ditches. Fridges chucked into these places, as well as looking awful, are actively continuing the damage to the ozone layer, as the CFCs leak from them. And it is our grandchildren who will cop it.

But at least we know about CFCs, and we have done something about it. Global warming is a second, completely separate environmental situation. We are looking now at a different part of the sun's rays and a different component of the atmosphere. The sun shines down upon the earth. The heat is carried to us as infrared radiation, which enters the atmosphere, warms us up, bounces off the earth and is reflected back into outer space. It comes and it goes. It is just like when a ball hits a wall, the wall slows down the speed of the ball and reflects it back in the opposite direction. Similarly, the heat rays are slowed down when they hit the earth and are reflected back out again at a slower speed than when they came in. And this slowing down of the heat rays changes their wavelength. They are longer when they are going out than they were coming in.

There are certain components in the atmosphere that are very responsive to these wavelengths. They will let them in all right, but the longer, changed shape can't get out again through them, and so the heat is trapped. The gases in the atmosphere that do this (block the infrared radiation from bouncing back, away from the earth) are called 'greenhouse gases' and chief among them is carbon dioxide. If the atmosphere was all carbon dioxide, no heat would escape, and this planet would be far too hot to live on. If we had no carbon dioxide at all, on the other hand, all the heat would escape and it would be too cold for us. But, like baby bear's porridge, the amount of carbon dioxide we have is just right, and we can live here grand. Or so we thought until recently.

Compared to oxygen (nearly 20 per cent) and nitrogen (80 per cent), we have very little carbon dioxide in the atmosphere – just .035 per cent or 35 parts per million. But it was only 27 parts per million two hundred years ago, which means that it has increased by a third over that period, and it is still increasing. Where does this carbon dioxide come from? Well, in the first place, carbon dioxide is not what you would call air pollution, as such. Every one of us breathes it out when we exhale. Plants take it in to grow as they carry out photosynthesis, and give out oxygen. We, and indeed all animals, breathe in oxygen and give out carbon dioxide. Neat, when the thing is balanced.

Now, plant bodies are made up of carbon, and as long as they stay as plants, this carbon is stored in them. But if they are destroyed or rot away, the carbon is released into the atmosphere as carbon dioxide. The amounts of carbon dioxide in the atmosphere have not always remained the same. We know that hundreds of millions of years ago, in the carboniferous era, there was much more carbon dioxide in the air than there is now, and the world was a much warmer place. It was covered with lots of forests that grew very fast. Just as our bogs today are great stores of plants that lived in Ireland hundreds of years ago, but did not rot when they died, the plants that lived at this time, millions of years ago, did not rot away either. They were compressed under the earth's surface and, depending on conditions, they became coal, oil and natural gas – in other words, fossil fuels. And the carbon dioxide that they took in from the air as they grew remained trapped in them. So, slowly, over millions of years, the carbon dioxide levels in the atmosphere were reduced, and the climate changed very gradually. (No nodding off at the back there, now.)

But in the recent past, we have found all these fossils fuels and we are burning them for energy. Oil for transport, coal for electricity, gas for heating, or vice versa. We get the energy and we release the carbon dioxide back into the air. What took millions of years to collect and store as fossil fuels, causing gradual change to the earth's climate at the time, we are releasing back into the air in one fell swoop, as it were, in tens of years, rather than millions.

And then, carbon dioxide is not the only greenhouse gas. Methane is one too. Anything that once lived produces methane if it rots away without any oxygen. This includes the contents of cows' stomachs where the hard-to-digest grass is fermenting away. (Michael Viney once described this phenomenon in *The Irish Times* as farting cows, and had to put up with 'refeened' people correcting him on what they presumed to be a typing error for 'farming cows'. It wasn't.) Landfill sites full of newspapers, old vegetables, chicken carcasses, don't just lie there quietly under their cover of soil when they are full and sealed. If they ever had any organic material, the contents are all fermenting away and producing methane. Left unattended to, this can be an explosive risk as well as a source of greenhouse gas. And, size for size, methane is much more efficient at trapping heat than carbon dioxide.

What would take some of this extra carbon dioxide out of the atmosphere? Well, large, fast-growing plants like trees would. Where are the greatest amounts and the fastest-growing trees in the world? In the tropical rainforests, that's where. And what are we doing to our tropical rainforests? (Don't all shout together, put your hands up!) We are cutting them down, that's what. Are we mad or something?

Is it any wonder that there is unprecedented climate change – and it may not be all global warming either. There is a possibility that the warm Gulf Stream off our coast may be redirected, if too much fresh water from melting icecaps enters it, and then we'd be goosed altogether – our Irish weather could end up like that of Labrador, with snow for six months of the year!

So, burning fossil fuels increases the amount of carbon dioxide in the atmosphere. Burning rubbish in your garden does not burn holes in the ozone layer, but it does cause air pollution. Anyone downwind of such a fire will have to breathe in the smoke and, depending on what you have been burning, there may be very nasty things indeed in the smoke. Anything with plastic in it gives off dioxins when burnt at the relatively low temperatures your back-garden bonfire-in-a-barrel would attain. Dioxins can cause cancer. Burning rubbish is against the law in built-up areas. Fine. But what about burning rubbish, plastics and all, in incinerators? They do this all over Europe, and they are not dropping like flies from cancer. There is even an incinerator in a main street in Vienna in Austria. The science is that, burned at very high temperatures – and we are talking here about eight hundred degrees centigrade – dioxins are destroyed. This is what happens in those countries that use incineration successfully as a means of getting rid of rubbish. But mention the possibility of having an incinerator in this country, and there is uproar. People who the week before were seeking my advice on how to get rid of foxes, wasps, badgers, ants, whatever, are now wanting me to come down to their part of the country to explain how the proposed incinerator will spoil the habitat for them. People who want and demand clean air for their children throng the parish hall in a 'No to the Incinerator' meeting and then one-third of them light up their cigarettes, when they finally get outside when the meeting is over. It is hard to take the protests of people seriously, when it is they who have created all this household rubbish and yet can't be bothered sorting it, recycling it, cutting down on it in the first place. In this country of only four million people, there should be no need for any incinerator. We should not be making enough rubbish to keep even one going. And it's not really the manufacturers' faults, you know. If we didn't buy their over-packaged, un-recyclable goods, they couldn't sell them, and they'd soon stop producing them. We should vote with our shopping baskets.

But of course we will do nothing but complain, until we are beaten into doing something. We all knew deep down that we didn't actually need all those plastic bags. However, in 2001 we used two billion of them – that's 500 plastic bags for every man, woman and child in the country. And our hedgerows were witness. But only bearded save-the-earthers in sandals carried shopping bags, or so the thinking went. At fifteen cents a bag, the plastic bag tax would have eliminated the national deficit in one year. Two billion by fifteen cents equals three hundred million euro. Noel Dempsey, the minister who introduced the plastic bag tax through thick and thin, would be assured of a place in the history books. Well, he has his place, not because our national coffers are bulging, but because of our totally improved hedgerows. Use of plastic bags dropped by 90 per cent in one year. People were seen juggling their messages in the air, instead of forking out for a plastic bag. Sales of embarrassing things, like toilet paper, dropped in small shops, and people didn't buy extras if they had forgotten their shopping bags. You could teach an old dog new tricks, but only if you used lots of stick and no carrot.

We all know we didn't learn this at school. Environmental education only began in 1971. But in the twenty-first century, this excuse is no longer good enough. We didn't have computers in school in the old days and we can still send emails and book foreign holidays as to the manner born. We used to have to go down the road to the phone box, to receive calls from Dublin, which came via several operators along the way and got through accompanied by a terrible racket as button A released all the money the caller fed into the box (if you were lucky!). Now we can send pictures to Australia from our mobile phones. We have no difficulty learning all these new technologies. We can do it right well if we want to. Sorting waste as you go, into different containers, isn't rocket science. Why don't we want to do it?

CHAPTER THIRTY-ONE

Flying in the Red Sea

Scuba diving is the nearest I'll ever get to flying. Really flying that is, like birds. When you want to go up, you kick your legs and up you go. When you want to go down, just put down your head and follow it. Correctly weighted, you are weightless under the sea and enjoy the same freedom that fish do. You can swim along over a rocky bottom and then, when you come to the edge of it, soar over the cliff down into the deeper water below. You can pause as you go down to examine the edge of the cliff and then stop going down and come back up when you want to. Just moving about in this weightless world is thrilling. When you factor in encounters with the denizens of the deep, the adrenalin rush can be mighty.

Plant life – large plant life that is – is surprisingly scarce under the sea. Seaweeds need light to grow. Not just any old light, but light with the correct wavelengths. Green plants, which contain chlorophyll, look green because they reflect green light. Seaweeds all have chlorophyll too, although they do not all look green. Brown and red seaweeds have other colour pigments as well, which give them different colours to our eyes, but it is the chlorophyll in them that enables them to do the business – the growing.

The wavelengths of light needed for growing cannot penetrate water very far, just down about ten metres in our not-so-transparent Irish waters, so all the growth in the sea by large seaweeds off our coasts takes place in the top ten-metre layer. The suspended algal plankton extends down somewhat further than this. Go down deeper than that in the sea, and you leave behind the world of plants. In fact, seeing seaweed is a sign that you have reached shallower water and is often a most welcome sight to a diver who has got a little lost.

Below ten metres or so, you also leave behind the world of colour as we are used to it. Although light may extend down to fifty metres or more, depending on the clarity of the water, all the rays of the spectrum won't, and so you see things down there in a sort of monochrome. Further down still, of course, are regions where light never penetrates – regions of perpetual darkness – but they are below the zones of sports diving so I can't report from there.

The furthest down I have ever been was to fifty metres and that was in the Red Sea in the Gulf of Aqaba. Here there is a great cliff going straight down to over three hundred metres just in off the edge of the sea. You trudge in off the shore in about forty degrees of heat in your thick, seven-millimetre rubber wetsuit designed for Irish weather, to the sneers of the affluent Germans in their three-millimetre suits: 'You must be such cold persons to need such thick suits.' But our skins are as thick as the suits and we ignore such comments. We have the wonders of the world to see and our thick suits will protect us from any nasty coral scrapes or over-enthusiastic fish! Ten steps in the water and we are at the cliff edge and down you go – carefully, carefully, keeping an eye on the depth gauge. The deeper you go, the shorter the dive, so if you go for the fifty metres, you'll only have about five minutes there. The pressure is about six times that at the surface, and the air in your bottle won't last long at that depth.

It's still bright down here, but it is not silent. You can hear every breath you draw shrieking through your air regulator. Is it really built for this depth? you wonder. If ever you depended on equipment, you're depending on it now. You can hear banging noises in the water and realise that it is pile-driving going on in Aqaba on the other side of the Red Sea, say fifty miles away. You can't hear that at all above. So it's true what the physics books say, sound travels better in liquids than in air. Bet the Native Americans could hear the trains miles away by putting their ears to the tracks and it wasn't just a figment of the *Beano* and *Dandy* illustrators' imaginations.

But I didn't come down here to think about the Dandy. What lives here? Well, sharks do, actually. Nurse reef sharks. These are large sharks that cruise just off the rock faces and, yes, I can see two swimming in a semi-circle around me as I gaze out with my back to the cliff. It says in the books that these are harmless and only attack injured fish. I hope that they have read the same books, that my swimming technique is better than that of an injured fish and that I am not sending out the wrong signals. Far, far below I can just make out other sharks with peculiar-looking heads. These are hammerhead sharks, so called because their heads look like the top of a lump hammer with an eye at the edge of each 'hammer face'. God only knows where their mouth is – hope I'm not about to find out. These sharks can be dangerous enough, but these particular ones are staying far below.

All the while, I am breathing normal air out of my bottle – 20 per cent oxygen and 80 per cent nitrogen, just like we all do every day. But down here the whole shebang is at six atmospheres of pressure, me and the air in the bottle. Nitrogen at this pressure in the blood can give rise to a condition called the narcs (which is quite different to the more notorious bends). Having the narcs is like being drunk – if I get up off this bar stool, I'll fall over – or, as it is known in the posher diving books, 'the Martini effect'. Divers are warned to be on the lookout for it in themselves and in each other. You don't know until you are down at this great depth whether you'll suffer from it or not, but look out for any odd symptoms. I knew I was getting the narcs when I saw, just in front of my mask, the weirdest-looking fish. It appeared to be bright green as I shone my torch on it, and it seemed to be very short and high, instead of long and slender and streamlined like fish are. This one looked as if someone had adjusted the vertical button too much and stretched it in the wrong direction. But what confirmed my suspicions was the fact that this fish had an enormous bump on the top of its head as if it had been hit over the head with a stick. Definitely time to move up, as the narcs wears off immediately you ascend and doesn't leave you with a hangover.

Moving up from such depths takes ages, because, as you come up, the pressure gets less. The effect is the same as releasing the lid on a bottle of soda water. Do it suddenly, and the carbon will fizz out of the water and cause it to overflow. Come up too quickly, and the air in your blood stream will react in the same way and fizz out as little bubbles, which, if they get to your lungs, will cause you to die from an air embolism – the dreaded bends. But come up slowly, and you're grand – there's plenty to see on the way. Glorious arrangements of coral are everywhere and each piece is inhabited by shoals of the most fantastically coloured fish.

Back in the open water, a shoal of stripy barracuda fish goes past, followed by a turtle swimming most elegantly. Just as the contents gauge reads empty and you are about to reach for the reserve valve, the surface is indicated by fronds of seaweed on the rocks. A quick clamber over the rocks, lugging the heavy bottle (still heavy although it is now empty), and you're back. The dive of a lifetime. 'Did you see this?' 'Did you see that?' we quiz each other. I don't mention the narcs or the funny-looking fish. We are all busy showing off how near we thought the hammerheads were to us. But later on that evening, looking through the fish book, trying to put names on the different brightly coloured fish that were darting through the coral, I was astounded to see a short thick green fish with a large bump on its head. Only occurs below forty metres, it said, and named it as a Napoleon wrasse (on account of its being so small and being full of its own importance, I suppose). 'Did you see this?' I casually asked the others. Would you believe it – everyone on that dive saw the Napoleon wrasse, and everyone thought they were hallucinating! Just as well the fish didn't hear the derogatory comments about its appearance or it might have acquired an inferiority complex.

That trip to dive in the Red Sea took place in 1979, when that part of Sinai was under the control of Israel after the Six Day War. We saw other parts of Israel too, besides the Red Sea coast. Much of that part of the world is in the Negev desert, where it hardly ever rains. But it had rained just before we arrived and there had been landslides. Deserts only come to life after rain and of course all the documentaries you see on television only show you the sudden flowering of the desert plants after the rain. We saw great sheets of yellow flowers, where dormant seeds had absorbed the rain and quickly germinated, grew, flowered and set seed again in a very short space of time. What the documentaries don't tell you is that hordes of flies appear after the rains too, and look for any food they can find to sustain themselves, while they mate and lay eggs that will survive in a dried-out state until the next rains. These flies are not particular about what they eat. They can visit the camp's makeshift toilet one minute and the lunch-time fish salad the next. One by one we succumbed: cramps, pains, the runs – just what you don't want on a diving holiday. Some of us were more resistant than others and got to go on most of the dives, but by the time we were scheduled to leave the Red Sea and go sightseeing, every one of us had had a dose or two. But we rallied. We were going to see and experience everything, and if we dived in the Red Sea, we were going to get into the Dead Sea as well.

The Dead Sea is one of the lowest points on earth, well below sea level, and the river Jordan runs into it. It doesn't overflow, however, because it is so hot that the rate of evaporation is very high. As much water evaporates every day as flows into the lake. But of course only pure water evaporates, and all the impurities are left behind. Whatever came in dissolved in the waters of the Jordan stays behind in the lake, and so the water becomes saltier and saltier. It is the saltiest sea in the world, and the water is very dense as well. You walk out into the lake, and by the time the water reaches your waist, it is able to support your weight. A few steps more and you are floating in a vertical position. You could lie back and read a paper, if you had a paper. Nothing can live in the water because it is so salty. Any living thing would shrivel up, as the liquid inside its body would try to achieve the same density as the water it was living in and so it would move out through its pores into the sea. Did we stay long enough there to shrivel up? Well, actually, no. We stayed in a very short period of time altogether. Very strong salty water is not the place to be after the affliction we had just suffered from, particularly considering that the toilet paper we had been using was more akin to sandpaper than double velvet. *Níl aon tóin tinn mar do thóin tinn féin,*[1] as they say. We spent a lot of time in the outdoor freshwater showers side by side – bending over to pick up the soap rather frequently.

[1] The proverb is correctly *Níl aon tinteán mar do thinteán féin,* which means 'There is no fireside like your own fireside' or 'Home sweet home'. The version used here means, 'There's no sore bottom like your own sore bottom.'

CHAPTER THIRTY-TWO

Hummingbirds: real and pretend

Hummingbirds are extremely acrobatic flyers that only live in North and South America. They are beautiful, multicoloured birds and they feed on nectar. They can beat their wings up to eighty times a second and if this is filmed and the film subsequently slowed down, it can be seen that their wings move in a figure-of-eight fashion. The wings move so fast when they are flying that they produce a humming sound – like a fan. Hence their name: hummingbirds. This flamboyant, speedy way of moving their wings means that, uniquely among birds, they can fly backwards, or even, in their more flamboyant moments, upside down. They only eat nectar, which they extract from flowers with their long bills.

So imagine the scenario if you are a hummingbird. You are hungry and you want a meal. The only thing you can eat is nectar, which is meanly kept by the flowers deep down inside their petals. You are a bird, not an insect, so you cannot land on the flower to eat. So you have to hover in front of the open flower, beating your wings like the clappers, and insert your long bill right into the flower and drink the nectar from its depths. It's quite unsatisfactory, really. First of all, after all this manoeuvring to get exactly into the right position to drink, there is only a small amount of nectar to be had. Any hummingbird feeling even slightly peckish has to visit quite a few flowers to get a half-decent meal. And secondly, the blasted flowers keep the nectar hidden as far down as they possibly can, and quite often the hungry hummingbird gets its face all covered in dusty pollen, which the flowers always seem to have hanging inconveniently just at the entrance. It really covers a hummingbird's facial feathers. If only there was a way to get the nectar without all this dusty palaver!

Well, one hummingbird species, which thinks it's very smart, has recently discovered a way. The robber hummingbird which lives, among other places, in Costa Rica, has worked out that it can get at the nectar by going around the back of the flower. It flies to the bottom of the petals and pokes a hole with its beak directly through the petal bases into the nectar well. It can drink all the nectar directly through this back door, as it were, without getting its face and feathers all covered in that dusty pollen. This is such a superior thing to do that this hummingbird species gets all its nectar this way and in fact has concentrated all its efforts on one particular species of flower that is easily poked open through the petals at the back. Clever, or what?

Well, actually, it is not all that clever. Hummingbirds don't realise (and how could they, sure they can't read wonderful books that would tell them) that flowers reproduce by sending their pollen – their sperm, as it were – off to the female parts of other flowers via the hummingbirds' facial feathers. Hummingbirds are being used as go-betweens. As far as the flowers are concerned, they are paying for these sexual services by providing a meal – a practice not unknown to the human race. The pollen is taken to the next flower by the hummingbird in search of the next course in the meal, and is thrust on top of the ripe female part, as the hummingbird seeks the deeply hidden nectar. And so the flower is pollinated and can go on to produce seeds and, in the fullness of time, more flowers with more nectar for hummingbirds. But the smartypants hummingbird who has short-circuited the process is not so clever after all. The flower's bribe, the nectar, is being taken, but the price in pollen delivery is not being paid. Before long, these flowers will become extinct, as new seeds are not being made. And there will be no more wells of nectar for these hummingbirds to feed on, as hummingbirds are specific to a particular species of flower. Both are on the road to extinction. Sometimes one can be too clever for one's own good.

Hummingbirds are fascinating birds. The smallest bird in the whole world is a particular species of hummingbird – the bee hummingbird – which is only two and a half inches long and weighs less than two grams, or one-sixteenth of an ounce. This is much smaller than our smallest bird, the goldcrest, which is a comparative monster, at three inches long and five grams in weight. In fact, the bee hummingbird is comparable with our large insects and has sometimes been confused with such by observers. Film-makers love hummingbirds because, as they hover in one place drinking nectar for a considerable period of time, relatively speaking, it is easy to focus on them and get wonderful pictures. As a result, they are among the film stars of the bird world and are very familiar to anyone who has ever spent any time at all looking at wildlife documentaries.

They are resident breeding species in North and South America, continents that are at least three thousand miles away from Europe. So why am I coming over all Discovery Channel describing them in loving detail if we are never going to have any of them in Ireland? Surely global warming is not advancing at such a rate that we can expect to be covered in tropical rainforest any time soon? Well, the truth is that listeners to the radio programme are reporting seeing hummingbirds in Ireland every summer. In fact, in 2003, a veritable deluge of them were seen in all parts of Ireland. How could they have got here? They are great show-offs when flying, but they haven't the stamina for the long haul. They could not fly three thousand miles across the ocean without refuelling regularly, and there are no nectar-filled flowers gracing the surfaces of the sea. The most they can manage is a five-hundred-mile hop across the Gulf of Mexico. Could it possibly be that our listeners are wrong? Are they hallucinating on their flower-filled patios on summer evenings? They definitely report hovering, backwards-flying nectar-drinkers approaching their nicotianas. And with the advent of these new camera mobile phones, they are taking their pictures and sending them in to us. What can they possibly be but hummingbirds? What, indeed?

Well, they are actually moths – hummingbird hawk moths, so called because they look and behave like the real McCoys, the hummingbirds themselves. They are much smaller, of course, smaller even than the smallest hummingbird, at about one and a half inches, but that is not a problem when you have never actually seen a real hummingbird to compare it with. And they do fly backwards and forwards in front of flowers. Their long tongue is visible sticking into the flower, drinking nectar. And their wings beat so fast they make a humming noise. Their back wings are orange and their front wings brown, but all you can usually see is a brownish blur as they hover in front of the open flowers. Their bodies are quite thick and scaly, particularly at the back, where it looks superficially like feathers. But birds they are not, they are moths. It can be hard to convince the senders of the pictures that this is what they are, so sure are they that the camera never lies.

Hummingbird hawk moths are native to southern Europe, and they migrate northwards in summer – sort of a population expansion. Adults can arrive here in July in a good summer and, as they are day-flying moths, they can visit our garden flowers during sunshine, when we might well be out in the garden ourselves. They lay eggs on plants from the bedstraw family – flowers such as lady's bedstraw, or robin-run-the-hedge – which hatch into caterpillars, great green dramatic-looking things with pale blue lines along the sides and a yellow-tipped blue horn at the rear. These complete their life cycle here, so that there can be hummingbird hawk moths seen at Irish flowers right up to the end of September, or even later if the weather is glorious. They have no going-home mechanism; they came here on a one-way ticket. Further south in Europe, adults hibernate and survive the winter in this way, but here in Ireland, while hibernation is theoretically possible, it rarely happens.

So that's what our 'hummingbirds' are – moths. It is amazing that the same form and shape should evolve in two different continents in two completely separate forms of animal life, birds and moths, just to exploit a source of food. Both of them carry out pollination as an unwanted nixer, except of course for the robber hummingbird. There is no record yet of moths being able to turn into robbers and avoid the pollen.

CHAPTER THIRTY-THREE

Talking wild in Costa Rica

'We're doing a world wild series,' says Derek to me one day. 'Where would you like to make a forty-five-minute radio programme?'

Oh, the possibility of it all! Considering various scenarios kept me awake several nights. The Antarctic maybe, the Amazon basin, the Great Barrier Reef, among the head-hunters in Borneo, in Honolulu looking at volcanic activity and colonisation of recent islands... the mind boggled. It didn't boggle for too long, however. This was one of a radio series, not a big film documentary; there was a tiny budget – a shoestring – it had to be done in a week, or less, preferably; it had to be in English so that our listeners would understand it; it had to sound well, as there would be no visuals. And I was to make the programme contacts. So that put paid to Antarctica and Borneo and the Great Barrier Reef – even I couldn't speak underwater.

What would sound well on radio? Our dawn chorus programmes had been very well received. Where would the birds sing louder for longer? Where else but in America, where everything is bigger and better! Tropical rainforests have half of all the animal species on earth – there were bound to be a few that would sound good on the wireless. Tropical rainforest extends north into the continent of North America. We had a better chance of finding people speaking English there than in deepest Africa, or the Amazon basin. And when I remembered that a friend of a friend of mine was a zoologist in San José, the capital of Costa Rica, then the decision was easy. I would make my 'world wild' debut among the rainforests of Central America, in Costa Rica to be precise.

Derek could only spare a few days towards the end of the week to make and record the actual programme itself. But it seemed to me an awful long way to go just for a few days, so by promising to pay for his flights and all his grub, I prevailed on my husband to accompany me there for an entire week. We landed in San José one dark night at the end of October, in the full knowledge, I must say, that it was the rainy season. However, it wasn't raining, nor was it the next morning, as we looked out over the city. It was like the nicest May morning you'd ever have in Ireland – sun shining, lovely blue sky with some white woolly clouds. There were big green mountains overlooking the city and the whole escapade looked full of promise. We had a driver and a van allocated to us for the week and, as Derek wasn't coming till Monday night, we had Saturday, Sunday and Monday to explore. We met Walter, our driver, at reception. The receptionist introduced us and said that Walter was at our disposal and was awaiting instructions. So we told her we wanted to visit the cloud forest in Monteverde. She told Walter, and off we went, bag and baggage.

Costa Rica is a country about the size of Ireland. It has the Atlantic on its east coast and the Pacific on the west. There is a great ridge of mountains like a backbone down the centre, which is part of the ridge that joins the Rockies to the Andes. The capital San José is – like Athlone – in the centre of the country. It lies about fifteen degrees north of the equator and the natural vegetation is forest. As the mountains rise, the temperature drops, so the type of forest depends on its position on the mountain. At the bottom are the hot, wet tropical forests and right at the top are the cloud forests of which Monteverde was one. There was a good road north for an hour or so, and then we came to the turn-off for Monteverde. The road deteriorated at once, and became a winding narrow track, which took several hours to negotiate and would not have accommodated anything bigger than our Hiace van. This is deliberate policy in Costa Rica, which depends a lot on eco-tourism and attracts rich tourists, mainly from North America. It is not in their interest to have large busloads of tourists swoop into their forest nature reserves, 'do' the place in a few hours and zoom off again. No value in that. You arrive half dead after your arduous journey, book into a nice chalet for two nights – dark six to six – and spend a whole day exploring the forest on foot and dining locally. A much more sustainable form of tourism than is seen in many another country. So we were there for two nights and, thanks to our early start with Walter, we had some daylight for our first exploration.

Well, was it crawling with wildlife? I'm sure it was, but how much did we see that first visit? The rainforest is dominated by broadleaved evergreen trees, so very little light penetrates to the forest floor. All the action takes place high up in the canopy, maybe fifty metres above our heads. We admired huge buttress roots, strangler fig trees that grew round ordinary, decent, unsuspecting trees and prevented them from expanding, lianas, epiphytes of all sorts, which are plants that grow way up on the branches of the main trees, bamboos, but few enough flowers. It was most amazing to stand there and see trees and ground shrubs and not to recognise a single one. I could see no species I knew until I rounded a corner and did a double-take. There, growing in a small light-filled spot, was a whole clump of busy Lizzies – the exact same plant that is so popular as a pot plant at home. This is where it lives in the wild – happy in cloud forest.

We heard lots of animal life, birds that sounded like a squeaky door, and screeches from monkeys high overhead. The most exciting thing, I have to confess, was the hummingbird feeder back at the entrance building, where lots of very brightly coloured hummingbirds were drinking nectar out of specially designed bird feeders. We arranged a dawn guided walk and retired to our chalet greatly pleased with ourselves.

It was a different story at dawn the next day. The forest birds were in fine fettle, out exploring and looking for food as soon as it was light. They are mainly extremely brightly coloured birds, such as toucans, quetzals, ruddy pigeons, yellowish flycatchers, and they communicate by flashing their gaudy plumage at each other. It's a visual thing, so the sounds they make are secondary in the communication stakes. Such a disappointment! Such loud raucous calls! Nothing like the sweet melodious music of our woodlands at dawn in spring, when our mostly nondescript woodland birds communicate entirely by song. Nothing like the thrilling arias of our thrushes and blackbirds. Of course it was a great thrill to see the emerald-green plumage of the quetzal – a bird whose plumage was once so valued that it bedecked the garments of the emperor only

– as it dined on wild avocados. We would get great sounds from the birds surely for the programme, but they would be bird racket rather than bird song. We went on our guided walk afterwards, and it was interesting to be on the receiving end of a tour for a change. And with expert eyes to notice and point out, we saw coati, white-faced monkeys, agouti, a coral snake – the dangerous one – and what seemed to be great big rat holes in the bank, but which turned out to be where the tarantula spiders live. And so it went for the day – every single thing was new. The butterflies were huge and dark violet in colour, with wings as big as our hands. Even the walk across to the chalet in the garden of the hotel was a field trip in itself.

Next day we were to go back to San José to meet Derek to make the programme. Walter took it into his head to show us the Pacific Ocean, so we detoured by Puntarenas on the west coast. Was there ever a town that could be described as the relics of auld dacency? Puntarenas had had its heyday, but it was now long past. It had been one of the elegant resorts visited by the cruise liners which sailed the Caribbean and came through the Panama canal just south of Costa Rica, but that was in the old days, and the cruise ships no longer come. It had the most splendid beach, with a whole line of magnificent buildings with balconies facing out to sea, but they were all faded, dilapidated, rusted. The ocean was great, though, my first time to see the Pacific. When we got back to the van, Walter, who seemed to consider this day as his treat, was waiting for us with our lunch at the ready. He had bought it from a roadside snack vendor and presented it to us with a flourish and an air of bestowing us with a great treat. It consisted of a banana leaf on which there was a mound of rice topped with tepid pork, then the pork crackling, then a salad of washed lettuce and tomato, topped with a dollop of mayonnaise. I thought weakly of all the advice we had been given about not eating from dodgy roadside stands, never eating tepid meat, particularly not pork, about avoiding washed salad and shunning mayonnaise-type dressings. I was only too acutely aware that even though I knew I was going to Costa Rica for ages, the exact dates were only settled at the last minute, and so there had been no time for any immunisations. I looked at Walter's beaming face and thought, 'What the hell!' and demolished the lot. It was tasty and I was hungry. In the van on the way back to San José, my husband, who had by now found Puntarenas in the guidebook, read aloud in sepulchral tones that Puntarenas was the only region in Costa Rica where cholera was still prevalent.

Halfway back, Walter's pager rang, and whatever message he got seemed to be important. But alas he had no English, and of course we had no Spanish. We stopped at a roadside café where the coffee was great. The girl serving the coffee which Walter had ordered came up and said, 'Your friend says, your boss is not coming.' What? What friend, what boss? After much to-ing and fro-ing, it transpired that the pager had rung to say that Derek's plane had been held up by a hurricane in London and he would not be along till the next day. Well, at least we wouldn't be meeting him at the airport as unwitting carriers of cholera – we'd surely know by the next day what our fate was going to be.

You can't believe everything you read in the guidebooks. Derek hopped off the plane all bright-eyed and bushy-tailed, half a day behind schedule and all set to reach the hot, wet tropical forest of La Selva before dark, so we firmly dismissed any thoughts of cholera and that was that. The hot rainforest was a completely different ecosystem from the cloud forest. Much hotter, much damper, full of flying insects which skidded off our insect-repelling cream as it slithered down our faces in the heat. We arranged to record the dawn sounds at five in the morning, the rain at midday and the night sounds after six. And that was how it was. The raucous birds duly performed as dawn broke and the moisture dripped off the trees. By nine o'clock the humidity was almost 100 per cent and we distracted ourselves looking at cacao trees with their long pods from which chocolate is made. Just before noon, there was an almighty howling from the trees above our heads – the howler monkeys who herald the rain. And then it rained – non-stop, in stair rods, for about three hours. The noise was incessant. And then it stopped and that was it. Except it wasn't. The water dripped continuously off the leaves for the rest of the day and you could nearly feel everything growing it was so hot and wet. Nothing is ever really dry there and clothes left hanging up for even a short length of time get covered in mould.

But we had a date with the darkness and, with Derek frantically trying to keep the recording gear dry and working, we sallied out when darkness fell. That is when the forests really came alive with sound. Such hot, wet forests are beloved of the amphibians, and there were frogs and toads everywhere. They were on the ground, up in the trees, along paths, behind stones, on leaves and all communicating with each other in one vast symphony of sound. Eric our guide could identify twelve different species calling at one time – poison arrow frogs, tree frogs, glass frogs, toads and salamanders. In all, forty species of amphibians occur here and none of them, it would seem, has taken a vow of silence. It was magnificent.

The Costa Rican government is now trying to replace the rainforest which had been cut down in a misguided effort to grow grass for beef, pineapples and now bananas, none of which has been a great commercial success in the protected, overpriced European markets. So they are turning the farmland back into rainforest in the hope that they will increase their tourist industry. This is not entirely a good news story, because where do the dispossessed farmers go and who compensates them for losing their land? We met some government officials, who assured us that all was well, and a dispossessed farmer who was still awaiting his compensation, which is to come, apparently, from the carbon taxes paid to Costa Rica by wealthy European and American countries for the use of their unneeded carbon allowance.

It's called Costa Rica – the rich coast – because when Christopher Columbus arrived, the inhabitants put on their best finery and went to welcome the visitor. And he, gazing upon their gold ornaments, thought, 'What a rich country this must be!' and promptly slaughtered all the inhabitants. But there was no gold in Costa Rica; the people had earned their ornaments by trading with Guatemala. All the people there now are of Spanish origin; there are no native Costa Ricans left.

We left the following Saturday, coming home by Miami, where a British Airways hiccup forced us to stay overnight, and by Heathrow, where they were experiencing the worst rain and floods in decades. We saw more water flying in over Britain than we had seen in Costa Rica, where it rained every day for four hours.

CHAPTER THIRTY-FOUR

Designed to kill

Natural selection for evolution is such a strong process that you would think that creatures have to be just right for the job or they would have long since gone to the wall. Any chink in the armour, any design fault, and there would have been a competitor waiting in the wings or indeed halfway to the spotlight to grab the opportunity and profit by the lapse. So if you look at bird design, say, you will see why the strong bills and talons of bird of prey have evolved and why they have such good binocular vision. If you are descending on a rabbit at great speed from the sky, you want to be sure first of all that it is a rabbit and not a rock or an abandoned rubbish bag. Secondly, as you are only going to get one chance at it, you want to be sure that you can grab it in your outstretched talons and carry it off. Birds of prey that foul up don't get too many chances.

So, you might think that a bird that lives entirely on fish must be an excellent swimmer. But there are birds – birds that we know well in this country – that live entirely on fish and cannot swim at all. What could God have been thinking of when He designed them? Was it His little joke to make kingfishers fish-eaters and yet be unable to swim and live in the water?

The kingfisher must be one of the most recognised birds in this country. Often when I am introducing a lecture on wildlife – particularly when I feel that the audience fancies itself on its wildlife knowledge or feels that they know all this anyway – I will show them a selection of twenty common birds (of a possible total of over four hundred that have ever been recorded in this country), and there is often confusion between rooks and jackdaws and between starlings and blackbirds. Pied wagtails are often an unknown species (although there was great protest when the plane trees they roost in on O'Connell Street in Dublin's city centre were under threat). But the one bird that everyone without exception can recognise from the slide is the kingfisher. The turquoise feathers and the pointy bill are unmistakeable.

And yet, when questioned, many of the audience will never have seen a kingfisher in reality. But they are so, so photogenic that every year they grace some calendar or other and so impinge upon our consciousness. But did you realise that the reason why they are so photogenic is because they cannot swim? When the kingfisher feels peckish and would like a bit of dinner, what it has to do is perch on a viewing post that has a grandstand view of the river flowing below and wait for a manageable-sized fish to swim past. Then, when this happens, it dives into the water like an arrow, on to the unsuspecting fish, and grabs it in its beak. But of course it can't stay there in the water and eat its hard-won prize. It can't swim, and drowning is not part of the plan.

So it must immediately scramble back up to the surface of the water and fly back up to its watching perch to gobble its meal. And any half-alert photographer who has been hanging around the river bank has plenty of time to focus the camera on the perch and get a beautiful shot of the kingfisher with the water pearling off its feathers and the fish draped artistically in its bill. No wonder we can all recognise kingfishers!

But they are seen much more often in photos than in reality, because life is hard if you are a kingfisher in Ireland, where many of our rivers are arterially drained. Obviously, if you are going to catch your dinner by diving headlong into a river from a perch some distance above the water, it has to be a fairly deep river or you will brain yourself. Kingfishers are birds of mature rivers, not of fast-flowing, shallow mountain streams. And if having to catch fish without being able to swim wasn't bad enough, the design spec for where the nest is to be beggars belief – not in a tree, where you might reasonably expect it to be, or even on the bank of the river, hidden among vegetation like other water birds' nests. No, that would be much too easy. The kingfisher's nest is at the end of a tunnel excavated in the river bank and entered – wait for it – by diving under the water and coming up the tunnel, the end of which, you'll be glad to know, is above the water level. How do you excavate a tunnel of any sort without it collapsing in on top of you, never mind one in the bank of a flowing river? Miners use pit props and so too do the kingfishers, who make the best of their lot in life. The pit props in their case are the roots of the trees which grow on the banks of the river. The kingfisher tunnels alongside a large embedded root and this sustains the route to its nest.

So trees on river banks are vital to kingfishers. They must have a convenient branch overhanging the water on which they can perch to scan the water for passing dinners – bridge parapets are no good at all, much too frequented by *Homo sapiens* and his associated traffic – and they need convenient roots alongside which to excavate their tunnels. But trees along river banks are much less abundant since arterial drainage was invented.

On the face of it, arterial drainage is a great idea. In the natural state of affairs, the river flows through your holding and your fields on either side become flooded whenever the river floods and the water table rises. But now, suppose the river could be excavated and made deeper: the water table would then be lowered and your fields would not flood. In our early days of being members of the EEC (as it was called in those days), this was considered such a great idea that grants could be had to do this. And so enormous JCBs were brought alongside the rivers and the beds scooped out and dumped in heaps on the river banks. To get access along the river, any trees in the way had to be removed. Of course this wasn't great news for the fish who used the gravels in the river beds for spawning, as this was all upset, but the rivers did recover after five years and fish came down again from areas higher up, which hadn't been drained, or else the rivers were restocked by anglers. But the poor kingfishers! They could hardly get leave of absence for five years while their devastated river bank recovered somewhat. They could hardly go to Tenerife on their holidays or start eating something else and making nests on top of the spoil heaps – and so their numbers crashed. The fields grew crops and supported cattle and enlarged the butter and grain mountains in Europe (remember those?) and our poor kingfishers paid the price.

If ever we need a quality mark for the river, a gold star as it were, it should definitely be the kingfisher. Not only will there be fish in the river if we see kingfishers, but the banks will be in good nick, there will be trees along the bank, there will be nice, undisturbed stretches and pollution will be minimal.

The kingfisher is not the only fish-eating bird that cannot swim. The heron comes into this category too. At least the heron has long legs and can wade about in the shallows, hoping to encounter a fish. And it isn't confined to fish. Herons are partial to frogs and, I'm sorry to say, the eggs and nestlings of other water birds, if they can nab them while unprotected. But fish forms a main part of the heron's diet and really this bird is the living example of the truth of the expression 'Everything comes to him who waits'. The patient heron standing motionless in the shallows of a river or at the edge of a lake, its long grey neck and body often merging with the vegetation nearby, is a familiar sight.

A measure of our familiarity with it is the number of names by which it is known in Irish – *corr éisc, corr ghlass, corr mhóna, corr riasc* as well as pet names like *Máire Fhada* and *Síle na bPortach*. Indeed, it is often called the crane, and in Irish the names given above refer also to the crane. Up to the 1600s, cranes were plentiful in Ireland as well as herons. They were much taller than herons, but they also frequented marshy places, particularly the raised midland bogs. They became extinct here in the seventeenth century, but the name in both Irish and English is often still applied to the heron.

The heron is actually quite well designed for catching fish, if you allow for the fact that it cannot swim. It stands patiently for hours in the water, hoping a fish will swim over its feet. The poor deluded fish swimming along thinks that it is a nice shady tree and swims right in under the shade. Quick as a flash, the rapier-like beak goes in, but in fact the heron does not impale the unfortunate fish on the end of its sharp bill. How would it get it off again, considering it has no hands? No, the heron has to wait all day pretending to be a tree in the hope of luring a fish and then when one comes, it has to catch it in an instant and swallow it head first. If it swallows it tail first the scales will be rubbed the wrong way and the heron will choke. It surely has to know whether the fish is coming or going.

The heron flies home in the evening with ponderous wing flaps and its long legs sticking out behind it in a most recognisable fashion. Amazingly for such a big bird, it nests in colonies – called heronries – at the tops of tall trees, and it has the ugliest chicks imaginable. Only their mother could love them. And did you know that herons can tell the time? But they can't read. At least this is the case for the herons in the Phoenix Park in Dublin. Some of them have copped that it is much easier to cadge a meal by hanging around the sea lion and the penguin enclosure in Dublin Zoo than by standing in the Liffey all day at Islandbridge. So come five to three in the afternoon, they begin to gather in the trees around this part of the zoo to apply for fishy handouts. And the keepers there are kind to them and fling the odd mackerel in their direction, as they dispense the food to the sea lions and penguins. But occasionally, feeding will not, after all, take place at three o'clock, and there will be a notice up to this effect, so that the public needn't wait in vain for the feeding spectacle. But the poor herons assemble anyway and look forlornly down over the area, unaware of – or perhaps unable to read – the notice. I wonder how long they wait. Is their patience as elastic in the trees over the sea-lion lake as it is in the river shallows? It is certainly more elastic than mine, as I never waited long enough to see them depart all disappointed.

Our listeners don't always love herons, however, particularly if they have just cleared their garden pond of goldfish. Brightly coloured foreign fish in a shiny pond in a built-up area must be really easily seen by the sharp-eyed aerial heron. All it has to do is land in the garden, walk a few steps around the pond and pick out the brightly coloured prey and swallow them (head first of course). You can't really expect them not to. But our listeners want their foreign exotic fish and are not impressed with the close-up views of a wild Irish heron landing in their back garden just beyond the kitchen window and providing excellent birdwatching material. How can we deter them? they plead in unison. There is a theory that you could place a strand of fishing line around the pond at a height of, say, a foot above the ground, and the heron would not see this and would walk into it and be scared off. But certain herons specialising in garden-pond raiding seem to be able to step elegantly over the strand of fishing line and hit the jackpot. Maybe you'd need two or three parallel strands, but then you'd probably fall over them yourself when you dashed out at the start of a shower of rain to bring in the clothes and kill the goldfish anyway by landing on top of them.

Another fish-eating bird that cannot swim is the osprey. Now, if you want a bit of drama, the osprey is your man. This is a bird of prey, known also as a fish hawk, although it cannot swim a stroke itself. It flies over a lake or estuary, and when it spots the fish swimming in the water, down it plummets and grabs the fish in its talons and flies off with it.

Ospreys are migratory birds, which spend their winters in west Africa. Some of them at least used to spend their summers with us. There are some who say that the drawing of an eagle in the ninth-century Book of Armagh looks more like an osprey than an eagle. However, there is archaeological evidence as well, so we really don't have to depend on the birdwatching skills of a ninth-century monk to know that we once had them in residence. But not now: gamekeepers in the mid-eighteenth century saw off the last of them, blaming them for their diminishing supplies of fish.

Ospreys are resident in Scotland, the species having become re-established there in 1954, and they live in Scandinavia too. They breed there every summer and fly to and from Africa in spring and autumn. Sometimes their aviation route takes them over Ireland, so it is not beyond the bounds of reason that they are sometimes seen here. In fact, they can hunt and feed here if they feel hunger pangs en route. But if you didn't know that, if you had never heard of a bird of prey which caught fish with its feet, what would you make of the story, which made the Mayo newspapers, of a four-pound salmon that crashed through the roof of a house, breaking the roof tiles and shattering itself into smithereens? The newsroom in RTÉ were amazed and rang me to see if I could offer them and the listeners an explanation at one-thirty in the afternoon. No better woman! They were able to confirm that there had been no aircraft in the area at the time, so it wasn't a helicopter pilot's lunch. When I suggested that it might be an osprey, as it was the migrating time of year, and a four-pound salmon might have been just a tad too heavy to keep aloft for long, they were plainly astonished.

'Could it not have been dropped by a seagull?' they asked.

'How could a seagull with webbed feet carry a salmon?' says I.

'Perhaps in its bill,' they falteringly suggested, 'though, perhaps not…' they trailed off.

'No,' I pontificated, 'it was definitely an osprey.'

Although in fact, nobody had seen such a bird or indeed anything dropping a fish on the roof. You would think, if you heard an almighty crash on your roof, you'd rush out and look up to see what caused it. And further disappointment – the salmon was so shattered it couldn't even be eaten. Its size was determined purely by the remains of its head.

Derek Mooney told me later that he had been told it was common practice for aeroplane pilots to hurl salmon out of aeroplane windows as a joke. Out of sealed and pressurised plane cabins? Come on, Derek, whose leg is being pulled?

CHAPTER THIRTY-FIVE

Beautiful water police

The first time I ever spoke about wildlife on radio was in the 1970s to the late John Skehan, he of the wonderful voice. I had been invited on to say what was happening in the world of wildlife at that time of year and I happened to mention dragonflies. What were they and why should anyone be interested in them? John wanted to know. I was working in An Foras Forbartha in the Biological Records Centre at the time, and, while I had some class of information from the public on mammals and butterflies, I had none at all on dragonflies. I felt this was an opportunity to encourage people to observe and record them and send me in records. Foolish me! How would the public know one from another – or that they were even dragonflies in the first place? John, not unreasonably, asked me. Why were they important anyway?

And indeed almost thirty years later, the same questions might still be asked. My postbag often brings questions about and indeed photographs of the large dragonflies, with the inevitable question, 'What are these and what good are they?' Well, they are indicator species, no less, to give them the full benefit of modern jargon. In other words, they are extremely fussy creatures that will only live in the cleanest water bodies. Their young and teenage stages – the nymphs – last for several years and then they crown a reticent life with a flamboyant and exuberant adult flying stage. Anyone with an iota of observational skills, if they are near fresh water at all, cannot fail to notice dragonflies in flight. We have at least twenty-four species in Ireland and they fly, one or other species of them, all summer long. The earliest of them is on the wing by May, and you may still observe flying dragonflies at the end of September.

Unlike butterflies, dragonflies are carnivores and all stages of them, young and adult, will dine on their less fortunate fellow-creatures. Butterflies are herbivorous, as we know to our cost when we gaze ruefully at the remains of our prized nasturtiums, but they only drink as adults – no eating. Dragonflies, on the other hand, dine on underwater creatures during the two years or so they live down there. Then, when they become adults and get wings, they fly around catching and eating aerial prey very efficiently. I wonder does it taste very different and how do the dragonflies know that this is what they must eat from now on? Nobody teaches them anything – it is all hard-wired in, they know all this by instinct. (We, on the other hand, know very little from instinct and have to be taught almost everything. Either we learn vast amounts or we are slow learners, but it takes us at least fourteen years to get a working knowledge of life – and that's only an average figure.)

Dragonflies are part of the water police that monitor conditions in our lakes and rivers. A rummage through stones in a fast-flowing stream will reveal the nymphs clinging to the undersides. They are dull, greyish creatures, only noticeable because they move. They have six legs, three tails and two antennae. They lie there on the rock, grey and colourless, giving no indication of the glorious, exciting creatures they will metamorphose into during the second spring of their lives. They look innocuous enough from above – two large eyes and, in the case of the smaller, damselfly species, three tails, which are actually their gills, through which they extract the oxygen from the water. But if you look at the head from underneath, you may see that they have the most ferocious and efficient mouth. Their lower lip is like no ordinary lip you have ever seen – it is modified into an enormous, hinged food-catching apparatus. Just imagine a very long lower lip with two claws, called palps, at the outside end of it. It is folded in two and kept neatly under the dragonfly's head, where it acts as a mask concealing its face, all but its eyes. It walks around smartly on the bed of the river, hiding its real intentions behind this false face, looking for food. It spies a little worm some distance away. It flips out its lower lip, straightening the hinge to make it twice as long, and grabs the hapless worm in the claws strategically positioned at the end of its lip. Yum.

It grows big and strong quite quickly, and soon is too big for its skin. It can only grow by bursting its coat or moulting, and there are usually between ten and fifteen moults in the nymph's life. Sort of like birthdays, I suppose, each one marking a stage of growth. If there is lots of food available, they grow very fast and the interval between moults is short enough. In poor, cold waters it can take up to five years for a dragonfly to complete all the moultings. Surely a case, if there was ever one, where stuffing yourself at every opportunity can shorten your life.

At each moulting the creature becomes bigger, its eyes get larger in proportion, and wings begin to develop underneath the wing cases high up on its back. Eventually the nymph knows that this impending moult it feels coming on is the big one (they must feel something special, because they've hardly counted all the other ones), and they leave the water and climb up on the vegetation above.

This last moult changes them completely from a wingless, nondescript, underwater nymph to a glorious brightly coloured flying creature. It happens at dawn some bright summer's morning and the whole thing only takes a few hours at the most – unlike the butterfly, who can spend months in a cocoon changing from caterpillar to adult. Once the dragonfly is on the vegetation, it has a short rest, no doubt to recover after such unusual exertion. It then splits the skin at the back of its head and removes its head and upper body from it – rather like removing a balaclava by tearing it up the back. More rest, then, before the final, Trojan effort, which is splitting the rest of the skin covering the abdomen and pulling that out (think of getting out of your sleeping bag sideways). Adult dragonflies are much bigger than nymphs and have wings, so inflation has to be the next step. The dragonfly expands by pumping blood around its body and out along the veins of its wings. If you happen to see such an emerging dragonfly early one morning as you stroll by the lakeside, it is nothing short of magical to see how this thing expands to a full-sized dragonfly. It holds out its expanding and hardening wings until they dry off and with one mighty bound, it then flies off to explore the world. It takes a few days for the colour to develop but when it does, these are among the most brightly coloured of all our flying insects. Their eyes can be bright blue or emerald green or blood red, and they bulge out enormously on either side of the head. Each eye is as big as the head itself and is exceedingly efficient at spotting movement of any sort. It is very hard to catch adult dragonflies – they say black nets are better than white nets, but luck and speed are better still.

Their bodies develop the most beautiful colours – the males in particular, wouldn't you know. Even the very words used to describe them by normally sober scientists not given to flights of fancy are compelling – azure, Prussian blue, crimson, bronze, amber, emerald green, apple green, metallic green, saffron, ash grey. They fly about so very obviously in their gleaming colours and yet they are prey to very few predators. Their supremely efficient eyes detect any untoward movement in their direction and with four independently moving wings they are the fliers par excellence, being able to wheel and turn and dart to avoid capture. This dexterity also makes them extremely deadly predators. They are still carnivores, still starving, needing lots of energy for this continuous fast flight, and so they hawk up and down over rivers and waterways in hot pursuit of midges, mosquitoes and flies of all sort. Once they get within striking distance, they zoom up all their legs together, forming a basket in which they catch the prey. They can then eat it leisurely, with their toothed jaws. (The toothed lip seems to be a feature only of the nymphal stage, which is just as well, really, since the main aim in life of adult dragonflies is to find a mate and settle down in life, and really could you have a meaningful relationship with a partner with a protruding toothed lower lip?)

Flying up and down the river ostensibly looking for food allows the males to show off their sartorial beauty and their boy-racer flying skills, and it is not long before they are selected by a discriminating female as the love of their lives. Of course the male was expecting to be chosen and he has prepared himself very carefully for this moment. Insects in general have their reproductive structures at the tips of their abdomens and mate by pressing these tips together, as even a cursory glance at mating butterflies will illustrate. But nothing so mundane for our dragonflies. Uniquely among insects, the male dragonfly has reproductive organs on the second and third segments of its abdomen as well as the regular one on segment nine down at the end of the body. So, in the equivalent, I suppose, of tanking up with a few pints before going out on the pull, he transfers sperm from the opening at segment nine back up to segments two and three. He flexes the muscles in his claspers at the very end of his body – they are going to get great use and he must be sure they're up to the job – and off he goes. The first female that lovingly approaches, he grasps her firmly with his claspers by the back of the neck and they fly along in this firm embrace. The female has to curve her body right under his until her reproductive parts, which are in the right place at the end of her body, touch his segments two and three and pick up the sperm so thoughtfully deposited there by himself, who had all this planned. No spur of the moment falling in love here. But that is not the end of it. The sperm makes its way into her body and immediately fertilises the eggs she has ready there. She soon feels the urge to lay these eggs and no better man to help than himself, who still has his claspers firmly around her neck. Off they fly together, still in tandem, until they reach a likely-looking spot. They can see the suitable vegetation under the surface of the water below. And down they go. He flies right down and immerses her in the water just at the exact spot beside the plant. She quickly cuts a slit in the plant and inserts an egg while no doubt he whistles nonchalantly and looks at his watch. But soon he gets the nod, he hauls her up and flies off again to another likely plant. There he dunks her in again and waits while she does the business. Imagine the bonds of trust there must be between the pair: she has to be sure that he will actually pull her up when the job is done and not leave her below to drown, and he has to be sure that she will actually lay the eggs he has contributed his sperm to and not fake it. A whole pleasant afternoon is spent in this occupation – dragonflies can be seen flying in tandem for up to five hours in suitable habitats.

The eggs duly hatch out under the water and the nymphs climb down the plant into the depths to live chasing smaller creatures. They face a lifetime of fifteen moults before in their turn ascending to the upper world of flight and sunshine and colour. Meanwhile, the amorous parents have another two or three weeks of glorious life, maybe longer in exceptional summers. Since we have at least twenty-four species, there are always some on the wing on any good summer's day in suitable habitat.

So I gave John Skehan a glowing account of the riveting behaviour of dragonflies. And was I inundated with records? Well, no, actually – perhaps observers were so taken with the wonders they were looking at that they forgot to make records. However, there was a source – a wonderful source – of records, which had just come to my attention. Cynthia Longfield of Castlemary in Cloyne in County Cork had been in communication with the Centre and had offered to make her records available. In those days (the 1970s), I had no idea who Cynthia Longfield was. She sounded old on the phone (in the event she was eighty) and she wanted to give Irish dragonfly records to the Biological Records Centre – that's all I knew. Would I come down to Cork to make arrangements for this? Amazingly, I got official permission to go – expenses, mileage, the lot – and off I went, with an appointment to meet Miss Longfield at three o'clock in the afternoon. She lived in Park House in Cloyne and I didn't have to ask for directions. It was the big house in the area, although apparently a smaller house than the original Castle Mary, which was burned down in the 1920s during the War of Independence. I was ushered in by Cynthia's assistant, nearly as venerable as Cynthia herself, and asked if I would take tea. Cynthia received me in her drawing room, a woman of presence and vigour, with a commanding voice in the tones of the gentry. I was served afternoon tea – I still remember the green china – and Cynthia immediately began to discuss dragonflies. Well, discuss is hardly the word, as I had nothing of moment to say to this redoubtable woman, who had spent her life working on dragonflies, who had discovered quite a few new to science and who even had one species called after her. 'It is all to do with penis size and shape you know,' she declared firmly, when I made some inane remark about how would you tell a new species from one that might be similar. I withdrew to more familiar territory – to me anyway. How would we get all the records up to Dublin? They were interspersed throughout all her notes and papers, she said; she would have to go through them all and extract them. Writing was not easy for her now, with arthritis. There must be some modern way.

Well, there was. Dictaphones. I looked at her doubtfully and wondered would she be able to load the little tapes, press the right buttons, record her material so that it could be typed out later, keep track of what she had recorded, and post them all up to Dublin. Oh, the impertinence of callow youth! There was I thinking these thoughts of a woman who (I subsequently found out) had crossed Africa on her own – a woman traveller in 1934 – from Mombasa to Nairobi, to Uganda, to the source of the Nile, to the Belgian Congo, to Lake Tanganyika, through northern and southern Rhodesia to Cape Town five months later. She had visited South America, where, as well as collecting, she nonchalantly informed the Bolivians that the Paraguayan army was on the way to invade. She had crossed the Rockies on horseback. She had collected in south east Asia. She'd sailed to the Galapagos. Uncharacteristically – and fortunately – for me, I didn't embark upon a whole explaining process about how to work the machine, but left it there with the tiny tapes and hoped for the best. And every week the tapes arrived in Dublin with Cynthia's voice loud and clear on each one, wonderfully enunciating the records, spelling out the species' Latin names and giving precise locations of where they were recorded. Each one took up where the other left off, and, over the weeks, I was able to have the records typed up and to make the maps. She proofread every one and checked over each map. Of the records in that first atlas produced in 1978 – *Provisional Atlas of Dragonflies in Ireland* – over 80 per cent were hers. She continued working and became the first fellow of the British Dragonfly Society in 1983. But I never met her again and it was to be 1991 before I fully realised the impact she had made on the scientific world, when I read her obituary following her death at the age of ninety-five.

CHAPTER THIRTY-SIX

How to boil an egg in a sock

One of the perks of doing a wildlife radio show is that occasionally, very occasionally, one gets to leave these shores and go and see wildlife in other climes. Over the ten-year period that *Mooney Goes Wild* has been on the air, I got to go in an aeroplane four times in a work capacity. The first time was in 2000, when we spent an October week in Costa Rica. In 2002, we went to visit wetlands in Wales and in December 2003 we went to the Natural History Museum in London. In February 2004, Iceland was duly visited. All of these trips were memorable in their ways, but Iceland was something else.

This island, about halfway across the Atlantic, is a little bit bigger than Ireland and lies just south of the Arctic Circle. What would it be like in February? Would it be absolutely freezing, so that we'd have to dress like Shackleton? The newspapers were no help to us. We could see what the daily temperature was in Auckland and Washington and Rome and San Francisco, but no reading for Reykjavik. It's just above the pictures they show on the weather forecast on telly every night. You can get sneak views of the weather in France and Spain when the weather forecaster moves position slightly, but no matter how you try to look past them at Iceland, there's no joy. The guidebooks weren't much better – they don't seem to expect visitors in February. So being pragmatic, and thinking that there was no point in buying things I'd never wear here, I just wore my boots and overcoat, jumper, hat, scarf and gloves, and I packed my bathing togs in my hand luggage (which is all I ever travel with).

It was just below freezing when we arrived, minus two, and it varied between that and minus six or so for the whole time, so I got it right on the clothes. The big thing about Iceland in February was not the wildlife as such, but the wonderful geological sights, which of course are to be seen all the year round. We arrived on Sunday afternoon and were to leave on Wednesday morning, so there was no time to lose. Our guide Jon met us at the airport, which is about forty kilometres west of Reykjavik, and as soon as we got into his four-wheel drive the trip was on. First stop – a swim out of doors. Just as well I had the togs.

Iceland is perched over an area of instability in the earth's crust and this causes heat to rise up under the country. This heats any water it meets on the way up and if this water is within rocks under pressure, it heats to well over the hundred degrees that we associate with boiling water. The heat from this water can be used in heat exchangers to make electricity, and some of the Icelanders' electricity is made in this way. The cooled water at the electricity plant a few kilometres outside the airport is just poured away after use, back into the ground from whence it came, at a much cooler temperature of course, say only forty degrees. But over the last twenty years or so, instead of it all disappearing down cracks in the rocks, the impurities in the water have filled all the spaces and a lake has formed. This lake is pure white because the minerals that are precipitating out of the water give it this colour, and it sits among the blackest rocks imaginable, so that the whole effect is of a steaming lake of milk in a coal shed. Presumably it reflects the blue sky at times, as the whole area is called the Blue Lagoon.

Before you could turn round, there we were in a lovely changing room divesting ourselves of all our woollies and donning the togs for a dip. I assumed that there would be a heated tunnel leading from the changing rooms to the water's edge – but nah. You opened the door, walked outside in your togs and bare feet (being careful not to slip on the ice) and got into that lagoon in record-breaking time. And it was lovely – like the nicest bath you ever had. And it never got cold like a bath would. Getting out, of course, was not anticipated at all, and we made the first bit of the radio programme up to our necks in hot water – literally. But eventually it got dark and Jon wanted to get to Reykjavik, so once more a streak from the water across the icy ground to the hot showers and changing rooms.

On Monday we went to see the tourist sights – the Great Geysir (that is how it is spelt, and from that name comes our word 'geyser'), the beautiful Gullfoss waterfall and the part of Iceland where the American and European plates are parting company. Derek made a *faux pas* at breakfast and sleepily took an egg which he assumed was hard-boiled, only to discover after he had cracked it open on his plate that it was from a section of the buffet where breakfasters could cook their eggs to their liking. So this gave him the idea of taking another raw one with him to the Geysir to see if the water there was really as hot as all that. Would it be hot enough to boil an egg?

The Geysir was spouting merrily as we arrived. The superheated water was forced to the surface through a very narrow crack and, as the pressure on it was suddenly released as it emerged, it changed with a whoosh to a column of superheated steam maybe ten metres high. It made very satisfactory noises for radio, so we stood close by and 'interviewed' it several times. All around were bigger holes where there was no pressure on the water, so it reached the surface merely heated to boiling as opposed to being superheated and exploding as steam. One of these would be ideal to boil the egg. We could hardly drop it in, because we would have to retrieve it after four minutes. Our guide was amazed at such proceedings. Any other tourists he had ever guided here just looked, took photos and went away. We were mad, he said. We were too. A spare pair of socks was commandeered and I was volunteered to hold the egg over the boiling hole for four minutes. The hole didn't turn out to be a geyser, and I survived the experience. Let no one say I cannot boil an egg. It was perfectly cooked – white firm, yolk just runny. I didn't even get to eat it after all that – Derek and Jon polished it off between them.

On to Gulfoss, a waterfall which is frozen at this time of year, situated on a fast-flowing river, which emerges from one of the glaciers that covers so much of central Iceland. While there wasn't much snow on the ground, it was freezing hard and we saw no wildlife at all on the way there. There were Icelandic ponies to be seen, though, and lots of them. Apparently all farming was done with these animals until about twenty years ago, and the farmers couldn't bear to part with them. So they roam free in a desolate countryside with no fields, no grass, no hedges, and the farmers put out fodder drops for them, to tide them over the winter. The waterfall was magnificent – a sheet of gleaming white ice with the sun bouncing a rainbow off it, and in the distance we could see the glacier from whence it came. Ireland it was not.

On then to this great divide separating America from Europe, where the magma that comes up from the central Atlantic ridge hardens to form Iceland. It then begins to split in two separate directions, one lot heading west and the other side heading east. These phenomena occur only as fast as your fingernails grow, so we were not really in danger of the ground opening up and swallowing us. It didn't even make satisfactory creaky noises for the microphone and it got colder and colder as we stood there drawing word pictures for the folks back home. Enough of this! Back to Reykjavik for our feast, which Jon had assured us was going to be something else again.

People have lived in this country since the seventh century and they have devised ways of surviving the winter when no food could be grown. Freeze it, you might think, sure isn't the place called Iceland. But no, it's not reliably cold enough – it isn't Greenland, where you can rely on the deep-freeze effect all winter. Here, because of troughs of low pressure and high pressure and prevailing westerly winds, you cannot rely on it to stay cold enough all the time to keep food frozen all winter. So they smoke and salt things as people do in other northern countries, but their salted meat is made from lamb, rather than the ham or corned beef we are used to, and it was a new one on me. It tasted like ham when you first chewed it and then halfway through eating it turned to lamb in your mouth. Most amazing.

Actually, our meal was to be a mixture of two feasts. One was to celebrate the start of Lent, when salted lamb, dried peas and spuds constituted the traditional Shrove meal, and it was grand. The other feast really had taken place the week before and we were given just a sample of it, as we were not there at the right time. Just as well, really, since this earlier feast was to polish off all the food that had been kept over the winter, now that spring was here and they would no longer need it. Lamb and mutton is their main meat, since the land doesn't grow enough grass to support cows. As well as salting the lamb, they steep it in a sort of fermented yoghurt which has the effect of pickling it. They waste no part of the beast – the pickled testicles are served separately. They make haggis-type sausages from the sheep's stomach and dry these out so that they will survive. But this is the *pièce de résistance* – they actually use the winter period to make something edible that otherwise they couldn't eat: shark. The Greenland shark to be precise. Other species of shark are perfectly edible, and you see steaks of it on sale on supermarket fish counters, even in conservative old Ireland. But the Greenland shark is a huge creature, which was hunted by Icelanders for its liver, which could contain up to three barrels of oil. Its skin was fairly useful as well, because it was so tough it could be used for making boots and shoes. But the flesh contains cyanic acid and eating it would cause death from cyanide poisoning.

However, it was discovered (how *are* these things discovered?) that if the mountain of flesh was buried, it fermented and the acid leached out of it and it would then be safe to eat. So shark caught for oil and boots at the start of winter were then buried and, by the end of the winter, they were safe to eat. So pieces of this rotten shark were the high spot of the winter feast we were given, which also included the pickled sheeps' testicles, the haggis, the salted lamb and a small shot glass of clear liquid to wash it down. The smell was very strong and not particularly inviting. In fact, it smelt like a piece of Camembert you might find at the bottom of the fridge after being away for a month. The Icelanders stood around and kindly explained everything in perfect English. We started with the lamb and worked up to the shark, for which we were advised to keep our drink. And it did taste pretty bad. You couldn't imagine anyone looking forward to digging some up for the dinner. We gulped the drink, a burning aquavit called Black Death. Did it cure or cause the black death? I wonder. You'd want to be on your last gasp of hunger to want to eat the rotten shark – the *hakarl* – either that or be making a radio programme.

Reykjavik itself has the look of a frontier town. There is no timber in Iceland. Much less than 1 per cent of it is forested, and early settlers cut down what there was for fuel. The houses in the city are made from cement and local materials. The roofs are of corrugated galvanised steel, such as we are familiar with here on outbuildings, and are painted brightly. The lake in front of the town hall that day in February was full of Whooper swans. Whooper swans in Ireland are wild and hard to see, but these ones were coming up to be hand-fed with pieces of bread like the ducks in St Stephen's Green in Dublin.

And was it fierce expensive? Well, it depends on what you're buying, I suppose. Houses were cheaper than here, petrol just about the same or a little dearer. Lamb and fish in the supermarkets were about half the price they are here. Eating out and drinking out, what visitors do, was about twice the price it is here – which is saying something. Drink used to be prohibited, because people drank too much and lost the run of themselves, and beer has only been available on sale in the last twenty years. Wine at dinner in a restaurant seemed to start at about €40 for the cheapest plonk – wine that we could buy here in an off-licence for €5 and probably cost less than the cork and the bottle in the country of origin. Then again, things that you'd think would be ruinously expensive because of having to be imported, such as cut flowers, tomatoes, peppers, bananas, were surprisingly inexpensive, because it turns out they grow them there all the year round. No, I didn't have an overdose of Black Death – the fact is that greenhouses are common, heated by hot water which comes free from the ground and lit during the long dark winter by banks of light powered by cheap, renewable electricity from water both heated and flowing.

You always have to leave something to go back for. We'll have to go back to see the Northern Lights. The postcards on display were full of beautiful night skies suffused with crimson, emerald, acid yellow, but we saw none of them, even though we nearly froze gazing at the sky. They happen all the year there, we were assured, though not, of course, every night and not the three nights we were there. They happen in summer too, but the sky is too bright to see them. So the *Aurora Borealis*, which conjured up such images in our minds when we learnt the words in school, are still on the to-do list. Still, they probably wouldn't have made good radio anyway!

CHAPTER THIRTY-SEVEN

Deconstructing the tale of the salmon of knowledge

The Salmon of Knowledge is the fish of legends. He featured on the old two-shilling piece and was promoted to the ten pence piece after the money changed to the decimal system. He was the source of the wisdom of Fionn Mac Cumhaill, the leader of the Fianna. There's not a schoolchild going but knows the tale. But if he was such a smart fish, how come he got caught in the first place? The tale does not stand up to close scrutiny.

At the beginning of this story, we are introduced to the salmon, who lived in the river Boyne in County Meath. He got his wisdom by eating the nuts of the nine hazel trees that grew around the sacred pool at the source of the Boyne. So it was the hazel trees that had the wisdom really. They still have, as any dowser who uses a forked hazel bough to divine water will tell you. The druids at the time were well aware of the magical qualities of hazelnuts and indeed of the concentrating ability of the food chain. The salmon that ate the nuts gained all the wisdom, and the man who ate the salmon would in turn be the wisest man in Ireland. So the men spent their time on the banks of the Boyne trying to catch the Salmon of Knowledge. If it was so partial to magic hazelnuts, why didn't they use those as bait? (Maybe they did.) Eventually, one of their number, Finnéagas, managed to catch the salmon and recognised it for what it was – a potential source of all knowledge and wisdom. If you or I caught such a thing, do you think we'd let it out of our hands? We'd probably take a bite of it raw, sushi style, in order to get the knowledge immediately. But what did the druid, who is described as a scholar and a poet, do? He entrusted the fish and the cooking of it to a pimply teenage youth called Fionn Mac Cumhaill whom he was minding since his father was killed, told him to cook it carefully and not eat any of it and then went away and left the fish that he had been trying all his life to catch. No wonder the powers that be determined that he didn't deserve to get all this wisdom. A few street smarts instead of all this poetry would have been more useful. He wandered back when he felt the salmon should be done, having left all the collecting of the kindling and the making of the fire and the peeling of the willow branch for a roasting spit and the gutting of the fish and the turning of the cooking fish on the spit to the person at home slaving over the hot fire, like many a man no doubt. And I am not a bit sorry for him that he got his comeuppance. Fionn, being a resourceful lad, and no doubt now full of wisdom, had an excuse for his changed appearance when Finnéagas came home and spoke to him. He had merely pressed a burning blister on the skin's surface with his bare thumb (what was he like?) and, of course, oven gloves not having been invented yet, burnt it. A piece of burning salmon skin stuck to his thumb – well it would, wouldn't it? – and Fionn inadvertently ate it as he sucked his burnt digit. They were both lucky some marauding gull hadn't landed on the fish guts and eaten them first. Ever afterwards, the wisdom was concentrated in Fionn's thumb and he had to suck it every time he wanted to know anything.

We don't hear anything more about Finnéagas after this. Did he become vegetarian and concentrate on the nuts of the hazel tree? What good did all the knowledge do Fionn? Did it last him all his life? Why didn't it tell him not to be such a dirty old man pursuing poor Diarmuid and Gráinne all around Ireland in his later years? It might dawn on a man with no wisdom at all that a young one might prefer the young handsome Diarmuid to an auld fella like himself. Not so the deluded Fionn Mac Cumhaill. Maybe Finnéagas was better off without the gift of wisdom after all.

But what about the salmon? Well, salmon have always been associated with Irish rivers. So abundant were they in the old days that the labourers working on the building of the monastery in Graiguenamanagh had it written into their contract of employment that they should not be given salmon for their dinner any more than three times a week. We cannot imagine eating wild Irish river salmon in Ireland above three times a year now, never mind three times a week. What has changed and why?

The salmon has an interesting life cycle. It spends some of its time in fresh-water rivers in Ireland and some of its time in the deep Atlantic Ocean. It is born in Irish rivers. Mum and Dad, who have been hanging around for some time, finally decide one wet dark December night that the time is right. Both are full of roe. Mum excavates a shallow nest – a redd – in the gravel bed of the river, well upstream. Dad is keeping an eye on proceedings, he discourages all other rivals and swims up alongside her when the time is right. His comforting presence encourages her to discharge all her eggs into the gravel bed she has just excavated. As they emerge, he releases his milt in a cloudy white stream and the eggs are all fertilised in moments. She puts the gravel back over them and the job is Oxo. They are on their own from now on. The river water flows over them, continuously supplying them with oxygen, and in due course – a month or two later, depending on the temperature of the water – they hatch out. They have a large yolk sac attached to their body to feed them for the first month as they make their way to the top of the gravel so energetically placed over them by their mother. The emerging creature doesn't look a bit like a fish and is known as an 'alevin'. It soon uses up the reservoir of food in its egg sac and changes its shape to look exactly like a real fish, and now it rejoices in the name of 'fry'. It is now a carnivore and will feed happily on any small shrimps or larvae it can catch. The thousands of eggs laid by the mother need a territory each to provide food in these rather barren upper stretches of river, and so the salmon fry spread out over a wide area. Even so, only the strongest can hold territory and, like any sibling, have no compunction chasing away their brothers and sisters from their supply of food. The weakest in the family cannot hack it and so cannot swim strongly enough to stay in their own territory. They get carried downstream, where their hapless plight is quickly noticed by hungry brown trout or watchful herons and – snap! – they are no more.

The successful fry on the territories grow big and strong and spend between one and three years here, depending on how fast they grow. When they pass the three-centimetre mark, they are elevated to the status of 'parr' and they continue growing under this moniker until they reach a decent length of over ten centimetres. Whenever this magic length is reached, a complete change takes place in the body of the little salmon. Puberty was never like this. First of all it changes colour from the brown camouflage jacket it has been wearing since its egg-yolk days and it acquires a beautiful silver coat. It also feels a great desire to swim downstream, something that was only for losers a few short months ago. In fact the fish is responding to the call of the sea; it is swimming downstream purposefully to leave the river altogether to go to sea. This is a huge undertaking. The sea is much saltier than the river and if the parr went straight out into the briny it would shrivel up like a prune, as its freshwater contents rushed out through its skin in a vain attempt to establish an equilibrium. So the puberty stage must involve more than getting a new shiny coat. And it does. Changes also take place in the mechanisms of the fish's body so that it is able to deal with a salty environment. The default options are reset as it were. And so the creature, henceforth known as a 'smolt', heads off out to sea some April evening, two or three years after it was born, with the memory and the smell of where it grew up indelibly imprinted on its brain.

Where do they go? Nobody knew until recently. They just went off out into the ocean and were never encountered out there. Recent tagging studies carried out by fisheries' research officers have revealed that they swim north up the Atlantic to the Norwegian coast. They feed abundantly in the ocean and grow big and strong. About two years later, they feel homesick or broody or amorous or something, and so they leave the Norwegian coast to travel back. They can be up to two kilos in weight and – yes, you've guessed it – they have changed their name again and are now 'grilse' to all their friends. They swim back the way they came and they can recognise in the ocean the smell of their own river, their own place. Back they come into the estuary, the summer fish, on their way back home to the spot where they were born. But again they cannot dash straight in. They linger in the estuaries, becoming acclimatised anew to the fresh water and waiting for a summer flood, so that they can traverse even waterfalls in their unstoppable journey upstream. And they never feed in fresh water again. They have put on lots of condition in the ocean and this food has to last them for six months or more.

So what was the Salmon of Knowledge doing eating hazelnuts or indeed anything else? And if they don't eat, how come fishermen are out fishing for them with rods and lines? Apparently they haven't forgotten the eating habit and they make lunges at things, although they don't actually swallow them. Isn't that the pits? Just going for something out of boredom and curiosity, something you can't even eat anyway, and you get impaled on a hook.

They don't quite all get caught, however, and some will make it right back to the exact waters where they were spawned. As they swim back upriver again, their colour changes back from the sea silver to a more reddish-brown colour, which helps to camouflage them in the river waters. In the females, the eggs grow and, by the time they are ready to be laid, they will occupy the whole underside of her body, four thousand eggs, each the size of a pea. The male hasn't been wasting his energy either and he is making a large quantity of milt in readiness for mating. This activity affects his jaw, and the lower one changes its shape, developing an upward-curving hook called the 'kype'. There certainly is a lot of specialised vocabulary associated with salmon.

After mating, both parents are spent completely. Most of them die, having used up all their energy swimming back up here, mating and producing eggs and milt. Some of them do make their way back down again to sea, mostly females, it must be said, and go to sea again. These experienced ladies can now be called 'kelts'. Grilse are only between two and four kilos in weight, but there are salmon that are much bigger than that in Irish rivers. These are females that don't come back with the other grilse but head across the ocean to the Greenland coast and spend several more years there putting on condition again before returning. Apparently, only females do this. The males are so anxious to get home to mate the minute they are able to, that they don't make the journey across the ocean. Much research on salmon and where they go is carried out in Borrisoshrule in County Mayo, where the researchers fertilise the eggs and rear the young salmon in controlled conditions. They then tag them with an implant and let them off. The salmon instinctively home back again to the exact spot where they were released into the river and they can be caught again, examined, aged, sexed and their eggs and milt harvested for the next generation.

Fewer and fewer of our wild salmon are making it back to their spawning beds. And indeed they may not find them in any condition to allow breeding. The gravel beds must be there, not swept away in an arterial drainage scheme. The water flowing over the fertilised eggs must be oxygen-rich. Water that has organic matter added to it, or which has received too much in the way of nitrates or phosphates, won't do. And then the water in the ocean is changing temperature, with climate change, and the new temperatures are affecting the salmon. So is salmon farming the answer? Farming food is what we have always done when hunting-gathering is no longer viable. We farm beef, poultry, pork, so fish farming is more of the same surely? Yes, but... The salmon are farmed in fish cages in sea water and fed a diet decided by the fish farmer. Salmon are carnivores, so the farmed fish have to be fed a meat diet as it were. So fish are caught and processed to feed to the salmon. It takes four pounds of processed fish to produce one pound of farmed salmon meat, hardly a sustainable conversion, seeing as it is wild small fish species that are used. Salmon swim long distances in their lives, even the ones that only go to Norway. Muscle that works produces tasty flesh. The salmon in the cages in the fish farms don't swim very far and their muscles are not much used. The proof of the pudding is in the eating. The wild salmon wins hands down. Would that we could be offered it more than three times a week! The relative availability of both sorts is reflected in the price. Farmed salmon is one of the most inexpensive fish you can buy in the fishmongers (itself a vanishing trade in Ireland), and wild salmon one of the scarcest and the dearest. Perhaps ranching is the answer. This is what they do in Borrisoshrule – fertilising the eggs and rearing the young in controlled conditions of safety and then releasing them to take their chances. Their strong homing instinct ensures they return with well-toned muscles, having eaten a diet of food they selected and caught themselves.

So where does all that leave the Salmon of Knowledge? Were we ever told what weight it was? What time of year was it caught? Was it male or female? Did Finnéagas ever eat the rest of it? But maybe I am being far too pedantic and we shouldn't spoil a good story with the facts.

CHAPTER THIRTY-EIGHT

The exciting life of the courtroom scientist

When you are growing up and deciding what you want to be, anything seems possible. If you want to be an architect, you see yourself as standing up defending (successfully!) your plans for a thoroughly modern building before an oral hearing. If you want to be a train driver, it's the TGV in France or the like that you see yourself driving. If you want to be a zoologist, you picture yourself discovering animals new to science, which of course will be called after you. Unfortunately, reality rarely lives up to such expectations. But sometimes scientists do happen to be in the right place at the right time.

A customer drinking a pint of stout in a public house some time ago noticed a foreign object in the glass when he got to the end of his pint. Upon closer scrutiny, this foreign object turned out to be a slug. The customer was outraged. How come he had been served a pint of stout with a slug in it? This was not good enough. He was going to take the matter further. The glass, complete with slug, was kept as evidence, his solicitor was informed and the matter was brought to the attention of the public house. The public house determined to fight the case. They definitely had not served a pint with a slug in it and were not going to compensate the man for the fetch he had received when he saw the creature after the pint was consumed. As the man was able to complain and to engage a solicitor, he had obviously survived the experience.

The case was scheduled to appear before the district judge. The man and the solicitor had the glass with the – by now – remains of the slug in it. The public house, however, had a secret weapon – a scientist! This is why anyone would become a scientist, to investigate matters like this. Was it really a slug? If so, could it come out of a beer tap into a pint of stout and be visible at the bottom when the pint was finished? Imagine the fieldwork involved! First of all, the glass plus slug had to be officially borrowed to determine if it was really a slug that was there in the first place. That wasn't so difficult to determine. 'Afraid so, it was definitely a slug, your honour, that was in the glass.' Next question for the scientist – how could it have got there? The pub took this case so seriously that they donated a keg of stout to the scientist for the required series of experiments. Several slugs were added to the keg of beer. It was connected to the taps and all the pints that the keg held were pulled and examined for slugs.

Unfortunately for the poor slugs, none of them survived, in anything like their entirety, the journey up through the keg and the lines and the tap and into the glass. No recognisable bits of slug could be found in any of the pints, never mind a whole one lurking at the end of the glass, post-libation. What a waste of good stout! Perhaps the slug was in the glass when the barman went to pour the pint. But the barman was completely clear on this point – he had total recall, there definitely was no slug present, the glass was totally empty and perfectly clean. Scientific fieldwork had proved that it could not have come out through the tap with the stout itself. So it could only get into the glass after the pint was poured and settled and had been handed over. If it fell from the barman, it would land on the new head on a full pint. Would it sink straight through immediately, or would the head support it, so the customer would see it if it had arrived in this way? Further research. More slugs were collected and the pints were lined up. A slug was dropped into each glass on to the new head. And in no case did the slug sink like a stone through the fresh head. It was supported there by the head of stout and would have been plainly visible to any toper as he raised his pint to his lips.

'But there was a slug at the bottom of my pint, your honour. Everyone agrees that that is so.' The question was: how did it get in? The intrepid scientist established, with further bouts of fieldwork, that as a pint is drunk and the level gets lower in the glass, the head gets smaller and weaker. Generally, pints are not polished off in one go. Seasoned pint drinkers raise the glass, have a drink, then replace the glass on the counter or table and continue the conversation. At a certain stage in the drinking of the pint in question, the head would be reduced enough in size and strength to allow a slug through, if it fell into the glass at that precise time. This part of the research took some considerable time, as the pints had to be drunk just as they would be in a pub. Pouring away small quantities of stout every so often is not the same as drinking, and the fieldwork had to be done scientifically. So the pints were set up and drunk in a measured fashion. How many gulps, over what period of time, led to a situation where a slug would sink instantly on the remaining head? Hard work, but someone's got to do it. Finally a situation was arrived at where such a thing could happen.

Our man was adamant that he had not left his pint at any stage, so it couldn't have been contaminated by a slug-dropping passer-by. So the only possible solution was that the slug had somehow come from the drinker himself. Was this likely? Well, yes, as it happens. He worked outdoors on the land and might reasonably be expected to encounter slugs in his everyday work. If one had adhered to his arm or his sleeve, the scene was set. The judge was delighted. 'Tell me, how many slugs would you normally have out of a pint before you had it all gone?' On the balance of probability the man had inadvertently added the slug to the pint himself, just at the moment when the head could not support it and so it fell without a trace into the black depths of the half-drunk pint of stout. Gives a whole new meaning to the expression 'make a hole in that pint'. Case dismissed.

What would you have with your pint in the pub? Well, you might have a bag of crisps. Imagine the consternation of the woman eating her crisps with half an eye on the telly, when she discovered that her hand contained not only a selection of the best cheese and onion but a wriggling earwig as well. Nothing could dissuade her from the notion that the earwig was in the bag of crisps and that only for the programme on the telly was so brutal, she would have eaten it with the crisps. Mind you, if the programme had been riveting she might never have noticed. Maybe *Mooney Goes Wild* should be on the box.

Of course she was outraged and brought her complaint to the manufacturers of the crisps. And our intrepid scientist was called in once more, this time to defend the earwig, who was being accused of getting packaged with the crisps and loitering in the bag with intent to terrify decent citizenry. Was it possible? Could the earwig survive the crisp-making exercise and live in an airtight bag? Our scientist looked at the possibility. No earwig could survive the slicing of the potatoes, the heat of the oven, the salting procedures, the hygienic packing. No, it could not have emerged alive and kicking from a sealed bag of crisps, which apparently this was.

But it was there. Where could it have come from? Earwigs are well known to be thigmotaxic, which means they like being at rest in tight spaces, although not necessarily in ears, in spite of their name. So, if you scientifically examine a bag of crisps you will note that in certain sorts the bag has a fold up its backbone, as it were. And it was in this fold, outside the bag, that our earwig was having a grand rest when he was rudely disturbed by the bag being ripped open. He hastened to a darker place, which was inside the bag. His sojourn there was not long. He was soon grabbed, along with the crisps, in whose contours he had sought shelter.

So in court the scientific evidence was that a live earwig, as was found on this occasion, could not have come originally from inside a sealed crisp bag. It was worth the crisp manufacturer's while engaging the scientist as an expert witness. Case dismissed. But how did it get into the fold in the outside of the bag? And is it acceptable to sell bags of crisps complete with extra protein included on the outside? Well that was *scéal eile*, and one which our plaintiff did not pursue. I suppose look before you leap is good advice for crisp-eaters as well as earwigs.

But do the scientists always win when called to be expert witnesses? Certainly Richard Collins gave such a good account of the swan's feelings when it had not got enough sliced pan from its human feeder to lead the judge to declare that it was having a 'bad hair day' and find in its favour.

But what about our poor shopper who bought a pound of mince in the butcher's and when he came to eat it, found it covered in maggots? Of course he wished to sue the butcher. So the scientist was consulted by the defendant – the butcher – to establish what the maggots were, how long they could have been in the mince and in whose establishment the contamination could have occurred. So the scientist worked on the case. Maggots are the young of bluebottles. A female bluebottle would have to lay the eggs on unprotected meat. Where could this have happened? Eggs are tiny and not easily seen. They hatch out quickly in heat, but not in cold. They smartly grow to white maggot proportions on such lovely food if the temperature is right. Did the butcher have the meat in protected cold storage? Did the customer leave the messages hanging about? Could the fly have gained access while the meat was in his possession? How long after buying it did the purchaser decide to eat it? How quickly does the lifecycle of a bluebottle occur in the heat of the summer? How long elapses between eggs being laid and maggots appearing? Our scientist was in full pursuit of all the facts when the case was called. It was known in advance who the judge was going to be. And – consternation! – it was a man who liked his beef. He was partial to a good steak. He would not like to hear of a man with maggots in his mince. He would surely empathise with such a trauma. Better not risk it. The case was settled on the steps of the courthouse. If the judge was known to be a vegetarian, I wonder what the outcome would have been.

And to think that some people imagine that scientists are serious nerds looking down microscopes all day. There should be waiting lists to get into college to study science!

CHAPTER THIRTY-NINE

Not sailing to Australia

I used to be a member of the Irish Sub-Aqua Club, and a great coup of that club was their discovery of the wreck of the *John Tayleur* off the nose of Lambay Island. This wreck was discovered before I joined the club in 1976, but it was a favourite dive site all during my time there. The *John Tayleur* was a sailing ship that set out for Australia from Liverpool in 1853. It carried on board survivors of the Irish famine, among others, who were sailing to Australia with all their worldly goods, to start up a new life there. They took all their possessions with them – the women had gold coins sewn into their long skirts for security. They even brought gravestones with them, so that those who died in Australia would not go unremembered. It was a modern sailing ship at the time, with a new iron hull, instead of the more old-fashioned wooden hulls of earlier ships.

It left Liverpool under full sail, but quickly sailed into bad weather. Gales drove them off course and the captain wasn't too sure where exactly they were. Reading the compass, he calculated they were well down the Irish Sea and away from any dangerous land. But he hadn't reckoned with the fact that the steel hull was deflecting the needle of the compass, giving a false reading, and the mist and rain parted just in time for him to see that he was running before the wind, hard aground onto the rocks off the nose of Lambay Island, just north of Dublin Bay. The ship struck with great force and was held fast on the rocks.

The sailors were an ill-trained crew. Many of them had little experience at sea and their first reaction was to clamber up the riggings on to land and run away. Women and children first, how are you – this wasn't the *Titanic!* As it turned out, that was the only way to escape. The ship broke up very slowly and there was time for more orderly passengers to climb ashore and rig up a line from the rigging to land to help the others ashore. But the women on board couldn't climb up the rigging with their heavy, wet long skirts and they certainly weren't taking them off – not with their life savings sewn into them. The ship couldn't wait. It slipped away beneath the waves, bearing every woman on board to a watery grave, with the sole exception of the captain's wife. Many of the menfolk died too, but none of the crew. What an end to the poor souls who had survived a horrible famine and hoped for a new life.

Over a hundred years later, when we dived down to see the wreck, we got no impression of a ship lying beneath the waves on its side. It looked like a timber yard, a collection of boards and planks in a great heap on the bottom. As you swam alongside underwater, you could never see the whole wreck at the same time – visibility didn't permit it. But you could look though gaps in the planks and see the cargo of tombstones still there, marking the place of death, but with no names written on them.

In fact the whole place emanated an aura of something wrong. The water seemed colder here than anywhere else. The timbers had been down there for so long that they were colonised by a fauna of their own. One particularly common sight was a coral-like growth called, fittingly enough, dead man's fingers. This is a growth of soft coral which forms on surfaces and branches in strands the size of fingers. Each finger has tentacles on it, and these wave around in the water filtering out food from the sea water. They look dead white or pale yellow to the diver's eyes and, if touched, they retract their tentacles as if they were drawing back from the touch. Eerie enough sort of behaviour from underwater life.

Even the crabs down there seem a different colour, much pinker, sort of a rusty red. It would make you wonder what they have been eating, although reason dictates that any dead body still in the wreck would have decomposed completely long since. Swimming around the wreck, looking at the sand below, mementoes of the cargo can be found. A piece of blue willow-patterned delph, the handle of a walking cane – all destined for Australia – never got further than here. Many artefacts from the ship were salvaged and are on display in the

Dublin Municipal Museum, items such as the portholes and the ship's binnacle.

Coming back up to the sunlight and the warmer surface waters is welcome after such a dive, although you would want to be careful addressing remarks to your fellow diver whom you happen to spot on the surface. That black head in a rubber wetsuit with its back to you might not be what it seems. Seals breed off Lambay Island and are common in the surrounding waters. They are curious creatures and are not beyond coming along to see what is going on in their territory. Being mammals, they have to come up for a breath from time to time, so a black head breaking water near to where you are may not be a fellow-diver at all, but a curious seal. There are no records of seals ever interfering with divers – they are so much more obviously at home in the water than a diver is with a big heavy bottle – but discretion is usually the better part of valour and the field is left to the seals.

We have two species of seals off our waters, the grey seal and the much less frequently encountered 'common' seal. They are part of populations of seals that breed off the Irish and Scottish coasts, so this whole area is their territory. They come ashore to give birth and while they are at it they mate again for the next season – getting the two jobs done, as it were, for the price of one. Common seals give birth in June. They haul up on to the shore in secluded coastal spots and give birth to large pups about an eighth the size of their mother's weight. If we were to do the same, our babies would weigh over a stone at birth. They feed them for about a month on very rich milk, with up to 60 per cent fat. Then they seem to lose interest and are more concerned with queuing up for the attentions of the bull, who has the whole harem to attend to. After this they depart to sea, leaving the baby to fend for itself. The poor baby takes about two weeks to realise that Mammy is not coming back and that it will have to go fishing itself. Fortunately, it is so big and fat it can survive for two weeks until it cops on how to catch food for itself.

The story is the same for the grey seal. They haul out to have their pups around the end of September. They use the same breeding grounds each year and the adult female likes to give birth in the exact spot she used the previous year. So woe betide any new mother who happens to have plonked down here. She is sent off in no uncertain terms by the experienced mum. In fact, these maternity wards can be places of great turmoil and fighting. The males know that the mating time has come when the females are coming ashore to give birth. And while mating won't actually happen until the pups are weaned some weeks later, that doesn't deter the randy males from getting into pole position, as it were. They come ashore as well and try to make sure they are in the best place to meet the women. This may involve lying on the stretch of sand between the sea and the maternity unit. Indeed, if the stretch of sand is narrow and the mammies need all of it, they'll hang around in the shallow waters. And they occupy themselves as they wait by fighting with each other. They can inflict nasty wounds on each other's neck and flippers. There is no fair sharing out – the strongest males occupy the best vantage sites and try to mate with as many females as possible. They do not leave their hard-won territory at all, not even to feed, so they could be there for up to eight weeks without food. Isn't lust a wonderful sustenance supplier all the same! The females leave as soon as they have mated, but the males hang on until the end – they may have waited ten years for this stage of their lives and they are going to get the very last out of it. Then off they go to sea and don't come ashore again until the same time next year.

Seals are very popular with the general public. Perhaps it is because they have an appealing face. Perhaps it is because they shed tears if their eyes are too long out of salt water. Perhaps it is because of the tales that they contain the souls of people drowned at sea. Whatever the reason, people who find what they believe to be an abandoned baby seal are always very anxious that it should be rescued, and that is exactly what the Seal Sanctuary in north County Dublin does. Here the seals are cared for and nursed back to health and sometimes the seal has been released back to sea amid a welter of media coverage. We have begun the season of *Mooney Goes Wild* on more than one occasion with a seal release.

These releases are well-flagged beforehand and, on the day it is due to occur, a cast of thousands assembles on the appointed beach. I remember one such day in County Wexford, when, emboldened with the success of previous releases on the radio, it was decided to release one which would be covered by a simultaneous television and radio link. Was there ever such weather? The release was to happen live on both media at 10.45 in the morning, and precisely as the introductory music was rolling, an immense black cloud rolled in from the Saltees, darkening the sky, and the rain and wind drenched everyone. But the show went on. The seal emerged from its box, smelt the sea and made a beeline straight down the shore and into the water.

They don't always perform as well as that, as we were to learn the following year in Balbriggan in north County Dublin. There were two seals to be released this time, and the cast of thousands was augmented by local dignitaries. Keeping the crowd well back, the first was released and went straight down to the sea and practically waved at the cameras. All the VIPs got to speak on air and welcome this auspicious occasion. So the programme for the viewers at home was grand. However, after we went off air, the second seal was released. The crowds did not stand back so well this time – sure, wasn't the fuss at the first release unnecessary really! So when the second seal emerged, it got confused and, instead of heading for the sea, it made a rush at the crowd, and for a moment it looked as if it might bite the mayor on the leg. Where are the television cameras when you need them? This gave a great deal of amusement to the beholders who had remained at a safe distance. Eventually the second seal was rounded up and encouraged into the sea. A yellow mark had been placed on the seal's head to facilitate tracking it until its next moult, at which time the mark would disappear.

Fishermen aren't too fond of seals, though. They see them as rivals for scarce fish resources. And what really annoys the fishermen is the habit some seals have of taking a bite out of each fish it comes across impaled in a net by the gills. If they just took one away and ate it that would be bad enough, but to destroy a whole netful seems unforgivable. Of course, the seal is just acting on instinct. For thousands of years when seals encountered a lot of fish together, they worked as fast as they could, knowing that the shoal would quickly swim away and they'd be lucky to catch enough for a meal. How are they to know that this is not a loose shoal in the open sea, but one that is entrapped in a net? They are simply acting on instinct, trying to get as much food as possible. However, knowing why they do it doesn't make life any easier for the fishermen.

The seal releases do a lot for public awareness of wildlife and so have their educational value, but neither the grey seal nor the common seal are species which are in actual danger of extinction in our waters.

CHAPTER FORTY

Sex, drugs and rock'n'roll in the dark garden

Did you ever wonder what goes on out in the garden when you are all nicely tucked up asleep in bed? Among the wildlife that is! While we are creatures of the day and feel tired and sleepy when night comes, there is a complete world of wildlife that only becomes active when it gets dark. There are many reasons for this – some of them so compelling that you'd wonder why anything comes out at all during the day. One reason is that it is much cooler and damper at night, so if you feel you might suffer from dehydration, then you avoid the sunshine and heat and emerge when such threats have passed. Sharp-eyed birds are about in abundance during the daytime, so if you'd make a tasty meal for a thrush or a blackbird, then best stay under cover until they have all gone to bed. So it is no wonder that when we ourselves venture out into the garden at night and wander among the vegetables and herbaceous borders, it isn't long before we become aware of the abundance of snails and slugs that are there.

In fact, you may even hear them before you shine your torch on them, munching away at your pet hostas or prized basil plants. Snails and slugs, both members of the same group – the molluscs – have the most remarkable tongues. This structure rejoices in the name of 'radula' and is attached, if you could imagine such a thing, to the underside of the oesophagus. It is covered in rows of minute teeth, so that when the snail is eating a leaf, it rubs its tongue over and back, for all the world like a nail file – and the rasping sound is quite audible on a clear, still night. It never wears out or gets blunt either; the radula continues to grow during the creature's lifetime, with new teeth being formed on the growing bit. So you couldn't even begin to hope that old snails would have worn out their tongues eating and would thus be less efficient.

Indeed, the whole design of its body is most remarkable. Our blood is red, because it contains haemoglobin, formed from iron, to bind the oxygen. The blood of snails and slugs contains haemocyanin, a copper compound which binds the oxygen, but their blood is colourless. I wonder why it isn't the bright green shade copper becomes when it is exposed to the air – like the dome of Rathmines church in Dublin?

Their eyes are another interesting phenomenon. In fact, they could be a role model for teachers, for their eyes are out on stalks at the front of their bodies and they can use each one completely independently. If teachers had eyes like this, they could look at the blackboard with one eye and keep an eye on the class behind at exactly the same time. Snails and slugs actually have four horns, or tentacles to give them their proper title, at the front of their bodies – two long ones with the eyes at the end and two short ones. The short tentacles are what they feel and smell with, so really you could say their nostrils are out on stalks as well.

So far so weird, but it is in the reproductive department that the seriously bizarre bits are. For a start, your average common-or-garden snail is neither male nor female but both at the same time – in other words, they are hermaphrodites. But this does not in any way spoil their reproductive pleasures. They cannot mate with themselves, in spite of having all the necessary reproductive equipment, but must seek out another of the same species if they are thinking of starting a family. No problem there: on any given dark, damp, warmish night the garden is full of them. So they slither about rasping away at the lettuce leaves and keeping a stalked eye or two out for another equally minded individual. Having encountered just such a body, they snuggle up together in a slimy embrace. Their genital opening is just below their head, and both their male and female parts terminate in this one opening. Thrilling enough, you might think, but the anatomical arrangements don't stop at that. Snails and slugs have a third department to enhance their love lives even further. This is a special dart sac in the oviduct, and in here they manufacture a thin, sharp, pointed structure known as a love dart. (Honestly, I am not making this up.) During mating, they lie side by side in the required position. They each thrust a love dart into the other, apparently as stimulation, and they then exchange sperm. This makes its way up the opening into the female bit, and the eggs are subsequently formed and fertilised.

Later – several weeks later, and under much less exciting circumstances – the eggs are laid in the soil and covered with earth. The snail crawls away and never sees its eggs again. So, in spite of belonging to a one-parent family, where the parent is both the mother and the father – a perfect arrangement one might think – the offspring are homeless, abandoned orphans. But this is of no consequence. Each egg hatches out into a snail, complete with a voracious appetite, and gets to work on the garden plants that are so delicious and that the kind garden owner has so thoughtfully planted for them. Most eggs are laid in summer and autumn, and baby snails and slugs hatch out within six weeks. They take a year to reach maturity and then, all going well, they have been known to live for ten years or even longer. They hibernate each winter, sealing up the opening in their shells to keep out the cold and to prevent them from drying out.

Slugs belong to the same group as snails, even though they have no shells. To compensate for this, they produce an even stickier mucus than snails do and are much less favoured by birds, who really don't want their beaks full of sticky slime, all things being equal. This slime seems to be very strong, in some slug species at any rate, who use it to carry out what must be one of the most bizarre mating rituals of all that can take place in the garden. Astute observers among the listeners to the programme have recounted experiences of watching slugs lowering themselves from a height by their mucus and abseiling as it were, downwards, suspended by the sticky mucus. One listener went so far as to describe it as bungee jumping, but plump and stately slugs would never move with such frivolous haste. What are they at? What do you think? Making their mating process even more thrilling, that's what!

What happens typically is this. Two slugs of the great grey species meet on the ground and decide that theirs is a match made in heaven. They both then climb up a tree – the same tree – and out on to a branch. They then each begin to lower themselves off the branch into the air below, suspended only by a rope of sticky mucus. They lower themselves slowly and steadily over a period by painstakingly extending their mucal strings. When some critical distance is reached, they entwine first of all their mucal strings and then themselves, both upside down, and then their shiny white reproductive parts. Mating then takes place as normal – normal, that is, for love-darting hermaphrodites – and can last up to an hour. After this, one slug just drops off down to the ground while the other climbs back up the mucal string, eating it as it goes. I suppose it feels quite peckish after all its exertions. Amazing. All this activity going on in the garden while we sleep easily in our beds.

What else is disporting itself out in the garden under the cover of darkness? Earthworms, if you look closely, seem to live strange and exotic lives too when viewed from our perspective. For a start, they have no eyes, so you'd wonder why day or night makes any difference to them. They live in the soil and eat the dead plant material that is mixed up with the soil particles. However, to get at these, they have to eat the soil and digest out the food particles as they pass through their bodies. So they don't need eyes, they live in the middle of their food and just eat their way around, tunnelling through their food supply. But it's a lonely life down there and worm does not live by bread alone, as it were. At night, when it is cool and dark, they come up to the surface, up into the garden, to suss out the social scene. Although they have no eyes, they do have light receptors in their skin, so they can determine if it is still dark. They hate the light, as it fills them with fears of being heated up and dried out, not to mention being breakfast for those pesky early birds who are on the rampage the minute the first photon of light appears. No, they risk all coming up to the surface to meet other earthworms, although not ones of the opposite sex. Earthworms, like molluscs, are hermaphrodites, and have both male and female organs. Unlike the snails, however, they mate, as it were, one upside-down, the other right way round. Allow me to explain such *Kama Sutra*-like behaviour.

A worm's body is a series of segments. Number one is up near the head and number one hundred and fifty is down at the other end. The male organs are at segments nine, ten and eleven and the female organs are at segments thirteen and fourteen. (Are you with me so far?) Further along the worm's body, at segments thirty-two to thirty-seven, we come to a remarkable organ called the clitellum. It looks for all the world like a saddle on the worm's body. This produces an exceedingly sticky mucus, which is vital to the whole mating process. A typical encounter might go like this. An amorous earthworm, who has risked all in the pursuit of love, tunnels its way to the surface one dark, damp night. It slithers blindly around in the grass until it encounters another earthworm with similar intentions. Presumably it is able to distinguish between slugs and worms – I'm sure they must feel quite different, and anyway the slug, which can see, would be able to give the worm a wide berth. So having encountered the love of its life, our earthworm has to ascertain whether it is coming or going. It then sticks its clitellum (at segments thirty-two to thirty-seven, remember) to segments nine to fifteen of the other worm, and arranges the rest of itself so that its reproductive organs are glued to the other's clitellum. This would all seem to require a remarkable amount of co-operation and dexterity.

Then they begin to mate. One worm produces sperm at segments ten and eleven. This trickles down its own body in a special groove, until it comes to where its clitellum is firmly glued to the body of the other worm. The sperm then makes the crossing at this point into the body of the other worm at segment nine. Meanwhile, the other worm is doing exactly the same thing in the other direction. It is not a speedy process. It can take up to five hours, and if the dawn comes before the job is complete they could be caught in the act by a starving thrush who would get two for the price of one, or at least one anyway as they struggle to detach and slither away. Such a violent end would break a worm's heart, a not insignificant procedure, seeing as how worms have not one, but five hearts.

However, we will not contemplate such a nasty end for our worms, but assume that they manage to complete the business, disentangle tenderly and glide slowly away to their underground world before the sun comes up. A few days later, the clitellum springs into action again. It covers itself with a hard coat, detaches itself entirely from segments thirty-two to thirty-seven and begins to move up along the worm's body, segment by segment. As it passes segment fourteen it collects its own eggs that are waiting there and continues on its journey. As it passes segment nine, it picks up the sperm the other worm left there during the mating process and fertilisation of the eggs takes place in the clitellum during the last bit of the journey up to segment one. Sort of test-tube fertilisation, as it were. The clitellum now comes off the worm completely and is shed into the soil where it looks like a tiny yellow lemon. Only one of the fertilised eggs develops into a baby worm. This grows for up to three weeks in its clitellum swaddling clothes, and then it is ready to face the world as a fully fledged worm. Wouldn't you know that worms, which are good for our soil and more than earn their keep breaking down dead plants, only reproduce one at a time, whereas slugs and snails, which wreak havoc on our delicate garden treasures, can lay up to one hundred eggs at a time, all of which hatch out into new slugs or snails. It's just not fair.

Is it all just one big orgy that is going on in the garden at night under the cover of darkness? Well, there is a fair bit of violence and murder going on as well. The carnivores are using the cover of darkness to leap upon an unsuspecting meal. Centipedes can be particularly voracious hunters. These are misnamed creatures, as they rarely have a hundred legs exactly. Many of the fast-hunting garden ones have only fifteen pairs of legs, while some of the blind, burrowing ones can have up to eighty-three pairs of legs. But they all have poison claws just behind the head, which enable them to kill their prey very quickly. The garden centipede has about twenty-five tiny eyes on each side of its head, so it can get about very nicely at night. As one might expect, it catches and eats insects that are unwary enough to be in its way, but it can also catch and eat worms and slugs and is not above a spot of cannibalism if another centipede crosses its path. They are not waterproof and often lurk under flowerpots during the day to avoid drying out, but you'll notice, if you lift one suddenly and stay alert, that there is always only one centipede per flowerpot. Be careful if you are handling the bigger ones, because they are not above attacking us with their poison claws and these are sometimes strong enough to pierce the skin and inflict quite a nip. But if you hate slugs in the garden you will overlook such bad-tempered tendencies and rank the centipedes among the good guys.

In fact, if any enemy of the slug is a friend of yours, then you should grapple all the members of the ground beetle family to your soul with hoops of steel. Don't be calling this lot cockroaches, no matter how much television you watch. Cockroaches – the real ones – are not native to Ireland and cannot exist in the garden in the wild. They live in countries much warmer than ours, such as America and the countries of southern Europe, and are occasionally brought here by an unwary traveller. They can become established indoors, where it is always warm – places with the central heating always on, such as in hospitals, laundries, warehouses, factories, hotels, even in homes if you are very *flaithiúlach* with the heating, but hunting out in your garden at night – not so. You will always know a cockroach no matter what colour it is because it has enormous antennae. These emerge from their heads and curve around like whips and extend back halfway along the length of their bodies. And they are not hunters. They eat leftover food and insects that are already dead. No, the dramatic, exciting creature is not the cockroach but the ground beetle, who is on the rampage in your garden under the cover of darkness on a seek-and-exterminate mission.

The deadliest, the most cunning, the most ruthless, the most devious of them all is the devil's coach-horse, the largest of the rove beetle family. It is jet black and can be up to an inch long. Like all rove beetles, it has ferocious jaws, with which it eats slugs, caterpillars and any other small creature that has the misfortune to cross its path. It has a long, thinnish body, because, unlike other beetle groups, the front wings are not modified into roundy wing covers that cover the rest of its body. It has quite small upper wing cases, but it has functional back wings and can fly about terrorising the other garden inhabitants. When it meets something much bigger than itself, it is not above a spot of intimidation. It opens wide its jaws, cocks up its tail and squirts a little strong-smelling vapour in the face of the enemy. Certainly a creature you'd prefer to have as a friend rather than as a foe.

There are other interesting beetles wandering around the garden at night. People often ask where do all the dead birds' bodies go, as they are rarely seen just lying about. Injured birds often crawl away under bushes to die in the first place and then their freshly dead corpses are just lying there as a succulent treat for the burying beetles and the sexton beetles the following night. These beetles generally wander around looking for a dead body. They have a good sense of smell and soon locate just such a treat. The first one of each sex that arrives on the scene fights off all comers of the same sex. When the first one of the opposite sex arrives, the mood changes. The presence of all this smelly food inspires them with uncontrollable lust and they quickly mate. Having got that over with, they proceed to the main business – that of burying the body. They do this by removing the soil from underneath it so that it slowly sinks beneath the ground. They are well able to cut any impeding grass roots with their jaws and soon all that can be seen of the dead bird is a slight mound above the ground surface. The female then excavates a small tunnel leading off from the burial chamber and lays her eggs there. She is a very devoted mother and stands by while the eggs hatch out, feeding herself from the buried body. She brings chewed-up bird to the young while they are quite tiny and cannot fend for themselves, but soon they can smell where the food is coming from and they head off to dine themselves. With such an abundant supply of food, they quickly grow and get on to the next stage of their life cycle. They undergo three changes, ending up as a legless maggot. They then abandon the by-now nearly demolished carcass, burrow deeper and pupate into adults. They subsequently emerge and wander around the garden looking for a meal, a fight, a girlfriend and a good time, quite typical adolescent behaviour really.

There is one exciting beetle that we don't have in our gardens, at least not yet, and that is the glow-worm. These are beetles that do occur in Britain in areas of chalk and limestone and they rejoice in the Latin name of *Lampyris*. While we have such terrain in Ireland too, these creatures obviously never made it here under their own steam after the Ice Age. As only the males can fly, I suppose they would have had to give the females a piggyback if they were to establish breeding colonies in our island country. These beetles give out light from their bodies, but it is the adult female which gives out the most light of all. In the underside of her last three abdominal segments she has a large supply of luciferin, backed by a reflector of minute crystals. When oxygen and water are supplied to this area by the female, the three segments glow brightly with a pale greenish-blue light. This is such a concentration of effort that females have no wings or wing cases at all, and look for all the world like woodlice. When night comes and they are ready for action, they climb up on a blade of grass or a plant, send down the oxygen and water and raise their abdomen. The males who have wings and large, light-sensitive eyes are of course cruising the area looking out for just such a signal. She doesn't have to wave her light for long before he arrives. If, however, the light attracts the wrong kind of client, she can immediately extinguish it, so you couldn't quickly gather a jam jar full to light the way if the flashlight on your bike failed. Still, the lights will come back on again if one or two are left gently in a box for a while.

Like adult butterflies, adult glow-worms hardly feed at all, but their larval offspring make up for this. They feed on both snails and slugs in a particularly ghoulish fashion. They grab the poor little snails and slugs in their strong jaws and inject a digestive juice. This first of all paralyses the prey and then – horror of horrors! – begins to dissolve its flesh, which can then be drunk by the larvae. Maybe it's just as well we haven't got such creatures in this country. Do we hate our molluscs that much?

Fireflies are beetles of the same family, which occur in the tropics. The female adults with the luminous underparts can fly there, hence the name fireflies.

So in our gardens we may well have sex and drugs and rock'n'roll but, in true Irish fashion, no light is shed upon the matter. It is all conducted under the cover of darkness.

CHAPTER FORTY-ONE

The ones that got away

When my first book, *Talking Wild,* came out, I got letters from readers who were disappointed that I had not covered the particular creepy-crawlies that they were interested in, revolted by, intrigued with. I, of course, had cherry-picked and had only included the ones that I felt everyone would know and identify with – in a manner of speaking. And as we have at least 16,000 creepy-crawlies – or, to give them a more scientific title, invertebrates – in Ireland, that's all I am about to do this time too.

Silverfish are weird-looking things. People encounter them late at night when they go back downstairs for a drink of water and surprise them slithering around the kitchen sink. Someone asked me recently if silverfish were the nearest thing to a dinosaur that we had, which rather took me aback for a moment. After all, dinosaurs were reptiles, sometimes absolutely huge and indeed are now extinct, whereas silverfish are tiny little insects that are very much with us. But the connection would seem to be that silverfish are very ancient and primitive insects that have remained unchanged for millions of year and would indeed have been around at the time of the dinosaurs. They are silvery in colour and appear to us to move by slithering around wettish areas and so seem more like fish than the insects they are. They have no wings but have six tiny legs and three tails and two antennae straight out of their heads like horns, if you are in a mood to admire them. They belong to a group of insects called bristletails.

They are not a favourite of our listeners, however, and indeed samples in matchboxes come with the invariable plea: what is this and how do you get rid of it? Well, it's a silverfish and to get rid of it – or indeed of anything unwanted – you have to understand why it is there in the first place. If you are giving it food and excellent living quarters – no matter how inadvertently – of course you will have it in abundance. So what does it need to live? Well, first of all it needs your house – these are purely domestic insects and cannot survive out in the open. They like warm, damp conditions, so they frequent kitchens and bathrooms. They only appear at night – they apparently sleep during the day and come out for food after dark. They seem to love glue and wallpaper paste, so if there are any cracks around the sink – loose wallpaper that the damp has caused to come away from the wall, loose or cracked tiles that they can get in behind, an area where the sink is not exactly flush with the wall – well, they are at their granny's: food and damp and hiding places all at once. They will also live in food cupboards, feasting on bits of paper, carton glue and, as a great bonus, spilt flour. Actually, if you are going to leave spilt flour in your food cupboard for any length of time, you could do a PhD thesis on the creepy-crawlies that come to dine.

If you don't like them, ask yourself why. They are not dirty and don't carry disease. There is no smell from them. They didn't wreck the place and vandalise the tiles in the first place – they just came to live in the already broken tile. Stay out of the kitchen at night and you won't see them. Otherwise, you will have to do up your sink area – new tiles, waterproof paper, new grouting and sealant – and that will starve them out. Or get the landlord to do up the place: they are often encountered in bedsits.

They have a relation called the firebrat, which is able to withstand much higher temperatures and can be found around hot-water pipes. This is, however, quite rare and is hardly ever complained of. Perhaps our nocturnal wanderings to the hot press are much less frequent than our midnight forays to the kitchen.

I talked about bedbugs in chapter 16. They were just one of a myriad of creatures that could beset our person and indeed one of the less nasty types, I said. Even though they do bite us in bed, they do not carry disease. Fleas and body lice were much worse. But then a listener phoned in about strange creatures she had in her house – kind of like ladybirds without spots. Some type of woodworm she had acquired in a bed she had bought, she supposed it was. Would we come and look? Well, we came and looked – at a massive invasion of bedbugs that had even spread next door, and the resultant postbag, after we broadcast the item, would have put *Liveline* to shame. People from all over were writing in confessing that they too had bedbugs and they had never been able to talk about them before. Such shame was associated with them, that they felt decent, god-fearing folk would shun them. One especially long missive had the address cut off the top of the letter; obviously the writer had had second thoughts before posting it.

What was abundantly clear from all the letters was how persistent they were and how difficult it was to get rid of them. As they only come out at night to bite, there is no sign of them during the day. But they lay tiny eggs in rough timber, such as down cracks in floorboards and on the unplaned wood behind bedboards. Pest removal companies come and spray and fumigate, but short of throwing everything in the room out (through the bedroom window so that nothing drops off on the way through the house), they seem to be really impossible to exterminate. And indeed the psychological damage seems to be the worst. How can you know they are gone? The test is to make yourself into a sacrificial victim, sleep in the room and see if you get bitten – just the conditions to enable you to drop off into a deep sleep at once and stay asleep all night. They may have been brought to your house in furniture or they may have come with visitors, but one thing is certain – once news of their residence in your house gets out, visitors will vanish like snow off a ditch.

Certainly while Derek and myself were doing the 'Answering Machine Mission' in the house where they were first reported, we experienced mild disquiet. We were intrepid reporters on the job and I took back samples in a jar to confirm identification. However, I made sure that the jar rested for several days in my freezer before taking the beasties out to examine them with my hand lens and, confirming they were bedbugs, I disposed of the bodies afterwards with the care one would lavish on victims of the bubonic plague.

People are very good observers of wildlife when the wildlife is an unwanted occupant of their home. For some obscure reason, I am associated in the public mind with spiders, so people long to regale me with tales of their particular spider-infested home. Judging from the descriptions, a particularly obvious spider has taken up residence in homes in recent years. This spider has a small enough nondescript body, but by gum it has mighty legs. In fact it is often described as a daddy-long-legs spider and indeed that is one of the nicknames of *Pholcus phalangioides*, also known as the cellar spider. Now this spider has a great ability to spin webs in the corner of rooms, whether you are living there or not. They could be employed if one was creating a set for Miss Havisham's room in Dickens's *Great Expectations*. They are quite easy to see if you go to inspect any such web. The unusual thing about them is the frenzy they go into if you disturb them, however. They behave like whirling dervishes, bouncing up and down so fast that they become a blur.

We filmed one a few years ago for a series called *Habitats*. This programme visited various wildlife habitats and featured all the interesting filmable wildlife there. In the house-as-a-wildlife habitat we encountered such a spider, which was fairly uncommon at the time. I remember we affixed the poor creature to the wall with bits of Blu-Tack so that it could be filmed. I noticed, on my most recent visit to the house last year, the bits of Blu-Tack were still there, but not the spider itself. No doubt it had long since shuffled off this mortal coil, as small Irish spiders would be lucky to live for twelve months. They are much more frequently encountered now. A free fly-killing service – what more could you want?

CHAPTER FORTY-TWO

Carnival of the carnivores

Foxes have an uneasy relationship with humans at the best of times. What infuriates the owners of hens is the havoc the fox wreaks if it gets into the henhouse. It sidles in and, when the hens become aware of it, there is consternation. They all squawk and fly about in a panic. And this excites the fox into attacking and attacking until every last one is killed. He cannot possibly eat them all, but he kills and destroys wantonly, and no one else can eat them either. No wonder hen owners hate foxes. But what is really happening here is that the fox's natural hunting instincts are coming to the fore. In the days long before henhouses, a fox would be likely to come upon a sleeping roost of birds at night. Immediately upon attack, the birds would wake up and fly away. The fox's natural instinct would be to attack and kill as quickly as possible before they were all gone. He'd be lucky to get one or two. But in the henhouse, because there is a roof, the hens can't fly away and the panic, noise and clamour have the fox in a killing frenzy. Maybe the solution is a roofless henhouse, or exceedingly calm, placid hens.

Foxes get killed on the roads too, but not as many as badgers. Or maybe it's just that we don't see them because they are light enough to be thrown into the hedge by the speeding vehicle, as opposed to the heavier badger, which lands with a thump on the road itself. Or perhaps it is that the foxes are smart enough to run away when they hear vehicles approaching so that they don't get dazzled by the headlights.

In the 1950s and 1960s, a bounty could be claimed for every fox that was killed. The tail had to be handed in, no doubt to prevent a bounty being claimed over and over again for the same animal. It didn't make a blind bit of difference. Fox populations never went into a decline, and they are still quite plentiful. Their numbers are controlled by the amount of food that is available and the few that get killed for a bounty (or indeed that are taken by fox hunts) means that there is more food for those left behind and so more of their offspring will survive. It takes a really big reduction in their food supply, like myxomatosis in rabbits, before fox numbers noticeably drop. On the other hand, foxes will never wipe out a thriving colony of bunnies, because rabbits can breed faster than foxes can kill them.

Foxes are scavengers too, which means that they will eat meat that they have not killed themselves. Much of the mutton found in the stomachs of foxes was mutton before the fox ever came across it. Newborn lambs often die of the cold, particularly if they are born early in a cold spring, and foxes will certainly eat their dead remains. There was great excitement in the spring of 2004 with the invention of plastic coats for lambs, which kept them from getting cold and wet and also rustled and smelt strange to marauding foxes. They certainly reduced the mortality in newborn lambs, for whatever reason.

City people generally like foxes, as they get glimpses of them in their gardens at dawn or at dusk. We are rarely if ever asked how to get rid of them from city areas, though in fact there are more urban foxes now than there are in rural areas, as it is easier for a fox to make a living in our suburban sprawl. They are supremely intelligent creatures and can adapt to new sources of food easily. They know that our bins contain food-laden rubbish. They can manage to flip the lids of over-filled wheelie bins and extract whatever chicken bones and half eaten pizzas have been deposited inside. But what I hadn't realised was that foxes in Dublin could not only read, but could read Irish. At least the ones in Terenure can. When I was doing my civic duty on the residents' association committee, my neighbours felt that they could bring their environmental problems to my doorstep for resolution. So, one evening, one of my neighbours came around to report that the area was going to the dogs. Why, even his morning delivery of milk was not safe from light-fingered gurriers who had nothing better to do than to go round stealing the milk of law-abiding citizens. It struck me as strange that gurriers would be up at 6.30 in the morning stealing milk, so I asked him, reasonably I felt, how he knew it was gurriers. Had he actually seen them at it? Well, no. So I suggested that the thing to do was get the milkman to ring the doorbell as he delivered the milk and the neighbour should come down and conduct a stakeout on the milk, to see exactly what was happening. I thought that would be the end of it, and that I would hear no more about it.

Of course not. He was round again the next night with the next instalment of the tale. The milkman left the milk and rang the doorbell. Your man leapt out of bed and hastened downstairs. He was just in time to see a fox come round the side of the house, seize the milk in its jaws and return back to whence it came – the overgrown, neglected garden next door. There the fox ripped open the carton, drank the milk and proceeded to suckle her cubs who were waiting for her. And strewn around were the remains of many other cartons, which had featured on my neighbour's milk bill, if not his breakfast table. How did the fox know there was milk in the carton in the first instance? Sure, wasn't *bainne* written on it – that's how.

So I asked my neighbour what was he going to do. He said that he would get the milkman to put the milk inside his glass porch and close the door, and he was going to come downstairs the next morning to see the look on the fox's face when it beheld the unavailable milk. Poor Reynard!

Another favourite among city dwellers is the hedgehog. Whether the story of Mrs Tiggywinkle is indelibly imprinted in our minds or what, certainly callers to the programme are much more anxious to acquire a hedgehog than to seek to get rid of one. Hedgehogs are not native to Ireland. This means that they were not among the select few that made it to these parts under their own steam after the last ice age. They were, it seems, brought here by the Danes as a source of food. Apparently they were killed, covered in clay and baked in the embers of a fire. You then peeled off the baked clay, skin, spines and all, and the meat tasted like pork. Anyway, do not be tempted to try such a dish – hedgehogs are now protected here under the Wildlife Act. They are great travellers, and if you find one in your garden it does not necessarily mean that it has taken up residence there. It is much more likely just to be passing through. Why people want them so much seems amazing, given that they are covered in fleas, which may well hop off the creature and give you a bite, before copping on that you are the wrong host.

Hedgehogs feed on slugs and snails, and if there is one group of creatures at the top of every gardener's hate list, it is the aforementioned molluscs. A hedgehog in the garden is considered a great asset, as they will definitely keep snail and slug numbers down. Certain people have been known to stop their cars at night if they encounter hedgehogs on the road, get out and wrap the creature up in the car mat and take it home to the garden. And if it is a walled, enclosed garden, it may well stay, as it can't climb directly up walls to escape.

If the temperature drops suddenly in October, hedgehogs go into hibernation for the winter. They find a heap of old leaves under the garden shed or wherever and roll up into a ball, lower their metabolic rate and sleep until springtime. So you have to be very careful raking leaves in November not to inadvertently disturb them in their slumbers. It takes such a lot of energy to raise their body temperature back to normal levels and to increase their breathing and heart rate, that they won't have enough stores of fat to last till spring if you do.

Our listeners have brought a phenomenon to our attention about hedgehogs that may well be linked to climate change. Normal hedgehogs in normal circumstances have their young in June. They have all summer long to feed them and teach them how to feed for themselves. This is important, as hedgehogs less than a pound (about 450 grams) in weight do not have enough energy laid down in the form of fat to last the winter. But recently our listeners are reporting babies born in September – a second family perhaps, the female being stimulated to breed again because of our warmer summer nights. But these babies have very little time to put on condition, and when the cold of Hallowe'en comes, will not have enough fuel in the tank, as it were, to survive hibernation. Kind garden owners would like to feed such hedgehogs and this is a good idea. Do not, however feed them with bread and milk, no matter what Enid Blyton says. They are not calves but carnivores and they need meat. Tins of meaty dogfood are the business. Put this out for them every evening, with just plain water if you like, and this will surely help. You could, of course, collect a nice bucket of slugs for dessert if you were in the humour.

So fond are people of hedgehogs that they do not want to hear any bad-news stories about them. So the story about the harm the hedgehogs were doing on the Hebrides in Scotland went down like a lead balloon with some of our listeners. Hedgehogs had been brought on to some of these islands deliberately by people who wanted them in their gardens. But being wanderers, they didn't necessarily stay in the gardens eating slugs, but went rambling over the whole place. And those islands are particularly important as refuges for nesting seabirds in summer –

seabirds that build their nests on the ground. Wandering hedgehogs found these nests and saw the eggs as a very delicious source of food. Their numbers increased and multiplied, but not those of the seabirds, which were, alas, being decimated by the hedgehogs. Natural enemies of the hedgehogs are badgers, foxes, ten-ton trucks and pesticides used in gardens. None of these were particularly common on these Scottish islands, so the checks and balances that normally occur weren't there. So it was decided to cull the inadvisedly introduced hedgehogs, in the interest of the seabirds, which were rapidly becoming endangered. But people with gardens in hedgehogless parts of Britain thought, 'such a waste, why can't we have them in our gardens? We'd love them.' So there were the pros and the antis for hedgehog resettlement.

Why were there no hedgehogs in these gardens in the first place, if they were being touted as such good homes? The surroundings patently aren't suitable. On the other hand, taking your chances in a garden in the home counties surely is better than definite death at the hands of the cullers.

But why not introduce something into the islands that will naturally predate the hedgehogs, you might ask, and that would solve the problem. What? And make a bad story worse, when these hedgehog-eaters turn their attention to the seabirds as well? There are no easy answers. In fact I wonder are there any answers at all.

It was proving quite difficult to catch the hedgehogs on the islands, dead or alive, when we carried the story on the programme. It just goes to show that, usually, introducing a species of anything where it has not come by itself and established a balance naturally is A Bad Thing. We have so many examples of this here in Ireland – rhododendron in the Killarney woodlands, giant hogweed along our waterways, magpies, I suppose, in our suburbia, zebra mussels in our waterways, New Zealand flatworms in our soil, mink in our rivers, not to speak of rats and house mice which nobody wants. The list is endless. We just can't learn to leave well enough alone.

The only land carnivore whose private life hasn't been revealed yet is the pygmy shrew, so why should I leave you with an incomplete picture? This is our smallest mammal by a long shot – it is only between forty and sixty millimetres long and weighs only three grams in spring after a hard winter. When you consider that this is about the size and weight of the body of a large hawk moth and that mice are veritable monsters by comparison, having a head and body length of one hundred millimetres and weighing in at twenty-five grams, you can appreciate how tiny they are. They are extremely common and widespread, according to distribution records, but most people have never seen one, unless they have a cat. Cats – the horrible things – kill little creatures for fun, and then, as they don't in the least want to eat them, will often bring them in to their doting owners as presents. Pygmy shrews often feature on the present list.

Shrews live in fields, hedges, bogs and woodlands and are to be seen all the year round as they don't hibernate. Strangely for something so small, it is believed that this is one of our native mammals and that it managed to get here before the land bridges broke. There are no bones in the archaeological remains, but then they are so tiny and brittle, shrew bones wouldn't have survived. DNA analysis would give their breed, seed and generation for definite, so there's a project for an aspiring zoologist.

Pygmy shrews are welcome visitors to the gardens of those who are less than passionate about beetles, woodlice and spiders, and in turn are on the menus of owls and foxes who are not put off by the horrible smell that comes from their scent glands. You would imagine that, being so tiny, they would be very delicate and graceful feeders, just nibbling at their food. So you might think it to be a compliment to tell someone they eat like a pygmy shrew. Not so. Pygmy shrews eat their own weight in food every day and will die of starvation if deprived of food for more than three hours. So they are, in fact, real gobble guts. They have to feed by day and by night to keep going. They make a very definite squeaking noise and indeed are more often heard than seen.

They are the only shrew species we have here. Indeed, we have very few small mammals compared to Britain or mainland Europe – having only the pygmy shrew itself, two species of mice and the bank vole, which apparently was introduced to County Limerick in the 1960s. No wonder we only have two resident owl species – there's not a great variety of food for them to pick and choose from at night.

Top carnivores, at the top of their food chain, are – would you believe it? – ladybirds. Very few things eat ladybirds because they are full of formic acid and taste horrible. They exude this horrible tasting, smelly liquid through their legs and any inexperienced bird that may have it in its mouth at this time quickly drops it. The frog is perhaps the only thing in this country that can bring itself to swallow a ladybird, and even then only when the poor frog is desperate. But at least ladybirds have the decency to warn any would-be predator of their horribleness, by being brightly coloured. They do not skulk away and hide in vegetation, but broadcast their presence to the world.

As well as red ones with black spots, we have black ones with red spots, yellow ones, orange ones and brown ones. In fact, we have eighteen species in all in Ireland. There is a Dublin ladybird which is red with two black spots, one on each side. Because the city, with all its concrete, has a warmer microclimate than the rest of the country, this creature is able to survive here quite happily in urban gardens. It is smaller than its culchie relation, the seven-spot, another red ladybird with black spots, which is common in rural gardens. In fact, this one occurs in city gardens too, which must be the reason for the confusion people have about them. I am often told that ladybirds acquire more spots as they get older. Presumably, Dublin residents see the two species in their gardens and think that one is an older version of the other. This is not so: they are separate and distinct species.

We like ladybirds because they are red, which seems to us, if not to the birds, to be a friendly colour. They also please us by dining extensively on aphids, particularly greenflies, which are such a pest on roses. It has been estimated by people who find such matters riveting that a single ladybird will eat five and a half thousand greenflies over a season in your garden. Even more riveting, they have estimated that there will be nine separate generations of greenflies in your garden over a summer. So one greenfly in your garden at the start of the summer – and only one female is needed: this lot don't need men at all, the ultimate feminists – will give rise to 600 million aphids in your garden if left unchecked. So three cheers then for hordes of hungry ladybirds.

Ladybirds are actually beetles, in the same group as the devil's coach-horse and the big black clocks that people hate so much because, they say, they 'look horrible'. It's amazing what a touch of lipstick and rouge will do in the popularity stakes, but then, we women always knew that anyway!

CHAPTER FORTY-THREE

Timberrrrr!

Ireland is one of the best countries in the world for the growing of trees; not that you would think so from the miserly total of native trees we have – twenty-eight in all. Why, a mere national park in Costa Rica has over three hundred native trees in an area the size of County Louth! Our mild, wet climate, with few full days below freezing in winter and few really dry scorching hot days in summer, makes for ideal tree-growing conditions. The arboretum in Wexford – the John F Kennedy Memorial Park – is testimony to this. Trees from every continent grow here happily, monkey puzzles from Chile cheek by jowl, as it were, with eucalyptus from Australia and ginkgo from China.

So why have we so few native trees? Well, it all goes back to the ice ages, which have been sweeping down over Europe for the last two million years. Because of the direction of our European mountain ranges, delicate species could not escape south ahead of the ice, nor could they return very quickly from further south during the inter-glacial spells. At the end of the last Ice Age, Ireland was only connected to Europe for a thousand years or so before the melting ice raised the sea levels to cut it off entirely. Whatever speedy tree species got here before then, that was it. And twenty-eight it was. Trees are not able to move themselves. (Although, that said, I did see a walking tree in the tropical forests of Costa Rica. And no I hadn't been at the blue smarties! This tree grew by having a huge collection of thin trunks, rather as if it were being held up on a hundred stilts. And as time went by, the stilts on one side were more favoured than on the other side, so more of them grew there, while the unfavoured ones on the other side died off. So over its lifetime, the tree might move in the favoured direction, say twenty metres. New roots established themselves under the new trunks while the old ones died off. You'd be a long time walking to Ireland from France that way, though.)

The trees that established themselves here after the Ice Age are only considered to be native because they were not brought here by humans. Birds, mammals and the wind apparently are more natural than humans. Of course, no matter what kind of seeds arrived here they could only become established if conditions here were right. So the seeds of the mountain ash, excreted by birds who had feasted on rowan berries further south, could grow here quite soon after the Ice Age on the exposed tundra grasslands, but coconuts and avocado seeds swept here on ocean currents hadn't a snowball's chance in hell. In fact, they still arrive here and are noted in coastal high-tide detritus surveys, but we wait in vain for coconut-fringed islands with glorious sandy beaches. We do indeed have such beaches, but they are much more likely to be coveted by golf-course developers than greengrocers looking for supplies for the Hallowe'en market.

It is interesting to note that most of our smaller trees have either wind-blown seeds or berries. Thus forests of birch and willow could be set up as soon as there was enough soil and warmth to support the wind-blown seeds. The adventurous short-taken birds could rest in their branches and leave behind calling cards full of haws, sloes, holly, rowan, elderberries, cherries and seeds of the berries of spindle, guelder-rose, crab apple, juniper, whitebeam and yew. These all fell on fertile ground and their trees bore fruit encouraging the birds to stay. However, while the seeds in a juicy berry need to pass through the ins and outs of a bird's digestive system, the same cannot be said of nuts. Did anyone ever see an oak tree grow from a jay's dropping? Once a nut is eaten that's that, end of story.

So how did the oak, the hazel, the Scots pine and the alder get here, then? And, indeed, how clever is it of trees to put all their hopes for the next generation in tasty attractive seeds? Well, this is where the mammals came in. Ireland was still attached to Britain and France when red squirrels came whisking across with hazelnuts and pine seeds in their dear little paws. They thoughtfully buried these in the ground so that they would have supplies in the cold winter days ahead and then thoughtlessly forgot where they had stored them when the time came to eat them. Or maybe the winter itself was harsher than Squirrel Nutkin had bargained for and he never lived to dig up his store. But red squirrels don't eat acorns – far too many tannins for their delicate tummies – only their brasher cousins the grey squirrels, in the yet-to-be-discovered America, could eat these, and they themselves would only arrive here nine thousand years later, unnaturally brought here by humans. It is much more likely that oak trees arrived here as acorns in the bills of jays and rooks, who are rather partial to them to this day, and who like to bury the odd few to have a tasty treat when times get hard. Obviously, their memories are not a hundred per cent either, and the oaks that germinated from those forgotten acorns found the country very much to their liking. They quickly rose above all the others and only had to share their canopy status with the wind-transported ash and elm, which had been following hard on their heels. The sycamore, which also has wind-transported seeds and which does very well here today, started off from much further south in Europe and no easterly gale gusts could blow its seeds all the way from France across the sea, which surrounded Ireland by the time it had moseyed north that far. The nuts of the beech tree did make it to Britain without human intervention, but their mammal porters found the Irish Sea barring further progress, and beech had to wait for the Normans before adding Ireland to their list of 'countries we have visited'.

What about the arbutus, the strawberry tree? It has a decidedly odd distribution here. It is native in Cork and Kerry, so well known, in fact, that it is included in the place names: *caithne* is its name in Irish and Smerick in Kerry is called *Árd na Caithne* – the Height of the Arbutus. It is also native to Sligo, and nowhere in between. It is called the strawberry tree because it has a soft red fruit like a little strawberry. However, the resemblance ends there, as the fruit is not juicy and tasty to eat. It is edible – but you must wait until November, when it is really ripe, or otherwise you'll understand why it is called *Arbutus unedo* in Latin. According to Pliny, it is because a person will only eat one – *un edo*. However, as it is quite common in the Mediterranean regions, they make fruit tarts out of it, and in Corsica it is also eaten. They turn it into *gelée d'arbouses* there, according to Jane Grigson in her seminal *Fruit Book*. I must say I wasn't mad about the one I ate, nicked from a tree in a front garden in Rathmines in late November. It is no wonder that it only made the third division when the trees were being given importance in the old days. Useful trees like the oak, hazel, holly, yew, ash, Scots pine and apple were considered to be the nobles of the wood, and woe betide anyone who even cut a branch off one they didn't own. The second group, called the commoners, comprised birch, elm, wild cherry, alder, willow, hawthorn and rowan. The arbutus was lumped in along with blackthorn, elder, juniper, spindle, whitebeam and aspen in the lower divisions of the wood. It is a much more beautiful tree than any of the others in its group. Perhaps it just didn't grow near to whoever was making the divisions, or perhaps they ate the fruits when they were unripe, when they are in the same category as the sloes of the blackthorn of the whitebeam, which are always mouth-puckeringly sour. Certainly there was no sugar around in those days to make the fruit more palatable.

Trees were valued in those far-off days by what good could be got from them. If they had more than one benefit, then they were higher in the pecking order than ones that had only one use. Oak trees had the best of timber and its acorns could be used as animal feed. But who would have thought that they would turn out to be expert timekeepers and would be able to pinpoint down to the very year when events happened *fadó, fadó?* Because oak was such a fine timber for construction and because it grew so commonly in Ireland, it was used for roads, ships, chariots, castles – all sorts of construction was carried out in oak. If these timbers have survived to the present day, it is possible to say when they lived and died by looking at the rings in the timber. Growth rings form in trees that grow on a stop-start basis. At our latitudes, trees don't grow in winter. When the heat of spring and summer comes, they lash into growth, but come the shorter days in late autumn and winter, they down tools again until the following year. It doesn't really matter whether they are deciduous, losing their leaves in winter, or evergreen, like the northern pine and spruce. If it is too cold they stop growing whether or which. And this record of the stop-start growth is recorded in the growth rings. Years that were great for growth gave rise to very wide rings. Bad years for trees gave them narrow rings. And all the trees of the same species in the same country followed the same pattern. All the oak trees in Ireland grew poorly in a bad year and well in a good year. So by looking at the rings of a tree just felled, you could make a pattern of the rings over the years the tree was alive – bad, good, good, middling, not so good, bad, bad and so on. Of course, these patterns can be measured much more scientifically than this and a master pattern can be drawn up – the science of dendrochronology.

As older and older trees were found, the standard pattern got longer and longer and moved further and further back. It is for all the world like a bar code, with the growth pattern for oak trees in Ireland chronicled for every year. The pattern now extends back thousands of years. So any ancient piece of oak that is now found has the order of its rings compared with the master pattern, and we know exactly when that oak tree lived. So the oak timbers found in roads under the bogs in the midlands can be dated to the exact year. The road, obviously, was built from dead timbers, trees probably felled for that very purpose. Bog oaks that grew in Ireland before the climate changed and became suitable for blanket bog can be dated accurately and tell us when they died, suffocated by the growing blanket bog. Ships washed up on beaches by storm tides may well be ancient Armada ships. The venerable oak timbers will tell us the dates.

Trees nowadays are valued just for growing at all. By growing, they take in carbon dioxide from the atmosphere, and as long as they stay as timber and are not burnt or do not rot, they will hold on to that carbon. So if we want to remove carbon from the air in order to row back on global warming, then the thing to do is grow plenty of trees and keep the timber intact. The faster the tree grows, the more carbon dioxide it takes in. So in a new list of Irish noble trees, the willow species might get promotion, as they are the fastest-growing of all our native trees. Bring back the sally gardens!

CHAPTER FORTY-FOUR

Having a whale of a time

When humans discovered how to use and control fire, civilisation could make two enormous leaps. The first was that now food could be cooked as required, instead of taking advantage of a lightning-caused forest fire or, as Charles Lamb would have it (according to an essay of his that used to be on the old Inter Cert syllabus), waiting for a house to burn down with a pig inside it before enjoying roast pork – a likely story. The second great leap that being able to control fire allowed was the possibility of seeing in the dark. Burning brands of wood could light up places that were never exposed to daylight. Very early cave drawings were done in dark places, far from daylight, which indicates that the artists were part of a community that could use fire to provide artificial light.

Burning brands, however, didn't last very long. Who was it, I wonder, who discovered that oils and fats with a wick in the centre would make a light that was somewhat safer and would last much longer? Animal fats and beeswax were obvious sources for such candle material, and plants such as rushes could act as wicks. Animal fat, or tallow, gave smoky, smelly light and beeswax was a scarce enough commodity. But there was another source of oil – animals that lived in the seas had great quantities of oil, in the form of blubber, in their bodies, and it was discovered that this too could be used for light. Seals could be caught reasonably easily, as they had to haul out on to the land to give birth, and so were vulnerable to capture at this time. For millennia, seals have been hunted for oil for lamps.

There were other animals in the sea that also had stores of oil and, as man became proficient in making boats, these animals could be hunted. The Greenland shark was hunted by the Inuit and by Icelanders for its oil-filled liver. Sharks as a group have no swim bladder and, in the absence of such a piece of equipment, the oil-filled liver adds to their buoyancy and helps to prevent them from sinking. It is not as good as a swim bladder, however, and sharks have to swim continuously to stay afloat. The Greenland shark is a slow, lumbering creature that can be caught from small boats, but sharks in general never really featured as a major source of world oil – I wouldn't fancy asking a great white shark for a liver transplant, would you?

But bigger and better than any shark or seal, whales were the business when you were really serious about collecting oil. Once man had boats big enough, the whales, which of course never came ashore, could be hunted and killed for their oil. The earliest whalers used stone axes to kill whales, and there are records of whales being taken as far back as the Book of Isaiah, in the Old Testament, when it is the Lord who is being accused of punishing the Leviathan with his strong sword. We also have the biblical story of Jonah and the whale, but Jonah wasn't out whaling – he just got chucked overboard when his shipmates decided that he and his sins were the source of their troubles and cause of a huge storm they got caught in. Instantly, the sea was calm, but poor Jonah was swallowed by a whale with yawning jaws and ivory teeth. At least it wasn't a baleen whale, or he would never have got past the baleen filter. As it was, he passed straight through, unscathed, into the whale's stomach, where the digestive juices were put on hold, for some reason, allowing Jonah to be duly expelled, still unscathed, three days later, up from the whale's lower regions, back through his mouth on to dry land in the region of Nineveh, a city on the river Tigris. A Turkish mosque was built in Nineveh in honour of Jonah and, true to his means of transport, there was a miraculous lamp there which burnt perpetually without any oil at all.

Whaling, which is catching whales for oil and food, goes back to the Stone Age, when Inuit people caught whales from skin boats using stone harpoons and lines made of skin. Natives of northern Japan used to catch whales too. They struck them with poisoned spearheads and waited for them to die and float to the surface. The Norse certainly had a whaling industry going from the end of the ninth century. King Alfred of England writes, in AD 890, of a visitor to England who had come with a view to catching whales there. This visitor, one Octher, was proficient at catching whales in his own country – wherever that was; Alfred doesn't say.

However, it was the Basques who really got whaling going from the eleventh century onwards. They hunted the North Atlantic whale for five centuries in the Bay of Biscay. This was a manageable whale to hunt from small boats. It lived in shallow inshore waters, mostly within twenty miles of the coast, it swam slowly and, most important of all, it floated when it was dead. So it was known as the Atlantic 'right' whale. It provided lots of oil from its blubber – up to about twenty tonnes – and from its large tongue and lower lip. It also provided a commodity called whalebone. This was not what you might think – the skeleton of the whale – but great sheets of baleen, which hang from the roof of its mouth. The whale uses them for feeding. It draws in a great quantity of water through these big sheets, which act like a sieve. All the food in the water is filtered out by the baleen, and the water trickles back into the sea. The whale then licks the food off the baleen sheets with its tongue. This huge creature, which could reach up to fifty-five feet long and weigh over eighty tonnes, gets all its sustenance from the admittedly very large amounts of very small planktonic creatures which individually might be no more than three millimetres long.

This baleen or whalebone was of the utmost use in the days before plastic. It was much in demand for the manufacture of stays and corsets, those most restrictive of undergarments that no respectable woman would venture out without. Whalebone was flexible and long lasting and ladies' fashions from the Elizabethan age onwards demanded great quantities.

Whale-meat did not keep well, so it could only be eaten if the boat returned home pretty smartly with the carcass. Hunting the Atlantic right whale had been going on off the European coast for five hundred years when, at the end of the sixteenth century, great efforts were being made by European explorers to find the northwest passage. As they tried for years in the cold Arctic waters, they found something more immediately valuable – the Greenland right whale, known today as the bowhead. This whale has even more enormous quantities of baleen in its mouth. Each plate can be fifteen feet long and it has up to three hundred and forty plates on each side of its mouth. That sure was a lot of corsets and umbrella spokes! They hunted this enormous whale almost to extinction in less than a hundred years. It is still extremely rare and is totally protected today.

Even though there were now bigger sailing ships that could go further afield and hunt whales across the Atlantic, not just off shore, the blubber still had to be brought home and processed fairly sharpish. So it was considered a great advance when they could equip the whaling ships with the means to melt down the blubber at sea. This involved building a brick oven on the ship, where a fire could be lit and the blubber melted and stored in barrels in the hold. These try works, as they were called, were invented in the 1760s and meant that whaling ships could stay at sea for longer periods and hunt and kill many whales. Which was terrible really, as by this stage the stocks of right whales in the Atlantic were greatly diminished. Now with the try works on board, American whaling ships from Newfoundland could set off on journeys lasting up to four years and come back with their ships laden down with oil. They could sail around the Cape of Good Hope and Cape Horn and hunt in all the oceans of the world. And they discovered a southern right whale as well, which lived south of the equator. But they also discovered that they could catch an even more valuable whale – the sperm whale, which lived in the deepest waters, between forty degrees north and forty degrees south, and could not be caught by small boats from land. This whale has seasonal wanderings to polar latitudes and occurred in Atlantic waters at certain times of the year.

This whale is a toothed whale, not a baleen one, and it feeds on squid and octopus, including the almost unknown giant squid, which it catches at depths of 3,000 metres. Its ability to dive to these great depths and stay there for up to an hour at a time is facilitated by the fact that its huge head, which is a third the size of its body, is filled with a waxy substance called spermaceti. Deep down in the ocean, this cools and hardens, allowing the whale to stay down there. Upon rising, the whale can pump warm blood around it and so melt it and increase its own buoyancy, allowing it to float. This spermaceti was the treasure that the sperm whalers sought. It was the purest and most magnificent of oils. It made marvellous candles. In fact, a measure of light in the old standards – the candle power unit of illumination – was based on the illuminating power of candles made from this oil. The world depended on whale oil for light in the 1700s, and for half the 1800s too, and the sperm whale was the prized donor.

Herman Melville gives a first-hand account of sperm whaling in *Moby Dick*, written in 1850. It certainly wasn't a job for the faint-hearted. The big whaling ship, under full sail, got into waters where the whales were. The lookout from the masthead spotted the whale blowing as it came up for air. The ship sailed as near as possible and then the whalers left the ship in quickly launched, keel-less boats like *currachs*, and rowed after the whale. When they got near enough, the harpooner stood up in the front of the boat and threw a steel harpoon at the head of the whale. This had a long rope attached to it, the other end of which was held by the men in the boat. They wore the enormous creature out, and threw more harpoons into it as they chased it. Dangerous work. The whale could and sometimes did beach the boat with its enormous flukes at the tail, or by coming up under the boat. The water all round seethed with sharks lured by the smell of blood from the whale. Woe betide any sailor that fell out of the boat! The rope attached to the first harpoon moved at such speed, as it was paid out, that it could remove a limb from an unwary sailor. But worse than all of this, the whale met a terrible end. The hunters harpooned it till blood came up through its blow hole. Even if it dived and escaped, it still had the harpoon embedded in it, which would cause a slow, lingering death later.

Sperm whales have a very large brain relative to the size of their body. Whales share with elephants the distinction of having, relative to the size of their bodies, bigger brains than man. If size equals space to learn and remember, then it is no wonder that elephants and Moby Dick never forget.

Sperm whales were also hunted on their journeys across the Atlantic, going to and from their tropical breeding grounds. They would feed off the continental shelf in late summer and autumn and would sometimes come in to shallower, inshore waters, where they could be caught by European whalers in big sailing ships, before the invention of the try works, and brought ashore for processing.

An interesting substance was occasionally found in the intestines of the sperm whale. This was a waxy substance like soap, called ambergris or grey amber, though it has nothing to do with actual amber, which is fossilised resin.

This substance found in the sperm whale was beautifully perfumed and was in great demand by manufacturers of fine perfume as a fixative. Until relatively recently it was used by the some of the famous French perfume houses. Melville describes in great detail the collection of it from a dead, dehydrated sperm whale. He maintained that it only formed in the bowels of sick whales, that it was caused by indigestion and that they found hard parts of squid embedded in it. Whatever caused it, ambergris was certainly more precious than gold: the ship's mate was reckoning on a gold guinea an ounce from the druggists when he got back to land.

They were dangerous times. Whalemen often came back in a different ship to that in which they sailed, if they came back at all. But if they succeeded in landing four years' worth of sperm oil, their fortunes were made. As well as for light, the oil was also needed as a lubricant for machinery as the industrial age got going. But then mineral oil was discovered in America in 1859. Hydrocarbons could replace fatty lipids. Paraffin wax and oil could give light, and lubrication of all sorts could be provided by the mineral oil. There was no need to endanger life and limb any more, and what was left of the whale populations was saved, because right whales and sperm whales were no longer the only substantial source of oil. And indeed, for a very little while, the whaling industry declined. Fast-swimming whales such as blue whales and fin whales were impossible to catch from rowing boats, even ones launched from whaling ships at sea, and anyway their bodies sank when they were dead. So everything might have been OK for the whales, only that then, in 1864, a Norwegian named Svend Foyn invented a gun that could fire harpoons with an explosive head. These could be fired from the deck of the fast new steam-powered ships, and the fate of all whales was sealed. Everything was game now – not fair game, though, since no species of whale could now escape capture. These steamships, able to travel independently of the wind, could catch the species that up to then had remained unhunted.

Modern whaling began in the north Atlantic in 1870 and whaling stations were set up ashore to deal with the catches as they came back. We had such whaling stations in Ireland. Two Norwegian companies ran a whaling business in County Mayo, one on the south Iniskea Island from 1908 to 1914, and the other on the Mullet peninsula from 1909 until 1923 (interrupted for a few years in the middle because of World War I). And, unbelievable as it might seem to many of us who believe that whales are creatures of faraway waters, eight hundred and ninety-nine whales were processed in those two stations during that time. They were mainly the faster-swimming whales, which could now be caught and killed with the new equipment – 592 fin whales, 125 blue whales, 97 sei whales – but sixty-three sperm whales and five humpback whales were processed here too, caught in the Atlantic no doubt. What did they want these whales for now? What excuse was there for hunting, practically to extinction, the Leviathans of our waters? We had another source of oil. Bustles were going out of fashion. Why continue to hunt and kill? Well, people still wanted the oil, and ashore in the stations they could extract oil not only from blubber, but from also from the skeletal bones in pressure-cooker-type extractors. This oil was used for linoleum, margarine, soap, crayons, lipstick and ice-cream as well as for lamps. The leftover bones were processed for bone meal. The flesh was canned and sent to countries, such as Japan, Norway and Iceland, that had a tradition of eating whale-meat since the days of local catches. Inedible flesh was sold as animal food. At their height, these whaling stations could process an entire hundred-tonne blue whale within thirty-six hours of its being killed. They quickly fished the Atlantic out, and the European whaling stations closed for lack of whales in the early 1920s.

But things got worse. Large factory whaling ships were built that could process an entire whale at sea. As well as try works, now known as blubber boilers, these were equipped with refrigeration plants, meat and bone-meal plants and, worst of all, sonar and other ultrasonic devices to frighten the whales into flight and exhaustion. Whale-meat was sold in Britain during World War II, when there was a shortage of other supplies of meat.

Modern fleets now rely on radar, depth recorders and underwater range finders to locate whales, because, incredible as it may seem, whales are still being hunted in some parts of the world. After World War II, in 1946 (when cows became plentiful again!), the International Whaling Commission was established with the aim of exploitation without extermination. Their role was to establish, for example, how many whales could be taken each year without decreasing the stocks. It quickly became apparent that this was closing the stable door after the horse had bolted. Many of our whales were practically extinct by now and could never be hunted again. Were they so scarce in world waters that they could never meet each other to mate and breed? This was for the IWC to decide. All taking of the Atlantic right whale and the grey whale was immediately banned, as was all taking of females of any whale species with calves. But other species could be hunted and so they declined too. By 1963, the numbers of blue whale had declined to less than a thousand worldwide, from an estimated 200,000, once upon a time, in the southern hemisphere alone. This whale was given total protection in 1966, by which time it wasn't worth anyone's while going hunting it anyway, and so the whalers moved on to the fin whale and the sei whale, which were not banned. Having been practically fished out worldwide by the 1970s (the Atlantic had already been cleaned out by the 1920s), the fin whale was put on the protected list in 1976. Today, only an aboriginal population in west Greenland are allowed to catch a very limited quota.

And so, on to the next one. The smaller sei whale was now worth chasing, as there were no longer any bigger whales that could be hunted. This whale first became almost extinct in the North Atlantic, and then the chase pursued it to the southern waters in the big factory ships, and at one point 20,000 were being taken annually. It too was finally put on the protected list when there were no more to catch profitably – in 1978 for the southern hemisphere; none have been caught in northern waters since 1988. Sperm whaling was only stopped in 1985, and humpbacks, which were practically extinct by that stage anyway in the north Atlantic, were protected there in 1956 and eventually worldwide (no quotas or exceptions) in 1988.

Not all countries of the world are members of the International Whaling Commission. These countries don't feel bound by its rulings and they seek quotas for research purposes. Iceland is one such country, which wishes to have a quota of minke whales to catch each year. We spoke to their minister for fisheries during our visit there in February 2004, and his attitude was illuminating to us, coming from Ireland, the waters of which are a whale and dolphin sanctuary since Charles Haughey brought in the legislation in 1991. The Icelandic fishing minister pointed out to us how important the fishing industry is to Iceland (which the British know only too well since the 'cod wars' of recent times). With the practical extinction of other whales, such as the blue whale and the fin whale, the minke whale seems to have recovered somewhat quicker, by exploiting the food sources that would have been eaten by these slower-to-recover species. Minke whales, although they are baleen whales, feed on fish, which they trap in their baleen sieves, rather than on plankton, which is the food of other baleen whales. The Icelandic fisheries minister maintained that 10 per cent of their fish catch of cod was being taken by minke whales, and they were determined to go back to catching them in order to protect their fish stocks. When we ventured to suggest that this would be very bad for their tourism industry and that surely inviting visitors to whale-watch was the way forward, he practically snorted. Ten per cent of the fishing industry was worth more to the economy of Iceland than the whole of their tourism industry, and anyway he was the minister for fisheries, not tourism. They had been taking some minke whales under licence each year up to this, to ascertain what they ate, how quickly they bred and where they fed, and he was sure they were a threat to the fishing industry. And, yes, the whale-meat is good to eat, and those whales captured under licence ended up in the meat shops when the research was finished.

I couldn't wait to go looking for whale-meat on sale. Was it in the butcher's, the fishmonger's, the supermarket? In the event, it wasn't anywhere, as it is only on sale in the summer time, when the whales are caught, not in February, when we were there. But it got me thinking: what was whale like to eat. I consulted my trusty *Larousse Gastronomique*, and there it was on page 1006. Whale meat was called *crapois* in the Middle Ages in France and was sold as 'Lenten bacon', for eating on the many meatless days they had then. It was a staple food of the poor. The Basque fishermen, who caught the right whale in the Atlantic for its oil, did a nice sideline in whale victuals. But what was it like to eat? *Larousse* pontificates: 'The flesh of this cetacean is most indigestible and remains tough even after twenty-four hours' cooking.' No pressure cookers around then, obviously. And what does it taste like? *Larousse* doesn't fail me here either: 'Boil a piece of lean beef in water which has been used to wash a not-too-fresh mackerel, and you will have a dish that is similar to escalope of whale *à la Valois*.' I haven't tried it yet. However, I wasn't too impressed by the final sentence in the entry in *Larousse* under 'whale', written, admittedly, in 1938. I quote it verbatim: 'Is it not certain, is it not an inescapable fact, that all animals living on land, swimming in water or flying in the air must, sooner or later, play their part in the culinary repertoire of the world?' The French approach to food neatly encapsulated, *n'est-ce pas?*

Another source of worry about whales in recent times is the frequency of beaching occurrences. Whales communicate by sound underwater. It is feared that man-made sounds from blasting and exploring, seismic shocks and sonic booms all interfere with the whales' perceptions of sounds. And there is the increasing pollution of our waters with heavy metals, which build up in the food chain, becoming most concentrated in those who, like whales, are at the top of the food chain. And there is the conflict between the top predators for the fish stocks – man and cetaceans. Who is entitled to them? Cetaceans also get caught inadvertently in fishing nets. And climate change is affecting our oceans and our ocean currents.

Whales first evolved in waters around Pakistan about 50 million years ago. The *Homo sapiens* species is here a mere 170,000 years. Doesn't this account of us and whales make us so proud of our species and its attitude to the rest of the inhabitants with which we share the world?

However, amazingly, whales are not extinct. Some species are recovering better than others and the fact that our waters have been a sanctuary for the last thirteen years has helped. There are fourteen different whale species on the Irish list at the moment, including the blue, sperm and humpback whales. It is possible to see them from our headlands if you are there at the right time with your binoculars. The Irish Whale and Dolphin Group studies the distribution and status of our whales and organises whale-watching expeditions, so at least some members of our species have a better attitude to whales.

CHAPTER FORTY-FIVE

The state of our environment

In May 2004, ten new countries joined the European Union. A great deal of work had gone on beforehand to make sure that these accession countries were up to the standards of the EU and were 'fit' to join. The main areas where they had to reach our standards were in environmental matters, and in standards of health and safety in the workplace. It certainly was a far cry from thirty years ago, when we joined. We all voted in favour, we were willing and anxious to behave like good Europeans and, above everything else, we were dying to benefit from the structural funds and the money from the Common Agricultural Policy that Europe had to offer. But it very soon became apparent that we only wanted to benefit, not to put ourselves out. We were, of course, bound by EU legislation, but one of the first things our politicians negotiated was a derogation from the waste directives. We were so far back and unready that we could not possibly comply, and so a fifteen-year derogation was acquired. As a result, we had no waste or waste problems in Ireland until 1987! Well, we didn't have to measure how much waste we had, there were no standards for landfill sites – aptly known then as dumps – recycling was unheard of. New member states today are allowed no derogations of any description; they can only join when they are up to the mark.

But we did things our way. There were air-quality regulations too. There were limits beyond which our air could not deteriorate without breaking these regulations and incurring the wrath of Europe. We must measure our air quality every day. Which we did, but of course we never published the measurements until the April following the winter when the worst air quality occurred. So you knew in April what had killed you last November! Or at least you could find out then when the air quality in urban areas exceeded the EU limits. In fact, it was only after the terrible first week in January 1982, when a yellow pall of smog hung over Dublin for five days, that the public began to demand to know what the air quality was now, not in three month's time. The authorities were forced to release daily figures, public awareness grew and the subsequent ban on the sale of smoky coal in urban areas from 1990 on was accepted.

But it was in the area of water quality that we really showed our ignorance and apathy. Sure, haven't we loads of water, isn't it always raining, what's the problem? Where to begin to explain? To put it simply, we take in clean water for our various uses and we put out dirty water when we are finished. God sends us new clean supplies of rain, and aren't we grand? goes the thinking. But the Environment Protection Agency (EPA) measures our water quality and they are not so sanguine about it.

Let's take drinking water first. It is vital for a country to have plentiful supplies of clean, fresh, disease-free water. Our drinking water can come from surface supplies, such as lakes and rivers, or from the groundwater, which really means artificial wells. Most of us get our water from surface waters, pumped to our homes by public water schemes, for which we don't pay, and indeed many of us have no intention of ever paying for it. The public water-supply schemes ensure that the water they send out is free from any sort of contamination and, according to the latest EPA report (2005), they got it right 97.4 per cent of the time. However, we are not all on public water schemes. There are over five and a half thousand 'group' (privately run) water schemes in Ireland, many of which get their water from groundwater. A full 10 per cent of our population get their water from these schemes. In 2005, the EPA report showed that 30 per cent of them were contaminated with coliform bacteria, which only come from the intestines of humans and animals. And, in fact, 11 per cent in porous limestone areas are grossly contaminated. In other words, one and a half thousand private water schemes in Ireland are contaminated with sewage and slurry. Charming!

Where does this pollution come from and how does it get into our water supplies? Human waste is sewage, and this can't be discharged willy-nilly into the environment – or can it? The good old EPA have the story. There is, of course, an EU urban waste-water treatment directive, which we transposed into Irish law in 1994. The government target for full compliance, you'll be glad to know, was 2005. At that time, in 1994, 48 per cent of our urban sewage was discharged into our waters completely untreated, and another 35 per cent only received primary treatment, which just meant the big solid lumps were sieved out or settled under gravity, but the dirty water happily flowed into our seas, lakes and rivers. In case you can't bear to do the sums, I will – that was a massive 83 per cent of all our urban sewage. We got EU cohesion funds and fixed up the situation, however. Ringsend was upgraded, which meant that Dublin's waste water is now treated, since May 2003. Mutton Island treatment plant in Galway city is in operation since 2004. The latest figures published by the EPA in 2004 show that 18 per cent of our waste water is still untreated, while a mere 13 per cent remains in the preliminary category! We'll only know whenever the next EPA report comes out whether or not we made the 2005 deadline! There won't be any more cohesion funds, though – sure, hasn't Ireland's financial situation improved and aren't our new members much more needy? We don't begrudge them; we got more than our share of it in our time. We'll pay to improve our waste-water treatment from our own taxes – isn't that what they're for?

Of course, there's more to it than urban waste-water treatment plants. What happens if you want to live in an area not serviced by 'mains'? No problem – you build your very own septic tank on the half-acre and that takes care of everything. It does, if you do it right, if you desludge your tank frequently and refrain from killing, with bleaches and other horrible unnecessary toilet cleaners, the bacteria that are breaking down your organic waste in the properly sized percolation area. Otherwise, where do you think the stuff goes when you pull the chain? It ends up, unbroken-down, in the groundwater, in your neighbour's well, in the group water scheme, in the local river, in some cases in your own well if you really haven't taken care. There are group waste-water schemes, where the waste of up to a hundred individuals can be sustainably treated in an environment-friendly reedbed system. We actually have some such schemes in Ireland, but not many. We don't want to live near enough to anyone to share a waste-water scheme of any description. Between 2003 and 2005, sixty-four thousand one-off houses have been built in increasingly remote areas, because of the attraction of scenic isolation and cheap land. No mains sewage disposal possible then, or indeed clean water supplies either. We have in total half a million septic tanks in Ireland. Take out some shares in one of the bottled water companies who are laughing all the way to the bank.

But doesn't it rain great quantities of clean water down on top of us every season? It does, and we could use that water as it comes, if we caught it on our roofs and piped it into our homes to wash clothes, flush toilets and so on. It would save us having to use expensively cleaned fit-to-drink water for these things, but what the hell, sure we are not paying for the expensively cleaned water. Anyway, if it was that important, wouldn't there be building regulations making new houses built on half-acres with plenty of space have a rainwater collection system of downpipes and gutters and a dual water plumbing system? I used to live in such a house, which was built in the 1950s, but of course we are much more advanced now. All the rainwater that falls on our roofs nowadays is piped straight into the storm-water sewers and causes huge problems of waste-water volume at the treatment works during very wet periods. Or at least it would if there weren't overflow valves that could be opened, discharging the whole lot, rain and waste water together, into the nearest river. There is no time to hold it for treatment when there is such a volume coming through. Remember, we had no environmental studies taught in any of our schools between 1936 and 1971, so how could those in charge possibly know these things and how can we, the public, know either, to demand proper treatment of water and sewage? This excuse should be good for another ten years yet!

So the uncaught rain falls down onto the ground, and if the ground is not covered in tarmac or concrete (in which case the rainwater ends up in the storm-water overflows), it percolates down through the soil to replenish the groundwater supplies. Or it flows, with gravity, through the soil into the rivers and lakes. It's very good at dissolving things along the way, so what does the clean rainwater find in our soils? Do you really want to know? Could you bear it? Well, it finds all the things we put there to get rid of. Chief among these are animal slurries. In the bad old pre-EU days, our cattle lived out in the fields, ate the grass, grew slowly, put up with the winter and did their droppings as they went along, a cow pat here, another there. They were fairly healthy too, in the main – OK, maybe they had the odd dose of worms or scour, but they got over it. And the dung beetles broke down the well-distributed cowpats, and the bacteria helped, and there was nothing nasty left to be dissolved and washed down by the rain. But farmers weren't rich. In the 1970s, when we first joined Europe, we had a market on our doorstep that would pay good money for every bit of beef and every drop of milk we produced. Keeping cattle indoors in the bad weather increased production. We got grants to build slatted sheds, we got grants to 'improve' marshy wet places that weren't worth farming before and to remove hedges to make bigger fields, we got grants to arterially drain rivers in order to have more farmland, we could reseed our pastures with one or two species of grass instead of having to put up with whatever grew there naturally, we could add nitrates and phosphates to make the grass grow better, we could give our animals medicines to prevent the possibility that they might get sick, and no matter how much we produced there was always intervention to store beef and butter mountains and milk lakes – we got top price. We could spread the slurries, saved during the winter in the slurry pits, over the soil to increase the supplies of nitrates and phosphates. We could cut silage two or three times a year instead of having to risk the weather and save the hay. It was great.

It was, until the plain citizen of Europe realised how much of the whole EU budget was going on agriculture and called for CAP reform. Quotas were introduced. Grants were given for things that were needed, rather than things that were not. On a European scale, sheep were needed, so we all turned to rearing sheep. The ewe premium was introduced in 1980, and by 1992 the national flock had grown by 270 per cent. We had nine million sheep in Ireland in the early 1990s and, as a result, 20 per cent of our uplands are affected by soil erosion. More CAP reform followed, this time in the form of grants to farm wisely and REPS – the Rural Environment Protection Scheme – was introduced. The EU nitrates directive was issued in 1991 too, obliging all member states to take action to reduce pollution from too much nitrate, but sure what were we to do with our slurries? We ignored the directive as long as we could and only began to talk about implementing it very reluctantly in 2004. By the time it actually was forced on farmers in 2005, twenty-three per cent of our ground water as sampled by the EPA exceeded the permitted nitrate concentrations. So if the E coli bacteria in the well water don't get you, the nitrates will!

Does it matter? What is the state of the place now – particularly our water bodies? The EPA monitors away and produces reports regularly. The latest report, issued in 2005, makes depressing reading. To put it simply, our water quality is declining. Of the 13,200 km of rivers sampled, only 70.2% is unpolluted, which is EPA-speak for the fact that almost 4,000 kilometres of river channel has some degree of pollution. Our lakes are equally bad. There is information collected for four hundred and twenty-one lakes and, of these, sixty-eight are polluted, thirteen of them described as being highly polluted. Seven of these highly polluted lakes are in Monaghan and three are in Cavan. Fifty per cent of the springs and wells in the Burren are contaminated, particularly after rain.

What are we doing to our country and do we care? Well, no, it would seem. We have a God-given right to do what we like – to build wherever we like, but have piped water and flush toilets, to improve our land and farm intensively, to plant forests of Sitka spruce, regardless of whether they acidify or not. Anyone that has the temerity to point out the irreversible harm this is doing to our environment is shouted down or accused of being a snob. Proper, good county development plans are overturned by private councillors' motions to favour party voters. Attempts to make the polluter pay are outwitted by illegal dumping, littering and the growing tendency of using our bogs and hedgerows as repositories for the black plastic bags of rubbish we are too mean-spirited to pay for. What are bogs and hedges for after all? Our ten new member states greatly enlarge our European total of unpolluted water and pristine wildlife habitats. How long will it remain so? If their attitude to EU membership is anything like ours was, I don't give it very long.

CHAPTER FORTY-SIX

Teaching students – or *not* teaching them

Teaching can be wonderful. I should know. I come from a line of teachers on both sides, and I do a bit of teaching myself. Not that I am a teacher mind you. Full time, all day, every day, it must be one of the most demanding occupations ever. You are totally committed when you stand up in front of that class. You have to initiate proceedings, keep the show going. If your attention flags or you show boredom even for a minute, the whole thing collapses. Because the truth is that, in the main, pupils don't want to be taught. They might like being at school, all right, but they'd rather occupy themselves in any other way in class than in listening to a lesson. The feedback is instant. If the lesson is not hitting the spot, they are bored and they show it. It is very hard to hit the spot for five hours a day with a class of up to thirty individuals of varying motivation and interest. In an office job you could have a break, a cup of coffee or take a phone-call – not in class, you can't. Teachers deserve a high spot in heaven.

My teaching experiences are different, because I come into the classroom as a one-off – a novelty, someone who was invited. The teacher is present. The pupils are allegedly on their best behaviour. I may be talking to primary or post-primary pupils, and my only requirement is to be interesting enough to hold the attention of the pupils. If not, the reaction is swift and merciless. Unlike grown-up audiences, which, if bored, merely switch off and look out the window, pupils who are not enjoying their lessons make it known. They lean back on their chairs and indeed fall off them, which livens up proceedings considerably. They plait the hair of the girl in front of them. They reflect the sunlight on to your face with the front of their watches. They speak to each other – what they have to say is considerably more relevant than what they have to listen to – and, if they are a particularly obnoxious group, they join together to mock the accent of the speaker and find double meanings in everything that is said. But at least I never have to mark copies or correct exam papers at primary or secondary level, so I can continue with the self-delusion that if it was all right on the day, then what I said made an indelible impression and they have really understood and learnt.

My third-level teaching experiences are somewhat different. Here I am actually not a teacher but a lecturer, and that title somehow implies that the task merely means passing on information to rapt, enthusiastic young adults who have actually chosen further education after their Leaving Cert, and have specifically selected the area in which you lecture. Yes, well, maybe so, but the be-riveting-and-keep-my-attention rule applies here too. So you are, and you do, and you get through a whole year on the topic with a class still turning up at the end of the year and even the occasional one asking relevant questions.

And then come the exams. You have to set a paper on the subject you have taught and, under time pressure, in three hours, they return what I can only assume is their best attempt to pass, based on what they have learnt from you over the year. Could this be all they really know about the subject, after all your hard work and Oscar-winning lecturing performances? It's depressing.

I lecture in biogeography in a third-level establishment. This is a subject that covers what plants and animals live where in the world and why. Why are there kangaroos in Australia, llamas in South America and deer in Europe – all grass-eating herbivores, yet so different? The subject involves descriptions of conditions in rainforests and in deserts and explanations for what species we have or don't have in Ireland. So the exam questions reflect what I have covered. One year, I asked the pupils to describe deserts and the plants and animals that lived there. (Despite having written the word on the exam paper in the question, I got long accounts of desserts rather than deserts.) Plants and animals in deserts have to cope with great heat and a lack of water. Could my pupils perhaps tell me about some of these?

Well, you will be delighted to know that camels are really well adapted to desert life. One student told me that they can lose 400 per cent of their body weight through dehydration before any permanent damage happens to them. I tried to imagine such a camel. Another said that a camel can lose 25 per cent of its body weight before it becomes dangerous.

Some animals in deserts have extremely large ears. This part is actually true: it's so that they can dissipate heat through such a large surface area and survive. We use the same phenomenon to heat our houses. We have things with a large surface area giving off heat in our rooms. We call these radiators. They are filled with hot water and they lose heat rapidly through the surfaces and warm our rooms. (Got that?) Well, sensibly enough, the ears on the desert animals are also called radiator ears, because that's how they function too, and foxes, hares and hedgehogs in deserts in different parts of the world have them in order to survive. That's not how my students understand it, though. They tell me that radiator ears contract and expand during hot daily temperatures – a case of now you see them, now you don't, I suppose. They tell me that the animals can store water in their ears because they are radiators. They say that they reflect the sun – like car mirrors I suppose.

Their knowledge of desert plants is not much better. Plants in deserts grow downwards instead of upwards, they tell me. The creosote plant sends out seeds via its roots. Cacti are spineless. Desert plants excrete salt, but this often clogs up the sellers (sic). Some plants have adapted to desert conditions by having smaller leaves, while others survive by disappearing altogether. How could they think I told them that?

Some years, the exam question might be about rainforests – describe them and talk about the threats to them. Did you know that the rainforest has a fourteen-month year, and that the trees there take millions of years to grow? I didn't. The trees there have no seeds and will soon be distinct (sic). Rubber trees were very popular once and were cut down and used before plastic was invented, according to a student of mine; and another one told me that the rubber tree has often been cut down. (I suppose it must spring back again after each cutting so that it can be re-cut.) There is a teak-flavoured mahogany tree there, apparently. One plant called Bunka banks (whatever that might be) is a 'scented angiosperm' that drinks the sap of other trees. (Actually, most plants are angiosperms; it simply means that they have flowers and fruit.) The sun shines twenty-four hours a day there. Many of the animals are 'docturnal'. And on threats to the rainforest – once a tree is cut down, it won't grow. Well, well. When trees are cut down, the climate usually sores (sic). There is an increase in ground-freezing birds, whatever they are.

Their knowledge of Irish wildlife is not so hectic either. Another type of vegetation found in Ireland is the flora and fauna, according to my students. The trees in Ireland are very young – they are only 10,000 years old. Hedgerows are boarders (sic) for fields. Corncrakes have become scarce here because they are too long for the Sahara desert! When forest clearances occurred in Ireland, the eagles began to eat the grass and the small baby animals. Soils in Ireland exist in three states – solid, liquid and gas. Many soils in Ireland are broken into smaller soils. Many species became extinct when our forests were cut down, but some were able to stick threw (sic) it.

It's terrible reading this. What impression have they gone away with? What will they tell the young people of Ireland when they go out to teach themselves? But at least I haven't had to read what was written for one of my colleagues. He was lecturing about habitations – why cities are where they are, on trade routes, at river mouths and so on. But nowadays, he explained to his class, cities can actually be imposed on places that have no natural attraction for them. Some cities in the American desert have been entirely artificially created. All food and water is brought in by road and processed there. Why, they even have their own Coca Cola plant. This came back on the exam script as follows: it is possible nowadays to have a city anywhere; they have such a city in America where everything is supplied and the Coca Cola grows on trees.

CHAPTER FORTY-SEVEN

Mooney goes wild

After nine years on the air for half an hour a week, on a Sunday, the radio programme on which I work, *Mooney Goes Wild*, got promotion, as it were, in 2004, to an hour a week at the weekend primetime slot of 10 am to 11 am on Saturday morning (we are now on air on Friday afternoon at 3pm). Now, this is actually a live programme, much to the surprise of some people. We are all out in RTÉ way in advance of the programme on Saturdays, making sure it all happens without a glitch, on the hour. At times, when I am asked if it is live, I am tempted to respond, 'Barely', knowing, as I do, that many of the listeners are hearing the programme in bed, enjoying the Saturday-morning lie-ins they have that we don't.

The public are invited to phone in with comments and queries, and it soon became apparent that there was a different class of listener on Saturday than we were used to from the Sunday programmes. First of all, they seemed to be touchier. An innocent remark by our bird expert on the advisability of feeding birds through the hard times – 'Keep up the social welfare,' said he – brought a very incensed response. Social welfare recipients were entitled to their payments – they weren't handouts – what did our panellist mean by such remarks?

But we weren't to be repressed by such reactions. We are normally not amused by listeners ringing up giving out about wildlife, but shortly after a particular outcry in the newspapers about urban-generated rural housing and the increase in people who work in the city coming to live in the country – a lifestyle considered to be unsustainable, depending as it does on heavy use of private transport – we got the following call. The house-owner wanted to know how to get rid of the fox that walked across his manicured lawn in the country and, on occasion, even had the temerity to leave a calling card. Well, I pulled no punches. I said that living in the country was wasted upon such a person and that he should take himself back to the city from whence he came. Such impertinence, to seek to get rid of a creature that had always lived there, just because he wanted to impose his unnatural lawn on the surroundings! I was gratified to receive a plethora of calls saying, Right on – I did my business right. No dissenting calls at all, or maybe they just didn't get through.

Mind you, I am amazed that we get any calls at all while we are on the air. Surely if you are listening to such a fascinating programme, you'd be reluctant to get up and phone, in case you missed pearls of wisdom while waiting to get through. And the latest now is emailing while the programme is on. It may be easier to type and listen, but it sure isn't possible for us to broadcast and read our emails at the same time. We are not coming down with extra assistants on a Saturday morning, and the people we do have are more than fully occupied with the phone lines.

Calls, I suppose, can be divided up into several categories. There are always the 'How do you get rid of…' calls. These start in April with 'How do you get rid of ants?' and I feel you could broadcast the same response, even the same programme, for a month, as people don't seem to listen to what you say and ask about getting rid of ants every week. This moves on to how to get rid of starlings and other bird species that have unwanted nests on our personal and private property. In 2004, there seems to have been an unmerciful invasion of millipedes in certain areas. These are black worm-like creatures with allegedly thousands of legs that feed on dead and rotting vegetation. One man encountered them in his bath, and wanted to know if they came up the plughole or through the overflow outlet. A bit of experimental activity would have resolved the mystery of how they got in: put the plug into the plughole. Surely they are not so super-strong that they could lift that. If they still appear, put Sellotape over the overflow outlet. Are they stuck to the inside of the Sellotape?

If you have an infestation, as people will insist on putting it, you must be providing food for them. Animals and insects are not on a fasting pilgrimage as they crawl all over your house. When did you last clean out the gutters and shores of dead leaves? Are there old birds' nests in your eaves? How can I tell, up in Donnybrook, what the cut of your premises is? But one thing is sure, if you have an infestation of millipedes or ants or flour mites in the press or silverfish in the kitchen at night, whatever, you are, however inadvertently and unwillingly, providing them with a source of food. Elementary, my dear Watson. Find the food supply and get rid of it and you'll be free of the unwanted visitor. But of course sometimes this is easier said than done. Anyway, millipedes do no harm at all. They think they look lovely, even if you don't. Sweep them back out of doors where they belong.

Another category of caller wants to report unusual wildlife occurrences. These are great and are seized upon with great alacrity, as they can often make great radio. We had the blackbird couple in Limerick who reared a chick in a nest which they had built in the Christmas tree in the hospital grounds in the month of January. Obviously the light and the heat of the bulbs fooled the birds into thinking it was spring. We ran the story until the baby blackbird was successfully fledged and out of the nest. We have calls about squirrels and rats at bird tables, robins that come when they are called, and ones which carry out duets with householders out at the clothes line, wrens that nest in tracksuit tops on the clothes line, slugs that bungee jump out of trees, foxes that saunter around houses – inside, that is – and cuckoos heard in February. We are expected to provide an explanation for all these phenomena, even though they may be sprung on us live on air. Like children clutching comfort blankets, we go in each week armed with a veritable library of books on every wildlife topic imaginable, but of course on the air there is seldom time to consult any of these learned tomes.

Another category of listener delights in ringing us up to give us more information on a topic we may have discussed on air, or rarely – very rarely – to inform us that we are wrong. Often, the latter come in the form of emails to the programme, and indeed emails are a great medium of communication between ourselves and the listeners. Pictures can be attached to emails and in some cases a picture can be worth a thousand words. The woman with the hummingbird in her back garden sent in a picture of the hummingbird hawk moth. We get wonderful close-ups, sometimes, of spiders and webs. Butterflies are easily identified from pictures too. We get great pictures of bungee-mating slugs.

We also have a category of listeners who seem to dislike wildlife and consider it as the enemy. We got a cross email from a lady on a beautiful May day giving out about all the dandelions that are around. Such cheerful, happy flowers! She wasn't giving out about buttercups or primroses or bluebells or daisies. No, she seemed to be expressing some form of flower apartheid. Of course, the growing point of dandelions is down in the bottom of the flower, so mowing the blessed lawn only encourages them. Give up having a lawn – plant a tree instead and put a woodland wildflower garden in underneath. Dandelions don't grow in woods.

And what about the attitude of the sender of this email?

Would like to ask you a question. Grey crows and magpies are scavengers, they devour any animals that are killed on our roads, even rats, which we consider dirty animals. At present any amount of badgers are lying dead on the roads and remain there for many days without being touched. Why don't the crows and magpies eat badgers? Are farmers right that they are dirty, disease-carrying animals that nature itself won't even touch?

Such naked aggression and hatred for poor old *broc!* Of course, it is not true. We do see more dead badgers on the roads than other species that are lighter and swifter of foot. These lighter corpses are probably hurled into the hedges by our speeding motorcars as we thunder along at speeds in excess of what is safe, no matter what the speed limit says, particularly on smaller secondary roads. And is there a badger removal service? Not to my knowledge, so some natural scavenging process must be getting rid of them or we'd have wall-to-wall dead badger on the roads, such is their abundance in the first place and propensity to car slaughter in the second.

But it is the public response that makes the programme, and keeps it fresh and relevant. It keeps us on our toes, too, because, no matter how carefully the running order is planned in advance, the programme has a life of its own when it goes on air. We should make a programme some time consisting of the stuff we prepared earlier but never got time to broadcast on the day. But who's complaining when there is such public interest in the whole subject?

Bibliography

Armstrong, E, *The Folklore of Birds* (Dover; London and New York) 1970.

Burton, J et al, *The Oxford Book of Insects* (Oxford University Press; Oxford) 1974.

Chinery, M, *Field Guide to the Insects of Britain and Northern Europe* (Collins; London) 1973.

Chinery, M, *Garden Wildlife of Britain and Europe* (Harper Collins; London) 1997.

Fairley, J, *An Irish Beast Book* (Blackstaff Press; Belfast) 1984.

Fitter, R (consultant ed.), *Book of British Birds* (Reader's Digest and AA, Drive Publications; London) 1969.

Gleed-Owen, C, F Marnell et al, 'Origins of the Natterjack Toad *Bufo calamita* in Ireland' *Bulletin of the Irish Biogeographical Society* (23) 1999.

Hayden, T & R Harrington, *Exploring Irish Mammals* (TownHouse; Dublin) 2000.

Kelly Korky, J & R Webb, 'Resurvey, Biogeography and Conservation of the Natterjack Toad *Bufo calamita* in the Republic of Ireland' *Bulletin of the Irish Biogeographical Society* (23) 1999.

Mc Neill, J *Something New Under the Sun* (Penguin Press; London) 2000.

Mackay, J T, 'The Natterjack *Bufo rubeta* occurs wild in Ireland' *Magazine of Natural History* (9) 1836.

Marnell, F, 'The Distribution of the Common Frog *Rana temporaria* in Ireland' *Bulletin of the Irish Biogeographical Society* (23) 1999.

Mitchell, F & M Ryan, *Reading the Irish Landscape* (TownHouse; Dublin) 1997.

Ní Lamhna, É, *Provisional Atlas of Amphibians, Reptiles and Mammals in Ireland* (Irish Biological Records Centre, An Foras Forbartha; Dublin) 1979.

Ní Lamhna, É *et al, An Air Quality Survey of Cork City* (Irish Biological Records Centre, An Foras Forbartha; Dublin) 1983.

Ní Lamhna, É *et al, An Air Quality Survey of the Greater Dublin Area* (Irish Biological Records Centre, An Foras Forbartha; Dublin) 1988.

O'Connor, J & P Ashe, *Irish Indoor Insects* (TownHouse; Dublin) 2000.

O'Sullivan, P, *Irish Superstitions and Legends of Animals and Birds* (Mercier Press; Cork) 1991.

Phillips, R, *Mushrooms and other Fungi of Great Britain and Europe* (Pan; London) 1981.

Praeger, R L, *The Way That I Went* (Figgis; Dublin) 1969.

Ramsbottom, J, *Mushrooms and Toadstools* (Collins; London) 1953.

Roberts, M, *Spiders of Britain and Northern Europe* (Harper Collins; London) 1995.

Roinn Oideachais, *Ainmneacha Plandaí agus Ainmhithe* (Oifig an tSoláthair; Baile Átha Cliath) 1978.

Smith, M, *The British Amphibians and Reptiles* (New Naturalist Series, Collins; London) 1964.

Smith, T (ed.), *Complete Family Health Encyclopedia* (British Medical Association, Dorling Kindersley; London) 1990.

Stapleton, L, M Lehane & P Toner (eds), *Ireland's Environment: A Millennium Report* (EPA; Wexford) 2000.

Uí Chonchubhair, M, *Flóra Chorca Dhuibhne* (Oidhreacht Chorca Dhuibhne; Baile an Fheirtéaraigh) 1995.